CATALOGUE

OF

# EARLY CHRISTIAN ANTIQUITIES

OXFORD

HORACE HART, PRINTER TO THE UNIVERSITY

# CATALOGUE

OF

# EARLY CHRISTIAN ANTIQUITIES

AND

# OBJECTS FROM THE CHRISTIAN EAST

IN THE DEPARTMENT OF

BRITISH AND MEDIAEVAL ANTIQUITIES AND ETHNOGRAPHY

OF THE

## BRITISH MUSEUM

BY

## O. M. DALTON, M.A.

ASSISTANT IN THE DEPARTMENT

## LONDON

PRINTED BY ORDER OF THE TRUSTEES

*SOLD AT THE BRITISH MUSEUM*

AND BY LONGMANS AND CO., 39 PATERNOSTER ROW
BERNARD QUARITCH, 15 PICCADILLY; ASHER AND CO., 13 BEDFORD STREET, COVENT GARDEN
KEGAN PAUL, TRENCH, TRÜBNER AND CO.; PATERNOSTER HOUSE, CHARING CROSS ROAD
AND HENRY FROWDE, OXFORD UNIVERSITY PRESS WAREHOUSE, AMEN CORNER

1901

ﭣ

# PREFACE

THE following Catalogue has been prepared by Mr. O. M. Dalton of this Department, who is also responsible for the Introduction. I have compared the description with the objects.

CHARLES H. READ.

DEPARTMENT OF BRITISH AND MEDIAEVAL
ANTIQUITIES &c.
*November,* 1901.

# TABLE OF CONTENTS

## CATALOGUE OF EARLY CHRISTIAN ANTIQUITIES

### I. ENGRAVED GEMS AND RINGS

# LIST OF PLATES

# LIST OF ILLUSTRATIONS IN THE TEXT

Enamelled Byzantine Cross in the Victoria and Albert Museum,
South Kensington. Front.

# INTRODUCTION

THE objects representing the minor arts of the Early Christian and Byzantine periods in the Department of British and Mediaeval Antiquities were first united in 1893, in which year several rooms were assigned to exhibitions illustrating the various religions of the world.   But even now the whole collection is not exhibited in one place.   The need for safer custody involved the placing of jewels and objects of gold in the Room of Gold Ornaments and Gems, and the passage by which it is approached, while a few of the ivory carvings are in the Mediaeval Room where they form part of the large series there exhibited.   A number of objects are also to be found in other Departments, and with these the present Catalogue is not concerned.   For instance, much material illustrating the Christian art of Egypt, together with a large collection of Gnostic gems, is in the Department of Egyptian and Assyrian Antiquities, while the Department of Manuscripts possesses an extensive series of Byzantine leaden seals.   In the custody of the Department of Greek and Roman Antiquities are a number of mosaic pavements of the Christian period obtained in Northern Africa.

The collections included in the Catalogue are naturally somewhat miscellaneous in character, and the various divisions are rather unequally represented.   For purposes of classification the whole has been divided into nine sections, viz.:—gems and rings, jewels, ivory carvings, silver, bronze, glass, pottery, sculptured stone, and miscellaneous antiquities.   Of these classes the gems, ivories, silver, and glass are the most important. The section of rings and gems was chiefly enriched by the acquisition of the cabinets of the Abbé Hamilton in 1856, and of Signor Castellani in 1865 and 1872 ; while the bequest in 1897 of the collection formed by Sir A. Wollaston Franks, K.C.B., added some of the finest examples to the series.   The section of jewellery profited to an equal degree by the generosity of the same benefactor, who indeed contributed in a greater or less proportion to the increase of all the classes enumerated.   Of the ivory carvings an important part was acquired in 1856, with the Maskell Collection, which included valuable examples of Early Christian Art such as the two sets of panels from caskets (nos. 291 and 292), one of which is well known among the earliest representations of the Crucifixion.   Among other private collections from which this section has been augmented, may be mentioned those of Mr. Alexander Nesbitt, from which the *pyxis* with the martyrdom of St. Menas was derived ; of Mr. Felix Slade, which included the remarkable panel (no. 299) with the Descent into Hell ; and of Mr. Rohde Hawkins, to which the series is indebted for a similar panel (no. 300) with the scene of the Nativity. The nucleus of the series of glass is formed by the fine set of gilded glasses (*fondi d'oro*) chiefly obtained by the purchase in 1854 and 1863 of the collections belonging to the Chevalier Bunsen, and the Counts Matarozzi of Urbania. Two exceptional pieces of the same class (nos. 628 and 629) came from the Disch and Herstatt Collections at Cologne, the more remarkable of the two (no. 628) having been bequeathed by Mr. Felix Slade in 1868. The two curious vases, perhaps chalices, of dark blue glass (nos. 658 and 659), one forming part of the same bequest, the other from the Pourtalès Collection, are also worthy of especial note. The section consisting of objects in silver is chiefly remarkable for the various Treasures which it contains. Foremost among these is that found in 1793 on the Esquiline Hill, including the famous Bridal Casket of Projecta (no. 304). The other treasures, that from Carthage (nos. 356–375); that found at Lampsacus in 1848 (nos. 376–396) comprising a set of inscribed spoons; and that discovered in Cyprus in recent years (nos. 397–424) are all worthy of mention, the last two being of especial interest from the occurrence on four vessels of several Byzantine stamps. The bronze section has a good series of weights and lamps, the latter including a fine example of a *polycandelon* (no. 529). The class of pottery, in addition to representative collections of lamps and pilgrims' flasks, contains in the so-called Constantine Bowl a remarkable example of the potter's art of the fourth century. Of all the sections, that of sculptured stone is the least satisfactory: the collection as a whole is pre-eminently one of small objects, sculptures and monumental inscriptions being alike scantily represented.

As far as the Early Christian Antiquities were concerned, the desirability of publication was long ago recognized, and in 1899 it was decided to print a catalogue. But as soon as a beginning had been made with the work, it became clear that the miscellaneous small objects in the possession of the Department illustrating the minor arts of the Christian East under the Byzantine Empire might be included with advantage. Exigencies of arrangement had brought the two classes together in a small room, and it seemed obviously appropriate that they should be comprised in a single volume. There was another reason which this course rendered desirable. Recent years have witnessed a remarkable revival in the study of Byzantine history and archaeology. In Germany and Russia reviews have been issued entirely confined to these subjects[1]. In France, and in a far less degree in our own country, a number of valuable books and monographs have been published, while Russian and Modern Greek scholars are devoting themselves to investigations for which they are so advantageously situated[2]. As a result of this activity, the evidence afforded by the minor arts is receiving more

---

[1] *Byzantinische Zeitschrift*, edited by Karl Krumbacher, Leipzig, from 1892; *Vizantiski Vremennik*, St. Petersburg, from 1894. The ' Materials for Russian Archaeology ' (Russian), published by the Imperial Archaeological Commission, St. Petersburg, also contains a number of important articles on Byzantine Archaeology. A new publication, *Oriens Christianus*, devoted to the antiquities of the Christian East has just appeared under the auspices of the German Campo Santo at Rome.

[2] Especial service has been rendered to students of the Minor Arts of the Christian East by the works of M. Gustave Schlumberger of Paris, and Professor J. Strzygowski of Gratz. To the study of enamels, silversmith's work, and ivory carvings, the researches of Professor N. Kondakoff, M. Smirnoff, and Dr. Hans Graeven are of fundamental importance.

and more attention from students of the history of the Later Roman Empire, so that the present moment seems propitious for rendering the collections in the British Museum more accessible by publication. But the proposal to include them in the Catalogue raised difficulties similar in character to those which had already affected the ordinary process of acquisition; it had to be decided whether all Byzantine antiquities were to be admitted, or only those which bore some obvious mark of Christian ownership. The latter alternative had been adopted for the beginning of the Christian era, with which period the Department of Greek and Roman Antiquities was equally concerned Theoretically no objects belonging to these early centuries were placed in the Christian Room which did not bear clear signs of Christian use, but contemporary pagan antiquities were included when they formed part of a single find with those of a religious character. This system was found to work well in practice, and is still continued. But in dealing with the period after the foundation of Constantinople, more especially in countries outside Europe, other difficulties arose, for the Greek and Roman Department does not acquire objects of so late a date. Byzantine antiquities which bore outward evidence of Christianity, that is to say a very large proportion of the whole, found their legitimate place in the Christian Room. But there were others without such evidence, which were in a sense beyond the pale, and might logically have been omitted. It seemed a matter of regret, however, that they should be altogether unrepresented in the National Collection, and they were consequently admitted on grounds of expediency. Their admission introduced an unavoidable complication, for it was now impossible to discriminate, as in the earlier period, between objects with signs of Christianity and those without; but it was felt that the material advantages of inclusion more than compensated for the want of uniformity. It was therefore decided that publication should follow the lines laid down for purposes of exhibition, and that the Catalogue should also comprise all objects of the Byzantine period without exception. This decision was confirmed by the acquisition of the above-mentioned Franks Bequest in 1897, which was separately exhibited, but contained a number of Byzantine objects which it was most desirable to make better known. The above development had, however, the effect of making the Catalogue unsymmetrical. Whereas for Eastern Christianity the close of the Middle Ages was adopted as a general limit, few western antiquities were admitted of a later date than the sixth century. The Romano-British, Teutonic, and Western Mediaeval Collections in the Department are destined to form the subject of independent catalogues[1], and the amalgamation of any part of them with the Christian Collection had never been in contemplation; Russian antiquities, which also form a class worthy of separate treatment, were omitted for similar reasons. An exception was only allowed in the case of one or two objects with Christian inscriptions, such as no. 541, which, though produced in countries under Teutonic dominion, stood in a more immediate relation to Roman civilization. The division thus adopted cannot

---

[1] A few Roman objects found in Britain, and now in the Romano-British collection of the Department, have upon them the sacred monogram ☧. They are four cakes of pewter stamped with the name Syagrius (see *Arch. Journ.*, vol. xvi, p. 38 and *Proceedings of the Society of Antiquaries of London*, Series II, vol. ii, p. 35); and a pewter dish found in Hampshire, on which the monogram is roughly scratched (see *Archaeologia*, vol. lvi (1898), p. 17).

but be open to criticism, for it is influenced to a certain extent by accidental conditions of arrangement; but it seemed that the publication of the available material should take precedence of all other considerations, and if the present opportunity had been allowed to pass, this might have been indefinitely postponed.

In the province of Early Christian Antiquities, which de Rossi and his numerous distinguished followers have so carefully explored, the date of most objects can be approximately determined. But in dealing with a subject like the minor arts of the Byzantine Empire, where there is so much untrodden ground, the case is very different. Here the danger of premature hypothesis must be set against the security of excessive caution. In the frequent absence of definite landmarks, conjecture is perhaps a greater evil than suspension of judgement, and it is better to err rather on the side of prudence than of temerity. Precise dates have therefore been sparingly assigned, and in many cases the age of an object has been left quite undetermined. But although decisive evidence is unfortunately rare, it is not altogether wanting. In a few cases objects are found associated with coins; for example nos. 252-255 were discovered with coins of Constantius, the ring no. 189 with coins of Heraclius, while the ring no. 210 contains a coin of Marcian. Internal evidence of a less conclusive nature is sometimes sufficient to date certain classes within comparatively narrow limits; for example, the occurrence of a particular form of letter or monogram, or the name of an office like that of Eparch which fell into desuetude after the sixth century, will often serve as a useful guide. Inscriptions cannot always be relied upon to afford exact indications of date, for where so large a proportion of objects are of the most varied material and the rudest workmanship, the different forms of letters cannot be easily differentiated; moreover, the study of Byzantine epigraphy has yet to be fully developed. The Museum has not the good fortune to possess one of those monuments which, like the Cross of Justin at Rome, the Reliquary of Cortona with the name of Nicephorus Phocas, or the ivory at Paris with those of Romanus IV and Eudocia, make explicit mention of historical persons. It is to rare instances of this kind that the most satisfactory attempts to introduce a chronological sequence in Byzantine antiquities are due; but even here the permanence of style which a comparison of dated ivories has revealed, proves that if Byzantine art was sometimes slow to rise it was often unexpectedly slow to fall. M. Molinier has truly said, that except in the rather improbable event of striking new discoveries, there must always be an element of uncertainty even in the dating of ivory carvings[1]. Much greater, therefore, is the chance of error in dealing with classes of antiquities which offer no such criteria as the dated ivories provide. In default of significant inscriptions, there remain other less direct indications which are not without value. Among these may be mentioned peculiarities of iconography; relation to historical epochs, or events such as the Arab invasions, the iconoclastic crisis, or the catastrophe of 1204; and finally the general style of workmanship and various technical or artistic affinities. But the value of these aids is naturally greatest in the case of the finer and more valuable works which have survived in the smallest numbers; the less pretentious objects do not lend themselves

---

[1] *Histoire générale des arts appliqués à l'industrie*, vol. i. *Ivoires*, p. 98, 1896.

so readily to exact classification, and it is of these that the collection is very largely composed.

Such are the data, scanty and inadequate at best, which enable us to associate different types or styles with different historical epochs. The early period which included the reigns of Theodosius and Justinian is not represented in the collection by many objects of artistic merit, though the lesser like the greater arts probably found their highest expression at that time. But the famous leaf of a diptych (no. 295) with the figure of the Archangel Michael, perhaps the finest surviving ivory carving ever produced in the East, is of this date; while some of the silver treasures are near enough in point of time to give a favourable idea of the silversmith's art. Of the workmanship of the iconoclastic interval and of the transitional period which followed it, marked as it sometimes was by a reversion to antique models often imperfectly understood, there are two examples among the ivory carvings (nos. 299 and 300) and perhaps one among the gems (no. 104). The period of the Basilian Dynasty, which witnessed so great an external expansion and so marked a revival of the arts within the Empire, is represented by fewer fine examples than are to be found in some other collections; but there are several rings and jewels (nos. 129 ff.) which can with probability be attributed to this time. The final phase of impoverishment and decay, initiated by the sack of Constantinople by the Crusaders, and concluded by the last victories of the Turks, is represented by work insignificant in character and feeble in execution. The difficulty in assigning accurate dates to Byzantine antiquities is perhaps greatest at the beginning and end of the Empire. Between the fourth and sixth centuries the respective claims of East and West are not easy to define, while at the opposite extremity it is hard to say where the Middle Ages pass into modern times. The desire to secure the publication of material which might otherwise remain unnoticed has prompted the inclusion of a few interesting objects, both early and late, which may ultimately be proved intruders. An instance of this latitude is afforded by certain gems in Section B (pp. 12 ff.), the attribution of which is by no means claimed as final. The point at which one archaeological period merges in another can seldom be exactly determined, for the time of transition is as indefinite as the twilight by which darkness is divided from day.

Although in the above paragraphs the word 'Byzantine' has been used for the sake of convenience, it will be observed that in the title, and generally in the Catalogue itself, it has been discarded in favour of the paraphrase 'from the Christian East.' The change has been made for several reasons. In the first place the word Byzantine implies too close an association with the metropolis of the Empire, to the exclusion of art-provinces like Syria and Egypt, the importance of which is daily being more widely recognized. It has been remarked by a French writer on Byzantine history that local differences even now stand out very clearly on the general background of artistic evolution. Thus there was a Byzantine art of Asia Minor, another of Syria, and a third of Egypt[1]. We can already anticipate the time when the antiquities of the Christian East will fall into their proper places in spheres well defined by local

---

[1] Ch. Diehl, *Justinien et la civilisation Byzantine au VI^{me} siècle*, p. 659 (Paris, 1901).

influence, and when that time arrives, the compromise here adopted will naturally be replaced by phrases of greater precision. In the meanwhile it may serve a useful purpose in so far as it suggests decentralization and implies that finality has not yet been reached. In the second place the term Byzantine has still for many minds a misleading connotation[1]. Although the old reproach of formalism is based upon a superficial view of the history and art of the Empire, the prejudice has struck such deep roots that the process of eradication must be slow. If the word as now too often used contributes even in a small degree to the perpetuation of an error, it is better that it should be abandoned where it is not absolutely necessary. A third advantage of the more general phrase is that it has no political associations, and thus permits the inclusion of isolated objects such as gems cut by Persian Christians (cf. no. 82), to which the terms 'Early Christian' and 'Byzantine' would not be wholly appropriate.

An attempt has been made in the index to illustrate the comparative fertility of different districts in Christian antiquities, the numbers of the objects being entered under the names of their respective countries in all cases where the localities are recorded in the Register of the Department. But as in a large number of cases actual records are wanting, the enumeration must not be taken as exhaustive; for instance, the prominence of Egypt and Syria would be yet greater if the index took account of probability in addition to registered facts. Yet, imperfect as they are, such lists serve a useful purpose by drawing the attention of the student to the geographical distribution of Christian remains. A metrical scale has been given on each plate, and a parallel scale of centimetres and inches will be found on p. 178. Throughout the Catalogue the dates immediately following the dimensions of objects indicate the year of acquisition.

The Trustees are indebted to the Society of Antiquaries of London, and to the Royal Archaeological Institute of Great Britain and Ireland, for the use of several blocks (pp. xiv, xxiv, and 186, and nos. 376, 379, 397–399, 400, 405, 424, 539) inserted in the text.

[1] On this subject *see* Professor Bury, *History of the Later Roman Empire*, vol. i, pp. viii and ix. (London, 1889.)

# LIST OF THE PRINCIPAL ABBREVIATIONS OF BOOK TITLES REFERRED TO IN THIS CATALOGUE

*Arch. Journ.*

    *The Archaeological Journal,* published under the direction of the Council of the Royal Archaeological Institute of Great Britain and Ireland. London, 1844 &c.

*Bonner Jahrbücher.*

    *Jahrbücher des Vereins von Altertumsfreunden im Rheinlande.* Bonn, 1842 &c.

*Byz. Zeitschr.*

    *Byzantinische Zeitschrift,* edited by K. Krumbacher. Leipzig, 1892 &c.

*C. I. G.* (1877.)

    A. Boeckh, *Corpus Inscriptionum Graecarum,* vol. iv. Berlin, 1877.

*C. I. L.*

    *Corpus Inscriptionum Latinarum.* Berlin 1863 &c.

D'AGINCOURT, *Peinture, Sculpture, &c.*

    Seroux d'Agincourt, *Histoire de l'art par les monuments.* Paris, 1823.

DELATTRE, 1890, 1893, &c.

    Delattre, Articles on terra-cotta lamps in *Revue de l'Art Chrétien.*

DE ROSSI, *Bullettino.*

    J. B. de Rossi, *Bullettino di Archeologia Cristiana.* Rome, 1863–1894.

DE VIT, *Onomasticon.*

    V. de Vit, *Totius Latinitatis Onomasticon.* Prato, 1859–1867.

FORRER, *Frühchristl. Altertümer.*

    R. Forrer, *Die frühchristlichen Altertümer aus dem Gräberfeld von Achmîm-Panopolis.* Strasburg, 1893.

GARRUCCI, *Storia.*

    R. Garrucci, *Storia dell' Arte Cristiana.* Prato, 1872–1880.

GARRUCCI, *Vetri.*

    R. Garrucci, *Vetri ornati di figure in oro.* 2nd ed. Rome, 1864.

GRAEVEN, *Elfenbeinwerke.*

    H. Graeven, *Frühchristliche und mittelalterliche Elfenbeinwerke in photographischer Nach-bildung.* Series I. Rome, 1898. *Aus Sammlungen in England.* Series II. Rome, 1900. *Aus Sammlungen in Italien.*

KING, *Antique Gems.*

    C. W. King, *Antique Gems and Rings.* London, 1860.

KRAUS, *Über Begriff, &c.*

    F. X. Kraus, *Ueber Begriff, Umfang, und Geschichte der christlichen Archäologie. Akademische Antrittsrede.* Freiburg, 1870.

KRAUS, *Real-Encykl.*

    F. X. Kraus, *Real-Encyklopädie der christlichen Alterthümer.* Freiburg, 1880–1886.

KRAUS, *Geschichte.*

    F. X. Kraus, *Geschichte der christlichen Kunst.* Freiburg, 1896.

*Mat. Russ. Arch.*

    *Materials for the Archaeology of Russia,* edited by the Imperial Archaeological Commission. St. Petersburg, 1888 &c. (Russian).

*Mitt. K. D. A. I.*

    *Mittheilungen des kaiserlich deutschen Archäologischen Instituts. Römische Abtheilung.* Rome, 1886 &c.

MOLINIER, *Ivoires.*

    E. Molinier, *Histoire génerale des arts appliqués à l'industrie du $V^{me}$ à la fin du $XVIII^{me}$ siècle.* Vol. i, *Les Ivoires.* Paris, 1896.

*Mon. Piot.*

    *Monuments et mémoires publiés par l'Académie des Inscriptions et Belles-Lettres, Fondation Eugène Piot.* Paris, 1894 &c.

PAPE-BENSELER, *Wörterbuch.*

    W. Pape, *Wörterbuch der griechischen Eigennamen,* edited by Dr. G. E. Benseler. Brunswick, 1863–1870.

PERRET.

    L. Perret, *Les Catacombes de Rome: architecture, peintures murales, inscriptions etc. des cimetières des premiers Chrétiens.* Paris, 1852–1855.

PITRA, *Spic. Sol.*

    J. B. Pitra, *Spicilegium Solesmense, etc.* Paris, 1852–1858.

*Proc. Soc. Ant.*

    *Proceedings of the Society of Antiquaries of London.* London, 1849 &c.

*R. Q. S.*

*Römische Quartalschrift für christliche Altertumskunde und für Kirchengeschichte*, edited by Dr. A. de Waal. Rome, 1887 &c.

*Rev. Arch.*

*Revue Archéologique.* Paris, 1844 &c.

SCHLUMBERGER, *Mélanges d'Arch. Byz.*

G. Schlumberger, *Mélanges d'Archéologie byzantine.* Paris, 1895.

SCHULTZE, *Arch. der altchristl. Kunst.*

V. Schultze, *Archäologie der altchristlichen Kunst.* Munich, 1895.

SCHULTZE, *Arch. Studien.*

V. Schultze, *Archäologische Studien über altchristliche Monumente.* Vienna, 1880.

SMITH and CHEETHAM.

Sir W. Smith and S. Cheetham, *A Dictionary of Christian Antiquities.* London, 1893.

STUHLFAUTH, *Elfenbeinplastik.*

G. Stuhlfauth, *Die altchristliche Elfenbeinplastik.* Heft ii of J. Ficker's *Archäologische Studien zum christlichen Altertum und Mittelalter.* Freiburg and Leipzig, 1896.

STUHLFAUTH, *Engel.*

G. Stuhlfauth, *Die Engel in der altchristlichen Kunst.* Heft iii of J. Ficker's *Archäologische Studien*, as above. Freiburg, 1897.

VOPEL.

H. Vopel, *Die altchristlichen Goldgläser.* Heft v of J. Ficker's *Archäologische Studien*, as above. Freiburg, 1899.

WESTWOOD, *Fictile Ivories.*

J. O. Westwood, *A Descriptive Catalogue of the Fictile Ivories in the South Kensington Museum.* London, 1876.

Enamelled Byzantine Cross in the Victoria and Albert Museum,
South Kensington. Back.

# CATALOGUE

OF

# EARLY CHRISTIAN ANTIQUITIES

## I. ENGRAVED GEMS AND RINGS

### A. Before 600 A.D. and mostly from Italy.

Those bearing symbols, such as The Good Shepherd, Anchor, &c., chiefly belong to the 3rd and 4th centuries. The reproductions in the plates I and II are twice the actual size.

### (i) GEMS.

#### (a) *Inscribed.*

1. BURNED PLASMA; the Good Shepherd standing full face and holding the sheep across his shoulders with both hands. To *r.* and *l.* the letters IH XP.

    > *Plate* I, *Row* 1.

    > L. ·4 in.  Hamilton Coll. 1856.
    > For the Good Shepherd on gems *see* Garrucci, *Storia*, pl. 477, nos. 1–17; Smith and Cheetham, vol. i, pp. 712, 713; and for a summary of the literature on the subject in general *see* Venturi, *Storia dell' Arte Italiana*, vol. i, p. 34 (Milan, 1901).

2. SARD; the Good Shepherd standing full face with head turned to *r.* regarding the sheep, which he holds with both hands across his shoulders. At his feet two recumbent sheep. Legend: Ӽ꙼Ѵ꙼Ꞓ꙼Ѵ, possibly a barbarized Greek inscription in Latin letters for 'Ιησοῦ υἱὲ Θεοῦ.

    > *Plate* I, *Row* 2.

    > L. ·56 in.  1865.
    > *See* Smith and Cheetham, vol. i, p. 712; King, *Antique Gems*, vol. ii. p. 30.

3. SARD; in the centre is a cross with bosses at the end (part of an anchor?) resting on a fish; upon the traverse stands a dove. The name IHC|OVC is inscribed to *r.* and *l.* of the anchor, and again at the top.

    > *Plate* II, *Row* 2.

    > L. ·56 in.  Hamilton Coll. 1856.
    > Perret, *Les Catacombes de Rome*, vol. iv, pl. xvi, fig. 7; Garrucci, *Storia*, pl. 477, fig. 46; Smith and Cheetham, vol. i, p. 713.  *See* also *C. I. G.* vol. iv (1856), no. 9089; King, *Antique Gems*, vol. ii, p. 29. A fragment has been broken from the upper part of the gem, upon which there was probably a second dove.

4. RED JASPER; an anchor with a dolphin upon the shaft. Legend: ΕΠΙΤΥΝΧΑΝΟΥ.

> *Plate* II, *Row* 2.

> L. ·5 in.  Hamilton Coll. 1856.
> Perret, vol. iv, pl. xvi, fig. 7; Garrucci, *Storia*, pl. 477, fig. 30; Smith and Cheetham, vol. i. p. 714.
> For the name of the owner Epitynchanus, cf. de Vit. *Onomasticon, s. v.*

5. GREEN JASPER; an anchor flanked by two dolphins; in the field the letters PLA.
> *Plate* II, *Row* 2.

> L. ·38 in.   Hamilton Coll. 1856.
> Perret, vol. iv, pl. xvi, fig. I; Garrucci, *Storia*, pl. 477, fig. 32.

6. SARD;  a dove standing to *l.* upon a fish and holding an olive-branch in its beak.  Before it is the sacred monogram; behind, the letters RVFI.
> *Plate* II, *Row* I.

> L. ·4 in.  Castellani Coll. 1865.
> Smith and Cheetham, vol. i, p. 713.
> The inscription gives the name of the owner, Rufus.

7. SARD; a hand holding a palm-branch.  Above, the sacred monogram; behind the wrist, the letter O of the word MNHMONEYE, the remaining letters of which are below.
> *Plate* II, *Row* 3.

> L. ·53 in.  Castellani Coll. 1865.
> Smith and Cheetham, vol. i, p. 716.
> On the formulae μνήσθητι, μνημόνευε, &c., *see* E. Le Blant in *Rev. Arch.* 1883, pp. 301–304.

8. RED JASPER, engraved with an inscription in four lines: MNHMON|EYEMOVΨY| XAPINAK|AKON.

> L. ·38 in.  1880.
> Cf. no. 7.

9. SARD; a wreath of two palm-branches enclosing the word IXθVC.
> *Plate* II, *Row* 3.

> L. ·52 in.  Hamilton Coll. 1856.
> *See* Smith and Cheetham, vol. i, p. 713, and cf. Ficoroni, *Gemmae Litteratae*, pt. ii, pl. xi, fig. 6; Garrucci, *Storia*, pl. 477, figs. 20, 21.
> On gems inscribed with ἰχθύς, *see* de Rossi, 'De Christianis Monumentis ἰχθύν Exhibentibus,' in Pitra, *Spicilegium Solesmense*, vol. iii, pp. 555, &c.

10. SARD; a triangle bisected by a straight line produced beyond the base, from which diverge two branches.  Across the apex is a rectangular bar, perhaps intended, with the vertical line to represent a T-cross. From the bar issue two horn-shaped objects, and across the triangle is the name MAPKOY.
> *Plate* II, *Row* 4.

> L. ·52 in.
> Cf. a gold ring, Garrucci, *Storia*, pl. 477, fig. 49, on the triangle as a Christian symbol, *see* de Rossi, in Pitra, as above, p. 514.

**11.** GOLD RING; the hoop of plaited wire with a thin wire along the middle and a pair of pellets on each side of the oval bezel, which is set with a red jasper, inscribed ΘΕΟC ΘΕΟΥ ΥΙΟC THPEI.

> L. ·34 in. Hamilton Coll. 1856.
>
> Perret, vol. iv, pl. xvi, fig. 14. The inscription *C. I. G.* vol. iv (1877), no. 9097. Cf. Smith and Cheetham, vol. i, p. 722.

**12.** SARD; the inscription DEVSDEDIT VIVAS IN DEO between the sacred monogram ✷ and a wreath.

> *See* figure.
>
> L. ·4 in. Castellani Coll. 1865.
>
> *See* Smith and Cheetham, vol. i, p. 717, and cf. Ficoroni, *Gemmae Litteratae*, pl. vii, fig. 20. For the name Deusdedit *see* de Vit. *Onomasticon, s. v.*

**13** BURNED CARNELIAN, pointed oval; Cameo inscription ISVVRASEN VIVAS IN DEO.

> L. ·7 in. Franks Coll. 1894.

**14.** SARD; cameo inscription ROGATE VIVAS IN DEO between two palm-branches.

> L. ·46 in. Given by A. J. Hanmer, Esq., 1886.

**15.** LENTICULAR AMETHYST; bust of a boy to *r.* with mantle fastened on the *r.* shoulder: legend: VIVAS IN DEO.

> *Plate* I, *Row* 4.
>
> L. ·5 in. Hamilton Coll. 1856.
>
> Perret, vol. iv, pl. xvi, fig. 16.

**16.** CHALCEDONY; male bust to *r.*; behind the head and before the chin a star; direct legend: DEVS AIY///ADISVNE?

> *Plate* I, *Row* 4.
>
> L. ·54 in. 1871.
>
> Mounted in a silver hoop of the seventeenth century.

**17.** BURNED CARNELIAN; a male figure wearing a mantle, walking to *r.* and extending the *l.* hand; over the *r.* shoulder is a cross. Direct legend: TAYPINOC.

> L. ·62 in. 1867.
>
> *See* Smith and Cheetham, vol. i, p. 716.
>
> For the name Ταύρινος *see* Pape-Benseler, *Wörterbuch, s. v.*, and J.-B. Chabot, *Index alphabétique . . . des inscriptions grecques et latines publiées par Waddington, s.v.* (Paris, 1897). The setting is modern.

### (b) *Uninscribed.*

**18.** RED JASPER, octagonal; the Good Shepherd walking to *r.* He wears a tunic and buskins, and holds a crooked staff in his *l.* hand. His *r.* grasps the legs of a ram which is carried across his shoulders. Near his *r.* leg is a sheep (?) and on the left is a tree.

> *Plate* I, *Row* 2.
>
> L. ·54 in. 1865.
>
> *See* Smith and Cheetham, vol. i, p. 712.

19. NICOLO; the Good Shepherd, between two sheep, holding another across his shoulders with both hands.

*Plate* I, *Row* 1.

L. ·52.   Hamilton Coll. 1856.

Cf. two gems at Ravenna, *Rev. Arch.* 1883, p. 300, pl. xii, figs. 1 and 4.

20. GREEN JASPER; the Good Shepherd, wearing a tunic and buskins, standing full face beneath a tree on which are two doves.  He supports the sheep across his shoulders with both hands: at his right foot is another sheep.

*Plate* I, *Row* 1.

L. ·43 in.   Hamilton Coll. 1856.

Perret, vol. iv, pl. xvi, fig. 6; Garrucci, *Storia*, vol. vi, pl. 477, fig. 15.

21. PYRAMIDAL ONYX, of three layers; hexagonal; the Good Shepherd, standing and holding the sheep across his shoulders with both hands.  On either side a fish.

*Plate* I, *Row* 1.

L. ·43 in.   Castellani Coll. 1865.

Garrucci, *Storia*, vol. vi, pl. 477, fig. 14.

22. RED JASPER; the Good Shepherd between two sheep holding another across his shoulders.  To *l.* a larger sheep; beneath, a tree on which is perched a dove.

*Plate* I, *Row* 2.

L. ·5 in.

Perret, vol. iv, pl. xvi, fig. 2; Garrucci, *Storia*, vol. vi, pl. 477, fig. 13.  *See* also Smith and Cheetham, vol. i, p. 717.

23. GREEN JASPER; two sheep standing to *r.* with three palm-branches.

*Plate* I, *Row* 3.

L. ·54 in.   Hamilton Coll. 1856.

Perret, vol. iv, pl. xvi, fig. 23.  *See* Smith and Cheetham, vol. i. p. 717.

24. SARD; four sheep standing upon an exergual line.

*Plate* I, *Row* 3.

L. ·5 in.   Cracherode Coll. 1799.

25. SARD; a composite subject.  To *l.* beneath a tree extending over half the gem, a figure with hands raised in the attitude of an *orans* flanked by two animals, possibly lions (the Prophet Daniel?).  In the middle, the Good Shepherd carrying the sheep across his shoulders; at his feet are two sheep, and below are two fish.  Above his head is a star, and beneath his *l.* arm a monogram, towards which flies a dove holding an olive-branch.  To *r.* is the Story of Jonah, with the ship, the monster, and the prophet reclining beneath the gourd, which extends over nearly half the gem, almost meeting the other tree.  Between the two trees is a star.

*Plate* I, *Row* 3.

L. ·7 in.   Hamilton Coll. 1856.

Perret, vol. iv, pl. xvi, fig. 8; Garrucci, *Storia,* vol. vii, pl. 477, fig. 8.  *See* also Smith and Cheetham, vol. i, p 717, and compare a gem at Ravenna, *Rev. Arch.* 1883, p. 300, pl. xii, fig. 2.

**26.** SARD ; the subject divided into two parts by a horizontal median line. In the upper part the Good Shepherd stands between two sheep with another across his shoulders. To *l.* is a hut or fold, and in the field above a dove. To *r.* Jonah reclines beneath the gourd, on which another dove is perched. In the lower part to *r.* is the monster perhaps swallowing the prophet as he falls from the ship in the centre ; to *l.*, a figure issuing from the ship, and apparently touching the heads of two kneeling figures. Above the ship is an anchor, below it a fish, while to the extreme *l.* a dove stands upon a rectangular object (the ark). Very rude workmanship. Originally in the possession of the Abate Foggini, *Sottocustode* of the Vatican Library.

> *Plate* I, *Row* 2.

> L. ·5 in.  Hamilton Coll. 1856.
> Costadoni, in Calogierà, *Raccolta d'opuscoli scientifici e filologici*, vol. xli, pl. opp. p. 246, no. xii (Venice 1749) ; Mamachi, *Originum et Antiquitatum Christianarum Libri XX* (Rome 1751), vol. iii, pl. ii, fig. 6 ; Perret, vol. iv, pl. xvi, fig. 5 ; Garrucci, *Storia*, vol. vi, pl. 477, fig. 12. Cf. also de Rossi, in Pitra, *Spic. Sol.* vol. iii, p. 577. Costadoni and Mamachi interpret in a different manner the subject of the lower part of the gem.

**27.** SAPPHIRE ; the sacred monogram combined with a ⊤-cross.

> *Plate* I, *Row* 4.

> L. ·4 in.  Hamilton Coll. 1856.
> Perret, vol. iv, pl. xvi, fig. 18. *See* King, *Antique Gems*, vol. ii, p. 28 ; Smith and Cheetham, vol. i, p. 717. Cf. for this form of monogram Aringhi, *Roma Sotterranea*, vol. ii, p. 705 ; Gorlaeus, *Dactyliotheca* (ed. Gronovius), pl. i, no. 211 ; Fortnum in *Arch. Journ.* vol. xxviii (1871), p. 271.

**28.** GOLD RING ; the hoop angular on the outer side ; projecting oval bezel containing a nicolo paste engraved with a composite form of the sacred monogram.

> *See* figure.

> D. 1·4 in.  D. of bezel, ·78 in.  Payne Knight Coll. 1824.
> *See* Smith and Cheetham, vol. ii, p. 1793.
> For this form of monogram *see* Roller, *Les Catacombes*, &c., vol. ii, p. 296.

**29.** BRONZE RING, with plain rounded hoop and oval bezel set with a red cabochon paste engraved in intaglio with the sacred monogram combined with an anchor.

> D. ·8 in.  D. of bezel, ·4 in.  Franks Coll. 1894.
> The hoop broken at the back.

**30.** CARNELIAN ; part of a ring cut from the solid, with flat oval bezel engraved in intaglio with a dove to *r.* holding an olive-branch in its beak.

> D. ·75 in.  L. of bezel, ·34 in.  Hamilton Coll. 1856.
> *See* Fortnum in *Arch. Journ.* xxvi (1869), p. 140, note 1. It may be mentioned here that the Fortnum collection of rings is now in the Ashmolean Museum at Oxford.
> The greater part of the hoop wanting.

**31.** GOLD RING, with plain hoop and oval bezel, with a pair of pellets at each end, containing an oval sapphire, engraved in intaglio with a dove to *l.* holding a branch in its beak.

*Plate* II, *Row* 1.

L. ·4 in. 1862.

**32.** OVAL PYRAMIDAL SARD ; a bird perched upon a tree.

*Plate* II, *Row* 4.

L. ·42 in.   Hamilton Coll. 1856.
Perret, vol. iv, pl. xvi, fig. 9.

**33.** ALMANDINE GARNET ; a dove to *l.* standing upon a branch ; above, a star.

*Plate* II, *Row* 1.

L. ·36 in.   Hamilton Coll. 1856.
Perret, vol. iv, pl. xvi, fig. 22 ; cf. Garrucci, *Storia*, vol. vi, pl. 478, figs. 7 and 8.

**34.** SQUARE CARNELIAN ; a dove to *r.* standing on a fish and holding an olive-branch in its beak ; before it, a palm-branch.

*Plate* II, *Row* 1.

L. ·38 in.   Given by A. J. Hanmer, Esq., 1886.
Set in a silver hoop of the 17th century.

**35.** SARD ; a fish to *r.* ; above, a shepherd's crook ; below, a palm-branch.

*Plate* II, *Row* 1.

L. ·45 in.   Hamilton Coll. 1856.
Perret, vol. iv, pl. xvi, fig. 3.   *See* also Smith and Cheetham, vol. i. p. 713.

**36.** SARD ; two fish above a hemispherical basket with two handles.

*Plate* II, *Row* 3.

L. ·4 in.   Hamilton Coll. 1856.
Perret, vol. iv, pl. xvi, fig. 24.   Cf. Garrucci, *Storia*, vol. vi, pl. 478, fig. 2.   On the fish represented with the basket, *see* de Rossi, in Pitra, *Spicilegium Solesmense*, vol. iii, pp. 564, 565.

**37.** SARD ; an anchor flanked by two fishes.

*Plate* II, *Row* 3.

L. ·4 in.   Given by A. J. Hanmer, Esq., 1886.
Cf. Garrucci, *Storia*, vol. vi, pl. 477, figs. 29, &c. ; *Rev. Arch.* 1883, p. 301, and pl. xii, fig. 5 (carnelian at Ravenna) ; Forrer, *Frühchristl. Altertümer*, pl. xiii, fig. 5 ; a gem in the Le Blant Collection, Bibliothèque Nationale, Paris ; Janssen, L., *Nederlandsche Romeinsche Daktyliothek*, nos. 183, 184, pl. viii (Leyden, 1844).

**38.** ONYX ; an anchor flanked by two fishes.

*Plate* I, *Row* 3.

L. ·36 in.   Hamilton Coll. 1856.

**39.** CHALCEDONY ; an anchor, on the traverse of which stand two doves.   On each side of the shank is a fish and a palm-branch.

*Plate* II, *Row* 2.

L. ·7 in.   Castellani Coll. 1872.

**40.** SARD; a galley with sail furled, the yard and mast forming a cross. It is being rowed to *l.*, three oars being visible with the heads of three rowers. Above the stern, a cross potent.

*Plate* II, *Row* 4.

L. ·36 in. Castellani Coll. 1865.

Smith and Cheetham, vol. i, p. 715. *See* also Fortnum, *Arch. Journ.* vol. xxvi (1869), p. 140 note; Schultze, *Arch. der altchrist. Kunst*, p. 304. On symbolism of the ship, *see* de Rossi, in Pitra, as above, p. 563.

**41.** CHALCEDONY; a palm-branch crossing a wreath.

L. ·54 in. 1881.

Cf. Ficoroni, *Gemmae Litteratae*, pl. iii, figs. 3, 5, 7, 9, &c.

**42.** NICOLO; Adam and Eve; between them the serpent twined round the tree.

*Plate* I, *Row* 1.

L. ·54 in. Castellani Coll. 1872.

**43.** CARNELIAN; the Crucifixion. In the centre, upon an exergual line, a nude figure of our Lord, facing the spectator, but with the head and feet turned to *r.* Behind the figure is a T-shaped cross, beneath the traverse of which the arms are extended without any apparent means of attachment. On each side stand six small draped figures representing the twelve apostles; above is the word IXΘYC. Owing to a fracture, the first letter of the inscription and three of the small figures are imperfect. A very early representation of the Crucifixion. Found at Constanza (Kustendje), Roumania, with other gems dating from the 1st to the 3rd century.

*Plate* I, *Row* 4.

L. ·54 in. Franks Coll. 1895.

C. H. Smith in *Annual of the British School at Athens*, 1896–7, fig. on p. 202 (discussed on pp. 202–206).

Cf. a gem with Crucifixion in Garrucci, *Storia*, pl. 479, fig. 15; a green jasper, in the Collection at Corpus Christi College, Cambridge, *see* Middleton, *The Lewis Collection of Gems and Rings*, &c., Class E, no. 1, p. 84, Cambridge, 1892; the ivory, no. 291 below; and the panel of the doors of St. Sabina, Rome, *see* Wiegand, *Das altchristliche Hauptportal an der Kirche der heiligen Sabina*, pl. iv, Trier, 1900. Other examples of the Crucifixion treated in a primitive and unrealistic manner may be seen on an amulet from Egypt in the Bibliothèque Nationale, Paris (Cabinet des Médailles), Fig. Schlumberger, *Byz. Zeitschr.*, 1893, p. 188 (6th or 7th century); on a Monza Ampulla (cf. Garrucci, *Storia*, pl. 434. 4); and on objects from Akhmîm (Panopolis) (Forrer and Müller, *Kreuz und Kreuzigung Christi in ihrer Kunstentwicklung*, p. 16 ff. Strasburg, 1894). The primitive type is also perpetuated on a silver dish from Syria, *see* Smirnoff, 'A Syrian Silver Dish from Perm' in *Mat. Russ. Arch.* no. 22 (St. Petersburg, 1899).

**44.** GOLD RING; the hoop rounded on the outer side and embossed on each side of the bezel with a meandering vine-stem, on which is perched a bird picking at a bunch of grapes; the ground is punched with small dots, and below the bezel on each side is a small embossed ring or circle. The bezel is oval, containing a pyramidal garnet engraved in intaglio with a draped

figure seated full face upon a cushioned stool with both arms raised as if in the attitude of an *orans*. On each side of the head is a cross.

    *See* figure.

      D. 1·1 in.   L. of bezel, ·64 in.   Castellani Coll. 1872.

      *See* Fortnum in *Arch. Journ.* xxviii (1871), p. 281, no. 3 ; Smith and Cheetham, vol. i, p. 716.

**45.** CARNELIAN ; male bust to *r.* flanked by two crosses.

      L. ·36 in.   Franks Bequest, 1897.

## (ii) RINGS WITHOUT GEMS.

### (a) *Inscribed.*

**46.** SILVER RING, with rounded hoop thickest at the back, where there is a revolving bronze key. To the front is applied a flat, oval, silver bezel, very rudely engraved in intaglio with a fisherman seated to *r.* drawing a fish out of the water with a rod and line. In the field the inscr. CALVATOP (?) in a mixture of Greek and Latin characters irregularly placed and partially reversed. The shape of the hoop, characteristic of a period much earlier than Christianity, the combination of two metals, and the peculiarity of the inscription, are all points worthy of remark.

    *See* figure.

      D. 1·2 in.   L. of bezel, ·36 in.   Franks Bequest, 1897.

      Cf. a gem in Garrucci, *Storia*, vol. vi, pl. 477, fig. 18.

      On the symbol of the fisherman *see* Smith and Cheetham, vol. i, p. 715 ; de Rossi, in Pitra, as above, p. 577 ; Macarius, *Hagioglypta*, p. 111 (ed. Garrucci, Paris, 1856), &c.

**47.** GOLD, CIRCULAR BEZEL of a ring engraved in intaglio with the letters MCSDR between two doves to *r.* each holding a branch in its beak.

      D. ·45 in.

**48.** GOLD RING ; the hoop is angular and fluted on the outer side, and has an oval bezel set with an emerald engraved in intaglio with a fish ; at the back is a second bezel slightly raised, and engraved in intaglio with a bird upon a tree, on either side and at the bottom of which are the letters of the name AEMILIA.

    *See* figure.

      D. 1 in.   L. of gem ·32 in.   Hamilton Coll. 1856.

      Perret, vol. iv, pl. xvi, fig. 4 ; Garrucci, *Storia*, vol. vi, pl. 477, fig. 22.

      *See also* de Rossi, in Pitra, as above, p. 577, no. 97 ; Martigny, *Les Anneaux chez les premiers Chrétiens*, &c., p. 17 ; Fortnum in *Arch. Journ.* xxvi (1869), p. 142, and xxviii (1871), p. 273 ; King, *Antique Gems*, vol. ii, p. 29 ; Smith and Cheetham, vol. ii, p. 713, and vol. ii, p. 1792.

      De Rossi, who erroneously supposes the ring to be set with *two* gems, says of it, *fuit in musaeo Imolensi Iulii Caesaris Ginnasii*. King assigns it to the early part of the 3rd century on the analogy of the Tarsus Treasure (*Antique Gems*, vol. i, p. 344).

**49.** GOLD KEY-RING ; the broad hoop fluted externally with twelve vertical channels, and ornamented above and below with a pierced and foliated scroll border. In the centre of the channel are pierced square apertures, eleven of which have reserved in the metal one letter of the inscription MVLTIS ANNIS, while the twelfth has a leaf. On the front are the words ACCIPE DVLCIS in two horizontal lines between three plain bands of metal, thus making the whole inscription *Accipe dulcis multis annis.* Above is a rectangular projection pierced with a diaper of nine Greek crosses connected by pellets ; it is ornamented laterally by a cable border, and on the top with a pierced scroll.

> *See* figure.

> D. 1·04 in. Franks Bequest, 1897. Found in Egypt.
> Fortnum in *Arch. Journ.* vol. xxix (1872), p. 305 ; Fröhner, *Les Musées de France*, pl. 38, figs. 9 and 10 (Paris, 1873).
> A ring of very similar style was found at Tirlemont in Belgium about 1894, and is believed to be in private possession. Cf. also a ring formerly in the Castellani Collection, and sold in Rome in 1884. *See* Sale Catalogue, no. 928, p. 120. For rings with similar openwork inscriptions *see* Fortnum, *Arch. Journ.* vol. xxvi (1869), p. 141, no. 5 (gold ring in Fortnum Coll.), and *Arch. Journ.* vol. vii (1850), p. 191 (gold ring found near Corbridge-on-Tyne, and belonging to the Duke of Northumberland).

**50.** BRONZE RING, with flat polygonal hoop engraved on the outer side with the sacred monogram ☧ between A and ⲱ, and the inscr. ARBORI VIBAS IN CRISTO.

> D. 1·02 in. Franks Bequest, 1897.
> For name Arborius *see* de Vit, *Onomasticon, s. v.*

**51.** GOLD RING, with flat polygonal hoop engraved on the outer side with a palm branch followed by the inscr. MARFINIANVS VIVAS.

> D. 1·08 in. Franks Bequest, 1897. From Brackeland near Jülich. *See Bonner Jahrbücher*, Heft lxxiii (1882), p. 85, note 1, & lxxiv (1882), p. 64.
> Cf. two rings described by Fortnum in *Arch. Journ.* vol. xxvi (1869), p. 140. The name Marfinianus is not given by de Vit, who only has Marfus and Martinianus.

**52.** BRONZE RING, with plain hoop and oval bezel engraved VIV|AS in two lines.
> D. ·88 in. L. of bezel, ·53 in. Franks Bequest, 1897.

**53.** SILVER RING, with plain hoop expanding into an oval bezel engraved VIBAS.
> D. ·74 in. Castellani Coll. 1872.

**54.** BRONZE RING, with flat hoop and rectangular bezel engraved with a reversed inscr. : VIVAS IN DIO in two lines.
> D. ·88 in. L. of bezel, ·45 in. Franks Bequest, 1897.
> Cf. bronze ring in Vatican ; *see* Fortnum in *Arch. Journ.* vol. xxviii (1871), p. 279, no. 6.

**55**. SILVER, CIRCULAR BEZEL of a ring engraved in intaglio with the bust of a youth to *r*., surrounded by the inscr. VIVAS.

> D. ·47 in.   Franks Bequest, 1897.   From Naples.

**56**. SILVER, CIRCULAR BEZEL of a ring engraved in intaglio with a male bust to *r*., surrounded by the inscr. GVRDA VI(VAS).

> D. ·4 in.   Franks Bequest, 1897.   From Naples.

**57**. SILVER, OVAL BEZEL of a ring engraved in intaglio with a male bust to *r*. surrounded by an inscription, C////C////IO, apparently a Latin name, at the end of which is V for VIVAS.
> *See* figure.

> D. ·34 in.   Franks Bequest, 1897.   From Rome.

**58**. GOLD RING ; the outer surface facetted horizontally, the bezel flat and octagonal with a circular medallion in low relief inscribed ARGYR VIVAS.

> D. ·64 in.   D. of bezel, ·36 in.   Franks Bequest, 1897.   From Rome.
> The name is possibly *Argyrius*; *see* de Vit, *Onomasticon, s. v.*

**59**. BRONZE RING, with plain hoop and projecting square bezel engraved with the inscr. in three lines MER|CVR|IVIV.

> D. 1·18 in.   L. of bezel, ·4 in.   Franks Bequest, 1897.
> Cf., for shape, ring figured by Fortnum in *Arch. Journ.* vol. xxvi (1869), p. 145, no. 20.   For the name Mercurius, *see* de Vit, *Onomasticon, s. v.*

**60**. GOLD RING ; the hoop double in front with oval bezels, on the upper of which is engraved BLITHIA, on the lower a monogram perhaps representing the same name.
> *See* figure.

> D. 1 in.   L. of bezel, ·4 in.   Castellani Coll. 1872.   Found at Orvieto.
> *See* Fortnum in *Arch. Journ.* vol. xxvii (1871), p. 281, no. 2 ; Smith and Cheetham, vol. ii. p. 1798.   The name may represent *Blitia* or *Blicia* ; *see* de Vit, *Onomasticon, s. v.*

**61**. BRONZE RING, with plain hoop ; the bezel in the form of the sole of a shoe and engraved with the direct letters OER between two crosses.

> D. 1 in.   Franks Bequest, 1897.
> On shoe-shaped ring-stamps, *see* Fortnum in *Arch. Journ.* vol. xxviii (1871), p. 289, and *Rev. Arch.* 1883, p. 53.

**62**. SILVER RING, with angular shoulders and pointed oval bezel engraved ·ⳁⲈⲨⲤⲈ.
> ᵇ

> D. ·92 in.   L. of bezel, ·5 in.   Castellani Coll. 1872.
> For the name Eusebius, *see* de Vit, *Onomasticon, s. v.*   The family of the Eusebii became prominent in the middle of the 4th century.

**63**. SILVER RING, with plain rounded hoop and flat oval bezel engraved in intaglio with a bird to *r*. holding a branch in its beak.

> D. ·82 in.   L. of bezel, ·36 in.   Hamilton Coll. 1856.

64. GOLD RING, with plain hoop expanding into a bezel engraved with a palm-branch, above and below which are characters probably representing the words AMA MƎ.
> *See* figure.
>
> D. ·7 in.  Franks Bequest, 1897.  Found at Carlisle.

### (b) Uninscribed.

65. SILVER RING, with plain hoop expanding into a bezel on which is engraved a palm-branch.
> D. ·74 in.  Hamilton Coll. 1856.

66. GOLD RING ; the hoop very slender at the back and expanding to an oval bezel engraved with a palm-branch.
> D. ·66 in.  L. of bezel, ·3 in.  Franks Bequest, 1897.

67. GOLD RING, with flat hoop expanding into a bezel engraved with a palm-branch, above which there rises from the edge a circular setting containing a green paste.
> D. ·6 in.  Franks Bequest, 1897.

68. GOLD RING, with flat octagonal hoop and circular bezel in low relief engraved with an anchor in a vertical position.
> D. ·74 in.  Franks Bequest, 1897.
> Cf. *Rev. Arch.* 1883, p. 53.

69. GOLD RING, with flat hoop and raised oval bezel engraved with a horizontal anchor.
> D. ·72 in.  Castellani Coll. 1872.
> *See* Fortnum in *Arch. Journ.* vol. xxviii (1871), p. 281, no. 1 ; Smith and Cheetham, vol. ii. p. 1795.

70. BRONZE RING, with plain slender hoop and oval bezel engraved in intaglio with a galley with six oars visible on one side ; mast and yard forming a cross.
> *Plate* II, *Row* 4.
>
> D. ·94 in.  L. of bezel, ·5 in.  Castellani Coll. 1872.
> *See* Fortnum in *Arch. Journ.* vol. xxviii (1871), pp. 274 and 281, no. 6 ; and cf. no. 40 above.

71. BRONZE RING, with spirally fluted hoop and projecting circular bezel engraved in intaglio with a galley to *r.*, above which is the sacred monogram inscribed in a circle.
> *Plate* II, *Row* 4.
>
> D. 1 in.  D. of bezel, ·5 in.  Castellani Coll. 1872.
> Garrucci, *Storia*, vol. vi, pl. 478, fig. 14.

72. BRONZE RING ; the hoop triangular in section ; flat pointed oval bezel engraved with the sacred monogram ⚸.
> D. ·96 in.  D. of bezel, ·5 in.  Franks Bequest, 1897.

73. BRONZE SIGNET RING, with plain hoop and circular bezel engraved with the sacred monogram  .
> D. ·8 in.  D. of bezel, ·3 in.  Franks Bequest, 1897.  Obtained in Rome.

**74.** BRONZE SIGNET RING, with plain hoop triangular in section; rectangular bezel engraved with sacred monogram ⳩ within a cable border.

> D. 1 in.   L. of bezel, ·34 in.   Franks Bequest, 1897.

**75.** CIRCULAR BRONZE BEZEL of a signet ring engraved with the sacred monogram ⳩ between two dots.

> D. ·5 in.   Franks Bequest, 1897.

**76.** BRONZE SIGNET RING, with plain hoop and oval bezel engraved with A ⳩ ω.

> D. ·9 in.   L. of bezel, ·52 in.   Franks Bequest, 1897.

**77.** GOLD RING, with plain hoop and circular openwork bezel containing the sacred monogram ☦.

> D. ·9 in.   D. of bezel, ·4 in.   Franks Bequest, 1897.

**78.** GOLD RING, with octagonal facetted hoop; the bezel is an applied setting in the form of the sacred monogram ☦, originally containing stones now lost.

> *See* figure.

> D. ·91 in.   D. of bezel, ·44 in.   Castellani Coll. 1872.
> *See* Fortnum in *Arch. Journ.* vol. xxviii (1871), p. 281, no. 5; Smith and Cheetham, vol. ii, p. 1793.

**79.** BRONZE RING; the hoop expanding to flat angular shoulders, on each of which is a star. The bezel is a square truncated pyramid of three steps engraved with an equal-armed cross.

> D. 1·16 in.   L. of bezel, ·32 in.   Franks Bequest, 1897.   From Catania, Sicily.
> Cf., for shape, Fortnum in *Arch. Journ.* vol. xxvi (1869), p. 143.

**80.** BRONZE RING, with plain hoop expanding to the front, on which is engraved a cross.

> D. ·72 in.   Franks Bequest, 1897.

**81.** SILVER RING, with plain hoop and flat oval bezel engraved with a cross.

> D. ·92 in.   L. of bezel, ·22 in.   Franks Bequest, 1897.

## B. From the Christian East.

### (i) GEMS.

#### (a) *Intaglios.*

**82.** CARNELIAN, hemispherical and pierced horizontally; two angels kneeling and holding a wreath over a cross between them. Below, a Pehlevi inscription.

> D. ·5 in.   1889.
> On other Christian gems of the Sassanian period *see* King, *Antique Gems*, p. 84; Smith and Cheetham, vol. i, pp. 721, 722; Chabouillet, *Catalogue Général des Camées et Pierres gravées de la Bibliothèque Impériale*, nos. 1330–1333 (Paris, 1858).

**83.** GREEN JASPER; a sheaf of corn or palm-tree between two birds, behind each of which is a palm-branch (?). Above, the inscr. Αναςασι τ8 δημ8.
*See* figure.

> L. ·75 in. Hamilton Coll. 1856.
> *See* Smith and Cheetham, vol. i, p. 715; and cf. no. 222.
> The character of the letters of the inscription points to a comparatively late date when the word δῆμος could only mean one of the factions of the Circus at Constantinople. The first word is therefore perhaps the proper name 'Αναστάσιος.

**84.** ROCK CRYSTAL; a draped figure with nimbus riding sideways upon a horse walking to *l.*, and extending the *r.* hand towards a cross potent in the upper part of the field. Before the horse walks an angel in a long mantle looking back towards the horseman.
*See* figure. *6th or 7th century.*

> L. 1·2 in. 1879. Obtained in Alexandria.
> The position of the rider with both legs on the same side of the horse is an indication that this gem was made in the East. With it may be compared a garnet intaglio of the Sassanian period in the British Museum (Assyrian Room, no. 587, Case J, figured by Smirnoff in *Mat. Russ. Arch.* no. 22 (1899), p. 38, fig. 12); a sard from Erbil at Berlin (Horn und Steindorff, *Sassanidische Siegelsteine*, Königliche Museen zu Berlin, 1891, no. 865 and p. 5); and a gem given by Furtwängler, *Die antiken Gemmen* (Berlin, 1900), pl. lxvii, fig. 6.

**85.** SILVER RING, with plain hoop and oval bezel with gold border containing a nicolo engraved in intaglio with an angel standing to *r.* and holding a long cross.

> D. 1·05 in. L. of bezel, ·6 in. Franks Bequest, 1897.
> With this and the following two numbers cf. a crystal intaglio from Cyprus in the Bibliothèque Nationale, Paris; Babelon, *Guide illustré au Cabinet des Médailles*, no. 2165 *bis*, p. 63 (Paris, 1900).

**86.** HAEMATITE, oval; an angel standing to *r.* and holding a long cross potent.

> L. ·44 in. 1881.

**87.** HAEMATITE; part of a larger gem. *Obv.:* an angel walking to *l.* holding a long cross potent. *Rev.:* a draped figure with radiating nimbus standing in front of, or seated on, a chair and holding out in his *r.* hand a long cross potent. Below, in the corner of the field, a cross potent with equal arms; round the edge a herring-bone border.
*See* figure.

> L. 1·18 in. 1881.

**88.** HAEMATITE ; part of a larger oval gem.  *Obv.* : a nude bearded figure standing to *r.* and holding in his *r.* hand a staff with a small cross at the upper end.  Round the side the inscription ΑΠΟΛΩΝΙϹ Ο ΤΟΥΑΝΕΟΥϹΜ · · ·  *Rev.* : a pharos approached by steps, on the top of which is a statue holding up the *l.* hand behind the head, which is surrounded by rays, and holding a globe in the *r.*  To *r.* and *l.* are buildings with gabled roofs surmounted by crosses, and in the background is the sea, on which are visible part of a ship with men in it, a fish (?), &c.  In the foreground a man fishing.

    *See* figure.

    L. 1·3 in.  1886.

    Apollonius of Tyana lived for some time at Aegeae (Aegae) in Cilicia (Philostr. *Vita Ap.* i, 7). The town was a naval station, and some of its coins have a lighthouse surmounted by a figure and with ships beside it.  *See British Museum, Cat. of Greek Coins* ; Lycaonia and Cilicia, p. cxv.

**89.** ONYX of two layers ; in the upper brown layer a rude intaglio representing two draped figures apparently with swords (?) at their sides, standing with their *r.* hands joined and holding a long cross potent.  Round the field and on each side of the cross a debased inscription.  The white layer is pierced for suspension below the figures.

    *6th or 7th century?*

    L. 1·4 in.  1884.

    Cf. an onyx intaglio at Paris, Babelon, *Guide illustré au Cabinet des Médailles,* p. 64, no. 2167 *bis* ; for gems of a similar rough style, *see* Horn und Steindorff, *Sassanidische Siegelsteine,* pl. i, no. 865, &c. (Berlin, 1891).

**90.** GREEN JASPER ; the Entry into Jerusalem.  Our Lord riding to *l.* upon an ass, sideways, with his *r.* hand raised.  Before him a bearded man advances with both hands extended as if to lay a garment in the way ; to *l.*, behind this figure, is a tree.  To *r.*, behind our Lord, are two other figures, one holding up a palm-branch ; in the field above these, a detached palm-branch.  Very rough workmanship.

    *See* figure.

    L. ·56 in.

    *See* King, *Antique Gems and Rings,* vol. ii. p. 31, and *Gnostics,* p. 140 ; Smith and Cheetham, vol. i. p. 718.  The gem is probably of Egyptian or Syrian origin.

**91.** BLACK JASPER, oval ; the Virgin with the Child enthroned between two standing figures in long garments, behind each of whom is a tree or palm-branch ; above, two flying angels.  Both the principal figures have the nimbus, that of the Child being cruciferous.  Very rough workmanship.

    L. ·6 in.  *See* Smith and Cheetham, vol. i, p. 719 ; King, *Antique Gems,* vol. ii, p. 31.

**92.** OVAL CHALCEDONY, engraved in intaglio with the Virgin seated full face on a throne with cushion and high back: on her knees is the Child. Rude workmanship.

*See* figure.

L. ·82 in. 1884.

**93.** OVAL PYRAMIDAL RED JASPER, engraved with a monogram; modern setting.

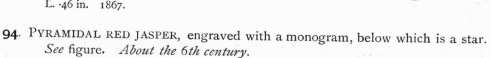

*See* figure. *About the 6th century.*

L. ·46 in. 1867.

**94.** PYRAMIDAL RED JASPER, engraved with a monogram, below which is a star.

*See* figure. *About the 6th century.*

L. ·6 in. Obtained in Athens. 1890.

**95.** PYRAMIDAL YELLOW JASPER, engraved with a monogram, below which is a recumbent jerboa (?) to *r.*

*See* figure. *About the 6th century.*

L. ·62. Obtained in Athens. 1890.

**96.** PALE SAPPHIRE, oval, engraved with a cruciform monogram  perhaps representing the name Thomas.

L. ·34 in. 1867.

**97.** STEATITE SEAL, bell-shaped, with pierced sides, perforated at top for suspension. It is engraved in intaglio with a figure of our Lord with cruciferous nimbus wearing a tunic, and standing with the arms extended horizontally. To *l.* is a bird; to *r.* a lion.

*See* figure.

H. ·8 in. 1888. From Cyprus.

**98.** STEATITE SEAL, of similar shape, engraved in intaglio with a figure of the Virgin in the attitude of an *orans.* On either side $\overline{\text{MP}}$ $\overline{\text{ΘY}}$ (Μήτηρ Θεοῦ).

H. ·6 in. 1896.

**99.** STEATITE SEAL, of similar shape, rudely engraved in intaglio with a bust of a saint. On either side the letters of an inscription.

H. ·84 in. 1888. From Cyprus.

**100.** STEATITE SEAL, of similar shape, rudely engraved with a half-figure of a saint in the attitude of an *orans.* Very rude work.

H. ·72 in. 1889.

## (*b*) *Cameos.*

With the cameos strictly so called are included small carvings in steatite and other stone. The best of these belong to the eleventh or twelfth century; the inferior examples are probably later.

101. ONYX of three layers, one of pale blue between two of deep brown. A bearded man in a biga to *l.*, his *r.* hand raised and holding a whip; the horses are guided by an angel flying above them.

> *See* figure.   *4th to 6th century.*

> D. ·92 in.   Hamilton Coll. 1856.

102. SARD; a horse to *r.* surrounded by the legend: ☩ ΚΥΡΙΗ ΒΟΗΘΙ ΙΟΥΛΙΑΝѠ (Κύριε βοήθει Ἰουλιανῷ).

> *See* figure.

> L. ·58 in.   Castellani Coll. 1872.

103. ONYX of two layers, white and red. A beardless bust to *r.* with a horn of Ammon above the ear, copied from a portrait of Alexander the Great. Legend: ΤΗC ΚΑΛΗC ΤΥΧΗC ΜΝΗΜΟΝΕΥΕ ΜΝΗΙΘΗΕΥΤΙ (μνήσθητι).

> *See* figure.   *4th to 6th century.*

> L. 1·1 in.   Franks Bequest, 1897.
> Cf. a cameo of the same class with a head of Jupiter Serapis and a similar inscription containing the word μνημόνευε, in an American Collection; *see* M. Sommerville, *Engraved Gems, their History and Place in Art*, no. 1431, pl. xlviii (Philadelphia, 1889). The usual formula has ψυχῆς instead of τύχης. But *see* Spon, *Miscellanea Eruditae Antiquitatis*, &c., p. 297, no. v (Lyon, 1685). On mottoes of this class *see* Millin, *Monumens Antiques Inédits*, &c., pp. 66–68 (Paris, 1806); *Bonner Jahrbücher*, xxxiii–iv, 1863, pp. 238, 239; *Rev. Arch.* 1879, p. 43, and 1883, pp. 303, 304.

104. ONYX of two layers, white on black; the Annunciation. To *r.* the Virgin with nimbus, standing in a long mantle drawn over her head, her *r.* hand raised. To *l.* the archangel Gabriel in the form of a nude winged genius holding up his *l.* arm as if speaking, while above his head is engraved a circle in which are conventional flames or rays of light. In the field, above, Ο ΧΑΙΡΕΤΙCΜΟC; lower, Ο ΑΡΧ ΓΑΒΡΙΗΛ and M̅P̅ Θ̅Y̅.

> *Plate* III (from a cast).   *9th century.*

> L. ·72 in.   Hertz Coll. 1859.   *Proc. of the Society of Antiquaries of London*, vol. xviii (1900–1), p. 365 ff.
> The style in which the archangel is here represented is most remarkable, and suggests that the figure was copied from a Genius or Cupid on an antique gem. The most probable date of such an adaptation is the eighth or ninth century, when, owing to the iconoclastic persecution, orthodox models had become difficult to obtain. A reversion to the antique is evident in the case of Byzantine ivory caskets of the same date, on which *see* H. Graeven, *Ein Reliquienkästchen aus Pirano*, in *Jahrbuch der kunsthist. Samml. des allerh. Kaiserhauses*, Vienna, 1899. Other Byzantine cameos with the Annunciation, but differently treated, are in the Bibliothèque Nationale, Paris; *see* Babelon, *Catalogue des Camées*, nos. 336–338, pl. xxxix.

**105**. SARDONYX; St. John the Baptist, clothed in a skin garment, standing to *r.* with his *r.* hand extended and holding in his *l.* a scroll on which is engraved METANO(EITE). Behind him is a tree, and in the field ΑΓ(ΙΟC) Ι Ω̄ (ΑΝΝΗC) Ο ΠΡ(Ο)ΔΡ(Ο)Μ(Ο)C, the last word in monogrammatic form.

    *Plate* III (from a cast). *11th century.*

    L. ·72 in.

    *See* Smith and Cheetham, vol. i, p. 719.

**106**. HELIOTROPE; bust of our Lord holding in his *l.* hand an open book on which is engraved an inscr. in two vertical columns of two lines each ΕΓ | ΗΜ | Τ Φ | Τ | ΚΟ|Μ, standing for: Ἐγὼ εἰμὶ (ἠμὶ) τὸ φῶς τοῦ κόσμου (St. John ix. 5).

    *Plate* III (from a cast).

    L. 1·66 in.   *Hertz Coll.* 1859.   In a modern gold setting.

    Cf. Babelon, *Catalogue des Camées de la Bibl. Nat.*, no. 333, pl. xxxix; M. Sommerville, *Engraved Gems, their History and Place in Art*, no. 575, pl. li (Philadelphia, 1889).

**107**. GREYISH SAPPHIRE; half-length figure of our Lord with cruciferous nimbus holding a closed book in his *l.* hand, and with his *r.* raised in benediction: on either side ΙC̄ Χ̄C̄.

    *Plate* III (from a cast).

    L. 1·1 in.   1869.

**108**. GREY STEATITE; to *r.* our Lord, with cruciferous nimbus, to *l.* a soldier in a chlamys and conical helmet laying his hand upon our Lord's breast. Part of a scene from the Passion.

    *Plate* III (from a cast).

    L. ·92 in.   1857.

**109**. SICILIAN JASPER, cut in low relief; the Virgin standing in the attitude of an *orans* upon a rectangular stool or pedestal. To *l.* and *r.* of her head the letters Μ̄ Θ̄ (Μήτηρ Θεοῦ).

    *Plate* III (from a cast).

    L. 2·5 in.   1869.

**110**. HELIOTROPE; the Virgin holding both hands over the breast with the palms outermost. To *l.* and *r.* Μ̄Ρ̄ Θ̄Ȳ (Μήτηρ Θεοῦ).

    *Plate* III (from a cast).

    L. 1·3 in.   1869.

**111**. STEATITE, pale grey-green, rounded at top and square below; bust of the Virgin, her mantle drawn over her head, and having on the front a St. Andrew's cross between four dots. Her hands are held over the breast with the palms outwards. To *l.* and *r.* Μ̄Ρ̄ Θ̄Ȳ.

    *Plate* III (from a cast).

    L. 1·9″ in.   1889.   From Tartûs, Syria.

**112**. STEATITE; a half-length figure of the Virgin with mantle as before with dots over the forehead, carrying the Child on her *l.* arm beneath a round arch supported by two columns.  To *l.* and *r.* of her head $\overline{\text{MP}}$ $\overline{\text{ΘY}}$ (Μήτηρ Θεοῦ) ; above the child's head $\overline{\text{IC}}$ $\overline{\text{XC}}$ ('Ιησοῦς Χριστός), above this again H ΑΛΥΠΟC. In each spandril is a bearded saint holding an inscribed scroll, that to *l.* appearing to read: ΠΙΑΝΟΙCΠΑCΙ ; that to *r.* THN TH/////. Along the upper rim are the much worn remains of another inscription, the greater part of which has been broken away.  The stone has been discoloured by oil and is almost black.

*Plate* III (from a cast).

L. 1·96 in.  Given by Major-General Meyrick, 1878.  Late work.

Cf. Babelon, *Cat. des Camées*, no. 339. pl. 40; Schlumberger, *L'Épopée Byzantine*, &c., *seconde partie*, *Basile* II, figs. on pp. 41 and 57 (two steatite panels in the Louvre with similar architectural motive).

**113.** HELIOTROPE ; half figure of the Virgin, veiled, or with mantle as before, with four dots in the shape of a cross over the forehead.  In her *l.* arm is the Child with cruciferous nimbus, his *r.* hand extended in the gesture of benediction.  In the field to *l.* $\overline{\text{MP}}$ $\overline{\text{ΘY}}$ ; to *r.* $\overline{\text{IC}}$ $\overline{\text{XC}}$.

*Plate* III (from a cast).

L. 1·42 in.  1869.

**114.** GREEN JASPER ; the Virgin standing and holding the Child, who has the cruciferous nimbus, in her *l.* arm.  To *l.* of her head $\overline{\text{MP}}$, to *r.* —C (part of the name $\overline{\text{IC}}$ $\overline{\text{XC}}$).

*Plate* III (from a cast).

L. 1.4 in.  1874.  Obtained in Smyrna.  Pierced with two holes at the top.  Rude workmanship.

**115.** BLACK STONE, rounded at top, square at bottom, and carved on both sides. *Obv.* : half-length figure of the Virgin, full face, supporting the Child in her *l.* arm. Both figures have the plain nimbus with dotted border.  On both sides in the field an inscr. in raised letters divided by horizontal lines: $\overline{\text{MP}}$ | $\overline{\text{ΘY}}$/// | IC XC ⫶ O E|ΛEHMON (Μήτηρ Θεοῦ· 'Ιησοῦς Χριστὸς ὁ ἐλεήμων). *Rev.* : two military saints standing side by side.  The one to *r.* holds a spear, and both have shields at their *l.* sides.  In the field an effaced inscription probably giving their names.

L. 1·1 in.  1869.  The stone is so worn and so highly polished that the details and features are obliterated.

**116.** PALE GREEN STEATITE in the form of a tympanum ; the Nativity and Adoration.  In the centre the Virgin lies on a couch ; behind her is the Child in the manger, above which are the heads of the ox and the ass.  To *l.* is Joseph seated to *r.* with his head resting on his *l.* hand ; to *r.* the three Magi bringing gifts ; a fracture makes the last group incomplete.  Above, H ΓENNHCHC ; below, another inscription /////ΠΑΠΑΝΤΕ ΙΗΡΑ MH///HCTOV conjectured by Venuti to stand for H ΥΠΑΠΑΝΤΕ ΙΗΡΑ MH ΧΡΗCTOY (ἡ ὑπαπαντὴ ἱερὰ Μητρὸς Χριστοῦ), which would refer to the Purification.

*Plate* III (from a cast).

L. 1·52 in. 1894.

In 1758 this object belonged to Venuti and is described by him in *Saggi di Dissertazioni accademiche pubblicamente lette nella nobile Accademia Etrusca dell' antichissima città di Cortona*, vol. vii (1758), pp. 45–47 and fig. no. xiv of the second plate at the end of his dissertation, which is entitled *Sopra alcune gemme letterate*. He calls the stone a glass paste and has thus misled subsequent writers. It is figured by Martigny, *Dict.*, s. v. *Nativité*; R. E. Kraus, vol. i, p. 607, fig. 214; M. Schmid, *Die Darstellung der Geburt Christi in der bildenden Kunst*, p. 31. *See* also Smith and Cheetham, vol. i, p. 735. It is possible that this panel was originally placed on the top of another of rectangular form, now lost, on which the Purification was represented.

**117** STEATITE. *Obv.*: bust of the prophet Daniel full face, wearing Oriental costume and in the attitude of an *orans*; the inscr.: O ΠΡΟφΗΤΗС (this word in mono-grammatic form) ΔΑΝΙΗΛ. *Rev.*: bust of St. Marina full face, wearing a hood and holding her hands over her breast; to *r*. and *l*. Η ΑΓΙΑ ΜΑΡΙΝΑ.

L. 1·34 in. 1889.

St. Marina (8th century, July 17th), Martyr of Antioch in Pisidia, or of Bithynia. On the former *see* H. Usener, *Acta Sanctae Marinae et S. Christophori, Festschrift zur fünften Säcularfeier der Carl-Ruprechts-Universität zu Heidelberg* (Bonn, 1886); on the latter, Migne, *Patrologiae Cursus, Series Graeca*, vol. 115, p. 347 ff.

**118.** SCHIST, rectangular fragment. *Obv.*: bust of a beardless saint holding his *r*. hand over his breast. *Rev.*: half of a cross pattée.

L. 1·3 in. 1869.

**119.** SCHIST, in form of a tympanum; half figure of St. Nicholas, bearded and in episcopal vestments. On both sides O ΑΓ(ΙΟС) | ΝΙΚΟΛΑΟС.

L. ·96 in. 1883.

## (ii) RINGS WITHOUT GEMS.

The date of these rings (nos. 120–226) is difficult to determine with certainty, but the majority belong to the period between the 6th and 13th century. Most of those with cruciform monograms like nos. 172 ff. perhaps date from the 8th–10th century, to which time lead seals with similar monograms are attributed (Schlumberger, *Sigillographie Byzantine*, p. 80). Many of those found in Egypt and Syria may naturally be earlier than the Arab invasions.

### (a) *Inscribed*.

#### I. ICONOGRAPHIC.

**120.** GOLD SIGNET-RING, with plain rounded hoop, and applied oval bezel engraved in intaglio with a bust of our Lord, between two crosses. Below, two adoring angels, and between them a cruciform monogram. Round the edge of the bezel is engraved: ΑΓΙΟС ΑΓΙΟС ΑΓ(ΙΟС Κ)ΥΡΙΟС СΑΒΑΟ(Θ).

*See* figure. *6th* or *7th century*.

D. 1·14 in. L. of bezel, 62 in. Franks Bequest, 1897. Cf. no. 189 below.

**121.** GOLD RING, with engraved and nielloed ornament. The flat and octagonal hoop has applied to one face a flat bezel in the form of a square with four lobes, on which is the Annunciation. To *r.* the Virgin, seated in a high-backed chair, to *l.* the archangel standing with his face towards her. Round the hoop beginning at *r.* of the bezel is the inscr. ✝ ΧΕΡΕ ΚΕΧΑΡΙ///////Ο Κ̄C̄ ΜΕΤΑ CΟΥ (Χαῖρε κεχαριτωμένη, ὁ Κύριος μετὰ σοῦ (St. Luke i. 28) within a herring-bone border.
*Plate* IV. *About the* 10*th century.*

> D. ·9 in. L. of bezel, ·76 in. Castellani Coll. 1872.
> The style of this ring is the same as that of nos. 129-133. Cf. also a ring with the Annunciation figured by G. Schlumberger, *Mélanges d'arch. byz.* p. 169, and *Byz. Zeitschr.* 1893, p. 191, and another, with bust of our Lord, in the Museo Civico, Venice. The niello is almost entirely lost from the figure of the angel and from most of the inscription. The hoop is much worn.

**22.** GOLD SIGNET-RING, with plain hoop and applied circular bezel engraved in intaglio with a bust of a bearded man full face, with his hair parted in the middle and wearing a diadem. Legend : CΑΛΒΑΤΟΡ.
*See* figure.

> D. ·8 in. D. of bezel, ·6 in. Franks Bequest, 1897. Obtained in Rome.

**123.** GOLD SIGNET-RING, with hoop of rectangular section expanding to a solid square bezel rudely engraved in intaglio with Orpheus seated near a tree playing a lyre ; in the foreground two recumbent animals. Legend : CΦΡΑΓΗC ΟΙΟΑΝΟΥ ΤΟΥ ΑΓΗΟ CΤΕΦΑΝΗΤΫ (σφραγὶς Ἰωάννου τοῦ ἁγίου στεφανίτου ?).
*See* figure.

> D. 1 in. L. of bezel, ·73 in. Franks Bequest, 1897. Found at Scutari.
> For the word στεφανίτης (*coronatus*) *see* Ducange, *Glossarium, s. v.*

**124.** SILVER BEZEL OF A RING, circular, engraved in intaglio with a figure of St. Leontius in military costume standing full face, holding a long cross in his *l.* hand and supporting a shield in his *r.* Direct legend : Ο ΑΓΙΟC ΛΕΟΝΤΙC.

> D. ·48 in. Franks Bequest, 1897. Obtained in Constantinople.

**125.** SILVER SIGNET, with plain rounded hoop and applied circular bezel engraved in intaglio with St. Leontius standing full face, holding a long cross in his *l.* hand, and supporting a shield in his *r.* To *r.* is a star or the sacred monogram. Direct legend : ΑΓΙΟC ΛΕΟΝΤΙ.

> D. 1 in. D. of bezel, ·5 in. Franks Bequest, 1897.

**126**. BRONZE SIGNET-RING, with rounded hoop and applied circular bezel engraved in intaglio with a standing figure of St. Demetrius, full face, in long garments and holding a cross over his breast in his *r*. hand. To left and right reversed inscr., in two vertical lines: ✝ Ο ΑΓΙΟС ΔΗΜΗΤΡΙС.

    D. 1 in. Franks Bequest, 1897.

### 2. MARRIAGE RINGS.

**127**. BRONZE RING, with flat polygonal hoop engraved on the outer side: ΧΡΥСΑΦΙΟΥ ΘΕΟΔѠΡΑС ; applied rectangular bezel, engraved in intaglio with a bearded standing figure in military costume holding a long cross in his *l*. hand, and a shield and spear in his *r*.

    D. 1 in. L. of bezel, ·7 in. Franks Bequest, 1897.

    For examples of the name Chrysaphius *see* Pape-Benseler, *Wörterbuch, s. v.*; Muralt, *Essai de Chronographie Byzantine* (1855), p. 50 ; Theophanes, *Chronographia*, year 5938.

**128**. IRON RING, with slender polygonal hoop and circular bezel engraved СΤΕΦ|ΑΝΥ ΓΕ | ΟСΙΑ(С)? Three lines, the letters direct.

    D. 1 in. L. of bezel, ·6 in. Franks Bequest, 1897.

    Perhaps the second name is Γελασία. Γελάσιος is known as a late male name. *See* Pape-Benseler, *Wörterbuch, s. v.*, and J.-B. Chabot, *Index alphabétique des inscriptions grecques et latines publiées par Waddington, s. v.* (Paris, 1897).

**129**. GOLD RING, with ornament engraved and nielloed. The hoop flat and octagonal; the bezel, in the form of a square with four lobes, applied to one of the faces. On the bezel four figures stand upon an exergual line, the two in the centre representing our Lord and the Virgin, the former turned to the bridegroom whom he blesses with his *r*. raised, the latter in a similar attitude with regard to the bride. In the centre above the group is a star, and below the line the legend: ΟΜΟΝΥΑ (ὁμόνοια). On each of the remaining seven faces of the hoop is a scene from the History of our Lord in the following order, beginning from the *r*. side of the bezel. The Annunciation ; the

Salutation ; the Nativity ; the Baptism ; the Adoration of the Magi ; the Crucifixion or *Ecce Homo* ; the Angel at the tomb on Easter morning. It is remarkable that the Baptism and the Adoration are out of their proper order.

    *Plate* IV. and figure. *About the 10th century.*

    D. ·75 in. D. of bezel, ·46 in. Franks Bequest, 1897.

    Cf. a similar ring in the museum at Palermo with the same scenes, figured Salinas, *Del Real Museo di Palermo*, pl. A. 1 (Palermo, 1873) ; *Arch. Journ.* vol. xxxviii (1881), p. 154; Kondakov, *Geschichte und Denkmäler des Byzantinischen Emails*, p. 264; another, formerly in the Pichon Coll., Sale Cat. (1897), no. 26, pl. ii, is also figured by Schlumberger, *Mélanges d'arch. byz.* p. 67. *See* also O. Pelka, *Altchristliche Ehedenkmäler*, pp. 105, 109. (Strasburg, 1901.)

**130.** GOLD RING; engraved and formerly nielloed, of similar shape but ruder workmanship. On the bezel our Lord stands full face with his *r.* arm extended and resting on the shoulder of the bridegroom, his *l.* on that of the bride. Behind the bridegroom is the letter **O**, behind the bride the letter **M**, commencing the word **OM(O)NYA** (ὁμόνοια), the last three letters of which are below the feet of our Lord, the second **O** being omitted. Below the feet of the bride is a star. Round the bezel, beginning from the *r.* is the following inscr. between dotted borders : **+ IPHNHN THN ЄMHN ΔHΔOMЄ** (St. John xiv. 27).

> *Plate* IV. *About the* 10*th century.*

> D. ·88 in.   L. of bezel, ·78 in.   Franks Bequest, 1897.   From Girgenti.

**131.** GOLD RING; engraved and nielloed with flat hoop and applied oval bezel. Upon the bezel our Lord stands upon an exergual line with his arms extended over a bride and bridegroom standing on either side of him ; below the line the legend **OMONV(A)** (ὁμόνοια). Round the hoop, beginning at the *r.* is a legend, *see figure*, possibly intended for θεοτόκε βοήθει, ἀμήν. +Θ·ΩЄTЄ·ΒϾΟ·Θ·HΑΜ

> *Plate* IV, and *see* figure. *About the* 10*th century.*

> D. ·82 in.   L. of bezel, ·6 in.   1856.
> *See Arch. Journ.* vol. xix (1862), p. 325, from which the figure is reproduced.

**132.** GOLD NIELLOED RING of similar shape to the last. The group upon the bezel is the same, and beneath the exergual line is the same word **OMONVA** (ὁμόνοια) Round the hoop beginning from the *r.* of the bezel is the legend ////**INHN TIN ЄMHN ΔIΔΩMI VMHN** (St. John xiv. 27).

> *About the* 10*th century.*

> D. ·78 in.   L. of bezel, ·51 in.   Franks Bequest, 1897.
> The inscription and bezel are both much worn. A great part of the niello is wanting from the former, and the whole from the latter.

**133.** GOLD NIELLOED SIGNET-RING, with slender, plain hoop and applied oval bezel, on which are engraved in intaglio the busts of a man and woman full face, divided by a nielloed cross pattée ; above the cross is a bust with nimbus (our Lord ?), on either side of which are the letters **Є|OΔ**, possibly part of the name Theodore. Below the cross the word **(O)MONOIA**. The inscriptions are nielloed.

> *See* figure.

> D. ·75 in.   L. of bezel, ·46 in.   Franks Bequest, 1897.   From Beyrût.

3. ACCLAMATIONS AND PRAYERS.

**134.** GOLD RING, with plain flat hoop expanding slightly at the shoulders, and oval bezel engraved with a star of six rays surrounded by the legend **+ H ЄΛΠIC MOY O ΘC** (ἡ ἐλπίς μου ὁ θέος).

> D. ·78 in.   D. of bezel, ·48 in.   Franks Bequest, 1897.
> Fröhner, *Les Musées de France,* pl. xxxviii, fig. 4.   Formerly in the Dimitri Coll.

**135.** Silver signet-ring, with facetted octagonal hoop narrowest at the back, and octagonal bezel in low relief engraved with the reversed inscription ΚΑΡΤ|ΕΡΕΙ in two lines.

D. ·92 in.   L. of bezel, ·5 in.   Franks Bequest, 1897.

**136.** Silver ring, with plain rounded hoop and high circular bezel engraved with a direct inscr. in six lines : ΕΙC ΘΕ|OC ΚΕ ο Χ|ΡΙCΤΟC ΑΥ|ΤΟΥ ΚΕ ΤΟ Α|ΓΙΟΝ ΠΝΕ|ΥΜΑ (Εἷς Θεὸς καὶ ὁ Χριστὸς αὐτοῦ καὶ τὸ Ἅγιον Πνεῦμα).

D. ·88 in.   D. of bezel, ·4 in.   Franks Bequest, 1897.

**137.** Silver signet-ring, with plain hoop expanding slightly at the bezel, which is oval with a reversed inscr. in three lines : ΚΕ Β|ΟΗΘΙ C|ΥΝΕCΙ (Κύριε βοήθει Συνεσίῳ ?).

D. ·8 in.   Castellani Coll. 1872.

**138.** Silver signet-ring, with plain hoop and oval bezel engraved with a reversed inscription in three lines : ΚΕ ΒΟ|ΗΘΗ ΝΙΚΗ|ΤΑ ΑΜ (Κύριε βοήθει Νικήτᾳ, ἀμήν).

D. 1 in.   L. of bezel, ·6 in.   Franks Bequest, 1897.

**139.** Bronze signet, once gilt and inlaid with silver, the hoop rounded on the outer side and narrowest at the back ; the bezel oval with a vertical ridge at top and bottom.  The outer sides of the hoop are engraved with floral scrolls inlaid with silver, and the bezel with a reversed inscription in four lines in which the gilding still remains : +ΚΕ Β' Τ|Ο CO Δ' CΤΕ|ΦΑΝΟ ΑΜ|ΗΝ (Κύριε βοήθει τῷ σῷ δούλῳ Στεφάνῳ, ἀμήν).
See figure.

D. 1 in.   L. of bezel, ·7 in.   Franks Bequest, 1897.

**140.** Bronze signet-ring, with plain hoop and flat oval bezel with reversed inscription in three lines : + ΚΕ ΡΟ|ΙΘΙ ΚΟCΤΑ|ΤΑΝΟΥ (Κύριε βοήθει Κωνσταντιάνῳ ?).

D. ·8 in.   L. of bezel, ·6 in.   Franks Bequest, 1897.

**141.** Bronze ring, with slender rounded hoop with a projection on each shoulder, and projecting oval bezel with channeled sides roughly engraved with a direct inscr. : ΧΕΒΟΗ|ΧΛΙ ? within a dotted border.

D. 1 in.   L. of bezel, ·5 in.   Franks Bequest, 1897.   From Catania.

**142.** SILVER SIGNET-RING, with flat hoop and applied circular bezel. Round the hoop beginning from the *r.* of the bezel is an inscr. (*see* figure). Κύριε βοήθει τῆς φορούσης. The bezel is engraved with a Medusa-like face from which radiate seven serpents. Above the head a cross.

See figure.

D. ·8 in.  D. of bezel, ·66 in.  Franks Bequest, 1897.

This ring was probably worn as an amulet. The design on the bezel may be compared with others of the same character, the use of which for protection against disease or accident is undoubted. *See* Schlumberger, *Mélanges*, &c., p. 136 ff.; C. W. King, *The Gnostics and their Remains*, pp. 167–169, and fig. 3; cf. also *Antiquités de l'Empire Russe*, Atlas, vol. i, pl. 23 (Moscow, 1849).

**143.** BRONZE SIGNET-RING; the hoop engraved on the shoulder with conventional ornament. The bezel is oval, engraved with a reversed inscription in three lines: ✝ ΚЄ ΡΟ|ΗΘΗ ΤΗC |ΦΟΡΫ (Κύριε βοήθει τῆς φορούσης) within a dotted border.

D. 1·04 in.  L. of bezel, ·64 in.  1853.

**144.** BRONZE SIGNET-RING, with plain hoop very narrow at the back and rectangular bezel engraved with a reversed inscr. in three lines: ΚЄ ΒΟΗΘ|Η ΤΟΥ ΦΟ|ΡΟΝΤΟC.

L. ·9 in.  L. of bezel, ·56 in.  Franks Bequest, 1897.  Obtained in Smyrna.

**145.** BRONZE RING; the hoop rounded on the outer side, the shoulders engraved with conventional ornament. The bezel oval, pierced in the middle and with a small projection at top and bottom. Circular direct inscr. within a milled border: ΚЄ ΒΟΘΙ ΤΟ ΦΟΡΟ (Κύριε βοήθει τῷ φοροῦντι).

D. ·94 in.  L. of bezel, ·64 in.  Franks Bequest, 1897.

**146.** SILVER RING; the hoop engraved on each side with a serpentine figure and three stars. Oval bezel with a channeled projection at top and bottom, and a milled band round the sides; the centre is drilled with a circular cavity surrounded by the legend: ΚЄ ΒΟΗΘΗ ΤΟΝ ЄΧΟΤΑ (Κύριε βοήθει τὸν ἔχοντα).

D. ·94 in.  L. of bezel, ·66 in.  Franks Bequest, 1897.  Formerly in the Castellani Collection.

**147.** SILVER RING; the hoop rounded on the outer side and engraved on the shoulders with conventional ornament; oval bezel with a projection at top and bottom, and direct inscr.: ΚЄ ΒΟ|ΗΘΗ ΤΟ | ΦΟΡΟ (Κύριε βοήθει τῷ φοροῦντι) in three lines within a circle.

See figure.

D. ·78 in.  L. of bezel, ·52 in.  Franks Bequest, 1897.  Obtained in Constantinople.

**148.** WHITE BRONZE RING, with broad hoop engraved on the shoulders with a much worn conventional design; oval bezel with a projection at the top and bottom, and a reversed inscription in four lines beginning KE BOHΘI, &c.

*See* figure.

D. ·9 in. L. of bezel, ·74. Franks Bequest, 1897. Obtained in Constantinople.

**149.** IRON RING, with slender hoop and circular bezel engraved with a direct inscr. in three lines: K(E BO?) | IAKOY | VΓIA (Κύριε βοήθει. Ἰακώβου ὑγίεια ?).

D. ·94 in. D. of bezel, ·6 in. Franks Bequest, 1897.

**150.** BRONZE RING, with slender hoop and vertical oval bezel engraved with a direct inscr. in four lines: VΓ̄I | IAN|NO|V (ὑγίεια Ἰωάννου ?).

D. ·94 in. L. of bezel, ·54 in. Franks Bequest, 1897. From Tartûs, Syria.

**151.** BRONZE RING, with slender polygonal hoop and applied oval bezel engraved in the centre with a plain Latin cross with direct inscr.: VΓIA IOANNY (ὑγίεια Ἰωάννου).

D. ·84 in. L. of bezel, ·56 in. Franks Bequest, 1897. From Beyrût.

**152.** IRON RING, with slender polygonal hoop and circular bezel engraved with a direct inscr. in three lines: + AN|TIOXY | VΓIA (Ἀντιόχου ὑγίεια).

D. ·92 in. D. of bezel, ·6 in. Franks Bequest, 1897. From Smyrna.

**153.** SILVER RING, with plain hoop and raised oval bezel engraved with a direct inscription in three lines: Φ | ZωH|C.

D. 1·04 in. L. of bezel, ·54 in. Franks Bequest, 1897.

**154.** BRONZE SIGNET-RING; the hoop rounded and ornamented with a trilobed projection on each shoulder; the bezel oval and engraved with a reversed inscr. in four lines: ΘEω|ΦYΛAK|TY ΠAT|POC (Θεοφυλάκτου πατρός).

D. 1·26 in. L. of bezel, ·7 in. Castellani Coll. 1872.

This is perhaps a mourning-ring worn by a son in memory of his father. For the name Theophylactus *see* Pape-Benseler, *Wörterbuch, s. v.*

**155.** BRONZE RING, with plain rounded hoop and applied circular bezel engraved with a direct inscr. in four lines: + CΦPA|ΓIC COΛ|OMONOC | BOHΘI (Σφραγὶς Σολομῶνος βοήθει).

D. 1·04 in. D. of bezel, ·64 in. Franks Bequest, 1897. Obtained in Rome.

For the use of Solomon's name on amulets *see* Schlumberger, *Mélanges d'Arch. Byz.* p. 120 ff. On Solomon's Seal *see* King, C. W., *The Gnostics and their Remains,* pp. 388 and 423 (London, 1887).

**156.** IRON RING, with slender polygonal hoop and flat octagonal bezel engraved with a Greek cross and a direct inscr.: + CΦPAΓIC COΛOMON.

D. ·9 in. L. of bezel, ·56 in. Franks Bequest, 1897. From Smyrna.

*See* note on no. 155.

E

**157**. BRONZE RING, with flat hoop and oval bezel engraved with a direct inscr. in three lines: OICATO|IKONE|NBOH.

> D. of bezel, ·6 in.   Franks Bequest, 1897.

**158**. BRONZE BEZEL of a ring, oval, engraved with a similar inscr. in three lines: OICA|TOIKO|NEN.

> D. ·7 in.   Franks Bequest, 1897.

**159**. BRONZE RING; plain hoop and oval bezel with a direct inscr. in two lines: ICKI|OI, within a dotted circle.

> D. ·9 in.   L. of bezel, ·4 in.   Franks Bequest, 1897.

**160**. BRONZE RING, with plain hoop and circular bezel with an inscription in characters symmetrically disposed.
> *See* figure.

> D. ·85 in.   D. of bezel, ·6 in.   Franks Bequest, 1897.   Obtained in Smyrna.

**161**. SILVER RING, with plain rounded hoop and applied rectangular bezel engraved with an inscr. in two lines: XEPE|IYJW?

> D. ·74 in.   L. of bezel, ·32 in.   Franks Bequest, 1897.
> The hoop broken.

**162**. BRONZE RING; the hoop of triangular section and engraved with chevrons on the shoulders, the bezel oval with channeled projections at top and bottom, and engraved with a very rough inscr. in three lines.

> D. 1·36 in.   L. of bezel, ·7 in.   Franks Bequest, 1897.

### 4. NAMES.

**163**. BRONZE RING, with slender hoop and oval bezel engraved with the name ΔOM|NOV in two lines within a dotted circle.

> D. ·1 in.   L. of bezel, ·64 in.   Franks Bequest, 1897.   From Smyrna.
> For the name Δόμνος *see* Pape-Benseler, *Wörterbuch, s. v.*

**164**. BRONZE RING, with plain hoop expanding to an oval bezel engraved with the name ΛEO|NTC (Λεόντιος) within a circle.

> D. 1 in.   L. of bezel, ·46 in.   Franks Bequest, 1897.

**165**. BRONZE RING, with rounded hoop and high circular bezel engraved in direct characters with the name MIX|AHΛ, in two lines.

> D. 1·16 in.   L. of bezel, ·44 in.   Franks Bequest, 1897.

**166**. BRONZE SIGNET-RING, with plain hoop and oval bezel with channeled projections at top and bottom, engraved in reversed letters with the name ΓЄOP|ΓIႷ (Γεωργίου), preceded by a cross.

> D. ·94 in.   L. of bezel, ·56.   Franks Bequest, 1897.

**167**. BRONZE RING, plain hoop and oval bezel engraved with a reversed inscr. in two lines: CЄPΓ(I)O for Σεργίου.

> D. 1 in.   L. of bezel, ·5 in.   Franks Bequest, 1897.   Obtained in Naples.

### 5. MONOGRAMS.

**168**. GOLD SIGNET-RING, with plain hoop and angular shoulders. Oval bezel, engraved with a monogram between two crosses, and surmounted by a star.
> *See* figure.   *6th century*.

> D. 1 in.   L. of bezel, ·62 in.   Franks Bequest, 1897.   Obtained in Constantinople.
> Cf. a gold ring in the Fortnum Coll., *Arch. Journ.* xxvi (1869), p. 146, no. 24; Smith and Cheetham, vol. ii, p. 1798.

**169**. BRONZE SIGNET-RING, with plain rounded hoop and applied circular bezel engraved with a monogram.
> *See* figure.   *6th century*.
> D. 1·1 in.   D. of bezel, ·58 in.   Franks Bequest, 1890.   From Tartûs, Syria.

**170**. GOLD SIGNET-RING; the hoop formed of three pearled wires, one above and between the others; oval bezel engraved with a monogram between two crosses.
> *See* figure.   *6th century*.

> D. ·8 in.   L. of bezel, ·32 in.   Franks Bequest, 1897.   From Beyrût, Syria.

**171**. GOLD SIGNET-RING; hollow inside, the hoop with three marked flutes which produce an octagonal bezel: on the shoulders a band of engraved chevrons.   Octagonal bezel engraved with a cruciform monogram perhaps forming the name Manuel.
> *See* figure.

> D. ·93 in.   L. of bezel, ·64 in.   Franks Bequest, 1897.   This ring has been ascribed to Manuel Palaeologus (1348–1425), an attribution which is not contradicted by the style of the work though unsupported by any evidence.   The type of ring is common in Italy in the 14th century.

**172**. GOLD SIGNET-RING, with plain solid hoop and oval bezel with a cruciform monogram.

> D. 1 in.   L. of bezel, ·46 in.   Franks Bequest, 1897.

**173**. BRONZE SIGNET, with plain hoop and oval bezel engraved with two monograms, two crosses and a star.
*See* figure.

> D. ·92 in.   L. of bezel, ·6 in.   Franks Bequest, 1897.

**174**. BRONZE SIGNET-RING, with rounded hoop and circular bezel engraved NK+|Kω (?) in two lines.

> D. 1 in.   D. of bezel, ·6 in.   Franks Bequest, 1897.   Obtained in Pozzuoli.

**175**. BRONZE SIGNET-RING ; the hoop very slender at the back.   Oval bezel engraved with a cruciform monogram composed of the letters ɤNω and M (?).

> D. 1 in.   L. of bezel, ·6 in.   Franks Bequest, 1897.

**176**. BRONZE RING ; the hoop very slender at the back.   Oval bezel engraved with a cruciform monogram.

> D. ·96 in.   L. of bezel, ·6 in.   Franks Bequest, 1897.

**177**. BRONZE SIGNET, with plain hoop and a projection on each shoulder ; oval bezel with a direct cruciform monogram.

> D. ·96 in.   L. of bezel, ·5 in.   Given by John Fewkes, Esq., 1891.

**178**. BRONZE SIGNET-RING, with plain hoop and oval bezel engraved with a direct cruciform monogram.

> D. ·9 in.   L. of bezel, ·64 in.   Castellani Coll. 1872.

**179**. SILVER RING, with thin rounded hoop and flat circular bezel with a direct cruciform monogram.
*See* figure.

> D. 1 in.   L. of bezel, ·5 in.   Franks Bequest, 1897.   Obtained at Smyrna.

**180**. BRONZE SIGNET-RING, with plain hoop and circular bezel engraved with a cruciform monogram within a circle.

> D. 1 in.   D. of bezel, ·46 in.   Franks Bequest, 1897.

**181** BRONZE SIGNET-RING, with plain hoop expanding from the back to an oval bezel with a slight projection at top and bottom, and engraved with a much worn cruciform monogram.

> D. ·97 in. L. of bezel, ·5 in. Castellani Coll. 1872.

**182.** BRONZE SIGNET-RING, with plain hoop and oval bezel engraved with a cruciform monogram with four characters Ⴘ, ω, Π and C (?).

> D. ·9 in. L. of bezel, ·6 in. Franks Bequest, 1897.

**183.** BRONZE RING, with plain hoop and oval bezel engraved with a direct cruciform monogram which perhaps reads Θεοτόκε βοήθει. On one shoulder is another cruciform monogram formed of five letters B ?, I, Λ, Ⴘ and T.

> D. 1 in. L. of bezel, ·56 in. Franks Bequest, 1897.

**184.** BRONZE SIGNET-RING; the hoop narrowest at the back; slightly raised circular bezel engraved with a circle containing a cruciform monogram with the letters N, Ⴘ, C and Є (?).

> D. ·94 in. D. of bezel, ·42 in. Franks Bequest, 1897.

**185.** BRONZE SIGNET; the hoop slender with a projection on each shoulder, and high circular bezel with channeled sides very rudely engraved with a cruciform monogram.

> D. 1 in. D. of bezel, ·54 in. Franks Bequest, 1897.

**186.** BRONZE SIGNET, with plain hoop and oval bezel roughly engraved with a cruciform monogram.

> D. ·96 in. L. of bezel, ·46 in. Franks Bequest, 1897. Found in Sicily.

**187.** BRONZE SIGNET-RING, with plain hoop narrowest at the back, and rectangular bezel engraved with a cruciform monogram.

> D. ·88 in. L. of bezel, ·56 in. Franks Bequest, 1897.
> The monogram reads Θεοτόκε βοήθει, and the four letters in the angles
> ΥΓΗΑ (ὑγίεια); cf. nos. 149–152 above.

**188.** BRONZE SIGNET-RING; the hoop thickest at the back. Oval bezel engraved with a monogram? of very irregular form.

> D. 1 in. L. of bezel, ·7 in. Franks Bequest, 1897.

### b. Uninscribed.

#### I. ICONOGRAPHIC.

**189**. GOLD SIGNET-RING, with plain rounded hoop and solid oval bezel, engraved in intaglio with a bust of our Lord, below which are two adoring angels with their heads · inclined towards each other.   In the field three crosses.
　　*See* figure.　*7th century.*

　　D. 1·14 in.　L. of bezel, ·58 in.　Franks Bequest, 1897.　Found in the East with coins of Heraclius.　Cf. no. 120 above.

**190**. GOLD SIGNET-RING ; the hoop forming seven oval medallions separated by pairs of pellets.　Each medallion is engraved in intaglio, with a standing figure in a long mantle, the end of which he holds in his *r.* hand ; all the figures are similar in character, the difference being that the heads are turned in opposite directions.　The oval bezel is engraved in intaglio with a beardless figure (our Lord?) with plain nimbus, wearing a mantle and seated upon a throne with a footstool.　His *r.* hand (impression) is held up in the gesture of benediction or discourse.
　　*See* figure.

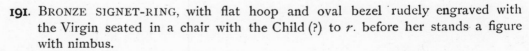

　　D. 1 in.　L. of bezel, ·56 in.　Franks Bequest, 1897. Obtained in Smyrna.
　　A ring of early date, perhaps 5th century.　It should be compared with no. 207.

**191**. BRONZE SIGNET-RING, with flat hoop and oval bezel rudely engraved with the Virgin seated in a chair with the Child (?) to *r.* before her stands a figure with nimbus.

　　D. of bezel, ·6 in.　Franks Bequest, 1897.
　　The hoop broken.

**192**. THIN GOLD RING, with flat hoop engraved with a chevron on each shoulder, and octagonal bezel on which is a half-length figure of the Virgin, very rudely cast and chased, with the Child upon her breast, and her hands raised in the attitude of an *orans*.　(*Panagia Blachernitissa.*)
　　D. ·78 in.　L. of bezel, ·56.　Franks, Bequest, 1897.

**193** SILVER SIGNET, with flat channeled hoop and applied oval bezel rudely engraved in intaglio with the Annunciation. To *l.* stands the Virgin with the basket and the wool (?) before her, to *r.*, the archangel Gabriel carrying a staff.

D. ·8 in. L. of bezel, ·38 in. Franks Bequest, 1897. From Beyrût.

**194.** BRONZE SIGNET-RING, with slender polygonal hoop and applied oval bezel rudely engraved in intaglio with a draped figure of a saint with nimbus and the hands raised in the attitude of an *orans*, standing between two animals. Probably St. Menas between two camels.

D. ·85 in. L. of bezel, ·51 in. Franks Bequest, 1897. Obtained in Alexandria.

**195.** BRONZE SIGNET, with plain hoop and oval bezel rudely engraved with a saint (St. George?) riding to *l.* and transfixing a serpent on the ground before him with a lance cruciform at the butt.

D. 1 in. L. of bezel, ·7 in. Franks Bequest, 1897.

**196.** IRON SIGNET-RING, with slender hoop and applied oval bezel very rudely engraved with a mounted figure riding to *l.* (St. George?).

D. ·9 in. L. of bezel, ·33 in. Franks Bequest, 1897. Obtained in Thebes, Egypt.

**197.** BRONZE SIGNET, with plain rounded hoop and high circular bezel engraved in intaglio with a horseman riding to *l.* carrying a lance with cruciform butt. In front of the horse is a cross, and above its head a crescent.

D. 1·04. D. of bezel, ·6 in. Franks Bequest, 1897.

**198.** IRON SIGNET-RING, with slender hoop and applied circular bezel engraved in intaglio with a mounted saint riding to *l.* (St. George?) within a dotted circle.

D. ·9 in. D. of bezel, ·56 in. Franks Bequest, 1897.

**199.** BRONZE SIGNET-RING, with plain hoop and circular bezel very rudely engraved with a mounted saint to *l.*, holding a lance. The field is filled with punched dots.

D. ·94 in. D. of bezel, ·74 in. Franks Bequest, 1897. Obtained in Constantinople.

**200.** SILVER SIGNET-RING, with slender rounded hoop and applied circular bezel rudely engraved with a saint carrying a lance and riding to *l.*

D. 1 in. D. of bezel, ·4 in. Franks Bequest, 1897. Found in Cyprus; formerly in the Cesnola Coll.

**201.** BRONZE BEZEL OF A RING (?) circular, with a winged figure in relief mounted on a horse and riding to *l.*

D. ·66 in. 1889.

**202.** IRON SIGNET-RING, with slender polygonal hoop and oval bezel engraved in intaglio with the bust of an angel, full face.

D. ·9 in. L. of bezel, ·5 in. Franks Bequest, 1897. From Tartûs, Syria.

**203.** IRON SIGNET-RING, with slender polygonal hoop and applied oval bezel rudely engraved in intaglio with the bust of a saint or angel, full face, and within a circle.

D. 1·04 in.    L. of bezel, ·6 in.    Franks Bequest, 1897.    Obtained in Smyrna.

**204.** IRON SIGNET-RING, with slender polygonal hoop and applied oval bezel engraved in intaglio with three standing draped figures within a circle.

D. 1·10 in.    L. of bezel, ·68 in.    Franks Bequest, 1897.    Obtained in Asia Minor.    Rough workmanship.

**205.** BRONZE SIGNET-RING, with slender rounded hoop and high conical bezel rudely engraved in intaglio with three draped standing figures.

D. 1·08 in.    D. of bezel, ·6 in.    Franks Bequest, 1897.    From Beyrût.

**206.** BRONZE SIGNET-RING, with slender imperfect hoop and high circular bezel, rudely engraved in intaglio with a standing figure with the arms raised in the attitude of an *orans*, between two other figures.

D. ·7 in.    D. of bezel, ·4 in.    Franks Bequest, 1897.    From Smyrna.

### 2. MARRIAGE RINGS.

**207.** GOLD SIGNET-RING; the hoop forming seven circular medallions divided by pellets (cf. no. 190), engraved with male and female busts alternating, each pair being identical. The lines are filled with niello, and on each side of the head in each medallion is a branch or flower of punched dots. The males wear a chlamys fastened on the *r.* shoulder by a fibula with square foot; the females have long hair parted in the middle and wear necklaces. The bezel is rectangular, deeply engraved in intaglio with a male and female bust confronted; above them a cross.

The man wears a chlamys with fibula on the *r.* shoulder, the female a mantle covering both shoulders, earrings and a necklace.

*See* figure.  *5th century.*

D. 1·02 in.  L. of bezel, ·5 in.  Franks Bequest, 1897.  Formerly in the Dimitri Coll. Fortnum in *Arch. Journ.* vol. xxix, p. 304, fig. 2.  Cf. no. 190.

**208.** GOLD SIGNET-RING, with thin flat hoop and rectangular bezel rudely engraved in intaglio with two confronted busts.

D. ·8 in.  L. of bezel, ·26 in.  Franks Bequest, 1897.
This ring has no definite emblem of Christianity upon it, but the subject, though very inferior in execution, resembles the preceding no., so that there seems to be some reason for assigning to it a Christian origin.

**209.** BRONZE RING, with flat polygonal hoop and raised rectangular bezel rudely engraved in intaglio with two confronted busts.  On the hoop on each side of the bezel are two panels, each engraved with a bird.

D. ·78 in.  L. of bezel, ·30 in.  Franks Bequest, 1897.

### 3.  MISCELLANEOUS.

**210.** GOLD RING, the hoop hollow and narrowest at the back, where there is a carbuncle in a raised setting ; the shoulders are moulded to represent hares. High circular bezel with pierced sides, containing a gold coin of the Emperor Marcian (450–457 A. D.) showing the obverse.

*Plate* IV.  *5th century.*

D. 1·3 in.  D. of bezel, ·98 in.  Franks Bequest, 1897.  From the Seine at Rouen.

**211.** GOLD RING, the hoop formed of a plain wire to which is applied a gold coin of Justinian, showing the reverse, within a pearled border.

D. 1 in.  Castellani Coll. 1865.

**212.** GOLD RING ; formed of three horizontal bands ornamented with punched dots, enclosing four circular open-work medallions, each containing a cross pattée.

*See* figure.

D. ·7 in.  Franks Bequest, 1897.  From Smyrna.

**213.** BRONZE STAMP-RING ; the hoop rounded with a pellet-like projection on each side of the bezel, which is square, pierced at each corner, and ornamented with a cruciform figure in relief.

D. 1·2 in.  L. of bezel, ·72 in.  Franks Bequest, 1897.  From Thebes, Egypt.

**214.** BRONZE SIGNET-RING, with rounded hoop and circular bezel deeply engraved in intaglio with a cross pattée.

D. 1·14.  D. of bezel, ·92 in.  Franks Bequest. 1897.  From Qûft, Egypt.

**215.** IRON SIGNET, with plain rounded hoop and applied circular bezel engraved with a cross with bifurcating ends.

> D. ·9 in.   D. of bezel, ·44 in.   Franks Bequest, 1897.   From Thebes, Egypt.

**216.** IRON RING, with slender hoop and applied circular bezel engraved with a cross with bifurcating ends.

> D. 64 in.   D. of bezel, ·34 in.   Franks Bequest, 1897.   From Luxor, Egypt.

**217.** BRONZE RING; with polygonal hoop and bezel in the shape of a cross pattée with traces of an inscription, the letter Ⲱ being in the centre and four other letters, two of which are H and Φ, at the extremities.

> D. ·82 in.   D. of bezel, ·4 in.   Franks Bequest, 1897.   From the Fayûm.

**218.** IRON SIGNET-RING; the hoop with three lines engraved on each shoulder; high circular bezel engraved in intaglio with a cross pattée between four dots.

> D. 1·14 in.   D. of bezel, ·64 in.   Franks Bequest, 1897.   From Thebes, Egypt.

**219.** BRONZE SIGNET; the hoop triangular in section, the shoulders channeled and cross-hatched.   The bezel is lozenge-shaped and engraved with a cross.

> D. ·92 in.   L. of bezel, ·36 in.   Franks Bequest, 1897.   From Naples.

**220.** GOLD RING, with flat hoop cut into four circular and four hexagonal panels alternating with each other.   The circular panels are engraved alternately with a bird and a palmette, the hexagons with an S-shaped line crossed by a bar, all the lines terminating in two or three punched dots.   All the designs are enclosed within dotted lines.

> D. ·63 in.   Franks Bequest, 1897.   From Beyrût.

**221.** BRONZE SIGNET-RING; the hoop moulded at the shoulders so as somewhat to resemble conventional monsters' heads.   The bezel is six-sided with very prominent corners, and engraved in intaglio with a bird to *r*. and three branches: below is an inverted pyramid of dots, and in front of the head a line of similar dots.

> D. ·94 in.   D. of bezel, ·66 in.   Franks Bequest, 1897.   From Smyrna.

**222.** BRONZE SIGNET-RING, with slender rounded hoop and high circular bezel engraved in intaglio with a palm-tree between two birds.

> D. 1·1 in.   D. of bezel, ·54 in.   Franks Bequest, 1897.   From Smyrna.
> Cf. no. 83.

**223.** BRONZE RING, with plain rounded hoop and applied circular bezel engraved with a bird (dove?) between two crosses pattée.

> D. ·94 in.   D. of bezel, ·45 in.   Franks Bequest, 1897.   From Luxor, Egypt.

**224.** BRONZE SIGNET, with rounded hoop and high circular bezel engraved with an eagle displayed, standing upon the back of a lion (?) to *l.*, below which is a serpent.

> D. 1·12 in.   D. of bezel, ·6 in.   Franks Bequest, 1897.   From Cairo.

**225.** BRONZE BEZEL OF A SIGNET-RING, engraved with a lion walking to *r.* ; above the back ΛƎON (?).

> D. ·7 in.   Franks Bequest, 1897.   Obtained in Smyrna.

**226.** IRON SIGNET-RING, with slender hoop and oval bezel engraved in intaglio with two rampant lions, confronted and divided by a staff (?).

> D. ·92 in.   L. of bezel, ·4 in.   Franks Bequest, 1897.

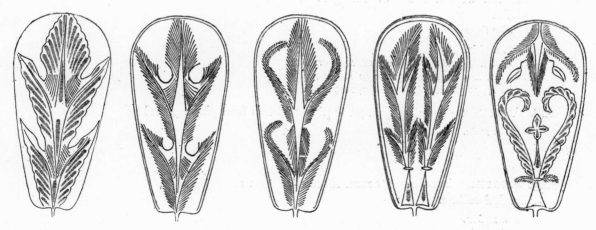

EXAMPLES OF THE DESIGNS ON THE BACKS OF SILVER SPOONS.   Nos. 400–424 below.

# II. JEWELS, PERSONAL ORNAMENTS, ETC.

## A. Found with various Silver Treasures.

(Nos. 227–241 form part of the Esquiline Silver Treasure, formerly in the Blacas
Collection, *see* nos. 304–345.)

**227.** SILVER FIBULA, of the cross-bow
type, the outer side of the bow ornamented with a band of triangles of
niello.

   *See* figure.

   L. 2·36 in.
   Visconti, *Lettera intorno ad una antica
   supellettile d'argento scoperta in Roma nell'
   anno* 1793; pl. xxv, fig. 8 (Roma, 1827).

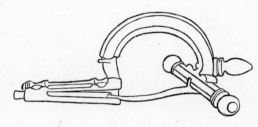

**228.** ANOTHER, of similar type; the pin and knob from the top broken.

   L. 2·18 in.

**229.** ANOTHER, bowshaped, ornamented with three
beaded collars.

   L. 1·76 in.
   Visconti, pl. xxv, fig. 7.

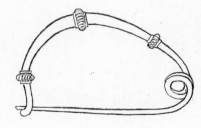

**230.** ANOTHER, bowshaped; the pin-guard punched
along one edge with a vandyke pattern.

   L. 1·9 in.

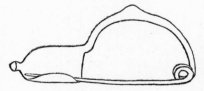

**231.** ANOTHER, distorted, with fusiform bow. The pin-guard is imperfect, now consisting of a flat plate, with extension, upon which are threaded two convex discs
face to face.

   L. 1·74 in.

**232.** SILVER PIN, in the form of a slender column with foliated capital upon which stands a figure of Venus, supporting her *l.* arm upon a Priapic term, and with her *r.* taking off her sandal.

    *See* figure.

      L. 4 in.   Visconti, pl. xxv, fig. 1.

**233.** ANOTHER, similar ; on the top a standing figure of Venus, holding in her *r.* hand a mirror, and in her *l.* a lock of her own hair.

    *See* figure.

      L. 3·3 in.   Visconti, pl. xxv, fig. 2.

**234.** PIN, with globular head.

      L. 2·8 in.   Visconti, pl. xxv, fig. 3.

**235.** HEAD OF A PIN (?), pewter, in the form of a left hand grasping a staff with a flat circular head, on one side of which is engraved the letter **M**, on the other **V**.   On the back of the hand is engraved **BYZAN**, and below it a plan of a building (?).

    *See* figure.

      L. 1 in.   Visconti, pl. xxv, fig. 10.

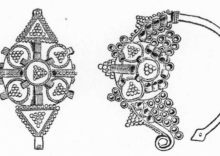

**236.** PAIR OF LOOP-EARRINGS; the upper part is in each case a plain wire ; the lower, a hollow sphere ornamented with spiral tubes and pyramids of pellets, and connected with the upper by two triangular plates similarly ornamented, the angles being filled in with spiral tubes, producing a honeycomb effect.

    *See* figure.

      L. 1·5 in.   Visconti, pl. xxv, fig. 5.   Cf. similar earrings found in the governments of Podolsk and Kiev, Russia.   *See Antiquités de la Région du Dnieper, Collection Khanenko*, pt. iv, pl. x, nos. 392, 394 and 396 (Kiev, 1901).

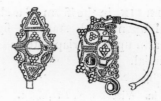

**237.** EARRING, similar to last, but smaller.

    L. ·84 in.  Visconti, pl. xxv, fig. 6.

**238.** FINGER RING, with plain hoop and oval bezel engraved in intaglio with a figure of Victory standing to *l.*  Behind the figure is an inlaid gold stud.

    *See* figure.

    D. ·86 in.  Visconti, pl. xxv, fig. 9.
    This is a Greek ring of the 3rd century, B.C.

**239.** CHARM ; a mouse eating fruit.

    L. 9 in.  Visconti, pl. xxv, fig. 4.
    Cf. Ficoroni, *Le Memorie ritrovate nel territorio della prima e seconda città di Labico*, p. 78. (Rome, 1745).

**240.** CHARM ; a panther, with body terminating in scrolls, lying down with its forepaws on a ram's head.

    *See* figure.

    L. 1·42 in.

**241.** ANOTHER ; a left forearm holding a torch.

    L. 1·42 in.

    Nos. 242–248 form part of the Carthage Treasure (*4th century*).  (*See* nos. 356–375.)  There are no Christian emblems upon them.

**242.** NECKLACE, of twelve polygonal rock emeralds, thirteen pale sapphires, and twenty-five pearls, united by gold links.  The pearls alternate with the stones.

    L. (doubled) 15·5 in.

**243.** PAIR OF EARRINGS, *en suite* with the last.  Each consists of a penannular gold ring, with a pendant formed of an emerald in a square setting, a pearl, and a pale sapphire, threaded on a gold wire and separated from each other by small gold beads.

    L. 2·25 in.

**244.** GOLD FINGER-RING, with hoop triangular in section. The bezel is a high setting formed of a quadruple claw holding a pearl, on each shoulder two pellets.

> D. ·86 in.

**245.** GOLD NECKLACE ; a chain of thin wire plaited in herring-bone pattern, having at each end a hollow ornament in the shape of a lion's head holding a ring in its mouth.

> L. 13·75 in.

**246.** PLASMA INTAGLIO, oval. A beardless male head of the type of Hercules to *r.*, wearing a skin from the head of a bull, with horns.

> L. 1 in.

**247.** NICOLO INTAGLIO, from a ring, octagonal. Fortuna standing with head turned back to *l.*, holding a sail with both hands. Behind her a rudder. In the field the inscription: NAVI GA | FELIX.

> L. ·64 in.

**248.** ONYX CAMEO of two layers, white on grey. Head of Minerva to *l.* Rude workmanship.

> L. 1·6 in.

Nos. 249 and 250 were found with the Lampsacus Treasure (*7th century*), *see* nos. 376–396.

**249.** GOLD, PART OF A NECKLACE, consisting of three rosettes with bases, each with a raised setting, two of which are empty, while the third contains a cabochon amethyst: the backs are pierced with a formal design. Attached to one end is a smaller circular setting containing a flat piece of plasma and fitted with a loop for attachment.

> L. 2·54 in. Given by Earl Cowley, 1848.

**250.** GOLD, PART OF AN EARRING, consisting of a piece of wire, a hollow setting, and a small gold bead.

> L. 1·1 in. Given by Earl Cowley, 1848.

## B. From the Christian East.

**251.** GOLD PENDANT, oval, set with a carnelian engraved in intaglio with a bird to *r.* perched on a branch. On the back is punched the sacred monogram ☧, above the word VERIAE.

> H. ·6 in. Franks Bequest, 1897.

**252.** GOLD PANEL, formed of two pierced plaques soldered together and confined within a heavy pearled border. On one side is reserved in the metal a female riding to *r.* with her *r.* hand unlifted and accompanied by a lion : round the

figure is scroll work, with a broad formal border and a leaf in each corner.   The
back is pierced with a diaper of similar leaves.

*Plate* IV.   *4th century.*

L. 2 in.   Franks Bequest, 1897.

Found with the following three numbers and six *aurei* of Constantius in Asia Minor.   For
pierced work of this kind *see* Riegl, *Spätrömische Kunstindustrie nach den Funden in
Oesterreich-Ungarn*, p. 143 (Vienna, 1901).

**253.** GOLD, PLATE OF A BUCKLE, with three heavy studs at the back, and tubes
for a hinge at one side.   In the centre is a small nielloed medallion with
a heavy pearled border containing the bust of a beardless nimbed emperor
wearing a chlamys with large fibula.   Above and below are three almond-shaped
lobes, the middle one in each case embossed to simulate a leaf.

*Plate* IV.   *4th century.*

L. 2·6 in.   Franks Bequest, 1897.   Cf. a bronze pendant from Kiev, *Antiquités de la Région
du Dnieper, Collection Khanenko*, pt. iv, pl. x, no. 260 (Kiev, 1901).

**254.** THREE FRAGMENTS OF A SIMILAR BUCKLE.   The circular medallion contains
a beardless male bust in a chlamys upon a nielloed background and within a
wreath ; each of the other two fragments consists of three ornamental lobes as
in the preceding number.

*Plate* IV.   *4th century.*

Franks Bequest, 1897.

**255.** GOLD, PART OF A NECKLACE, formed of
four strands of twisted wire with a loop
at one end.

L. 4.5 in.   Franks Bequest, 1897.   Found with
nos. 252–254.

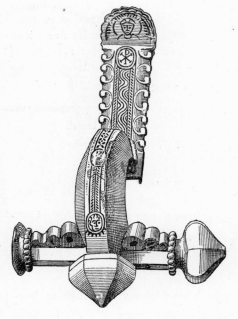

**256.** BRONZE-GILT FIBULA of the cross-bow
type, hollow, with hexagonal knobs at
the ends of the bow and cross-piece (one
wanting).   The bow has a band of ornament
divided into two equal sections by three
medallions, the upper half composed of
quatrefoils, the lower of herring-bones.
The lower medallion contains a rude human
face, the ornament of the other two is effaced.
The upper surface of the stem, which is a
sort of sheath, has a band of wavy ornament terminating at each end in a medallion, the upper containing the sacred monogram, (☧), the lower a head like that upon
the bow.   The edges are ornamented with raised pelta-like crescents with incurved

ends, and the upper end is turned up, having on the inner side a nimbed bust.

*See* figure.   *Late 4th century.*

L. 3·5 in.  1856.

Fibulae of this form have been found with coins from Valentinian I to Arcadius, and are seen on monuments of that period, e. g. the ivory diptych of Stilicho and Serena in the Cathedral of Monza (Molinier, *Ivoires*, pl. i).   Cf. an example figd. by de Longpérier in *Rev. Arch.* xiv (1866), p. 105.   Cf. also a gold fibula in the Kunsthistorisches Hofmuseum, Vienna (Riegl, *Die spätrömische Kunstindustrie nach den Funden in Oesterreich-Ungarn*, fig. 55, p. 149 : Vienna, 1901) ; a gold fibula found in the tomb of Childeric : Cochet, *Le Tombeau de Childéric*, p. 214 (Paris, 1859), and Lindenschmit, *Handbuch der deutschen Alterthumskunde*, p. 70, fig. D, (Brunswick, 1880) ; a gold fibula found in Scotland (*Proc. Soc. Ant.* ii (1853), p. 85) ; another, also of gold, from Odiham, Hampshire, England (*Arch. Journ.* ii (1845), p. 46) ; a gold example from Trèves in the Franks Bequest in the British Museum ; bronze examples are naturally more common and are preserved in numerous museums.   The above brooches fasten in different ways, some have had two pins, one piercing the other at right angles, others, like our own example, would appear to have had a spring hinge, as the sheaths below the stem have in each case a lateral slit which would be unnecessary if two pins were employed.

**257.** BRONZE FIBULA, of the cross-bow type, once gilt, the head and cross-piece terminating in melon-shaped knobs.   The bow is a broad ridge grooved on the upper edge and having on either side four triangular hollows ; the stem is flat, expanding to the end, and has in the centre a Latin cross in a ground

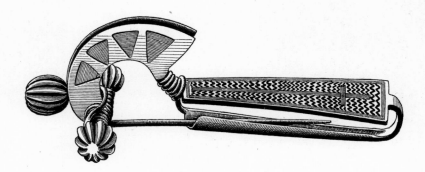

composed of herring-bones alternating in silver and copper.   The pin works on a spring, and lies in a groove formed by a continuation of the stem, doubled under and joined by a wire to the narrow neck of the bow.

*See* figure.  *Late 5th century.*

L. 3·82 in.  Given by C. J. Pocock, Esq., 1849.   From the Tombs of the Prophets, Jerusalem.
Cf. the more elaborate gold fibula from Apahida, now at Klausenburg, and the gold fibula found on the Palatine, now in the Museo delle Terme, Rome, *see* Riegl, *Die spätrömische Kunstindustrie*, pl. xvi, figs. 1–3, and p. 145, fig. 52, respectively.

**G**

**258.** RECTANGULAR PLATE OF A BUCKLE of gilt bronze, with a double-tongued buckle attached. It has on one side a nude male figure in relief standing full face, with crossed legs and leaning on a staff held in his *l.* hand. To *l.* is a tree, and in the *r.* hand lower corner a dog. The plate is enclosed in a pearled border, and at the back are two studs for attachment to a belt.

*See* figure.

L. 2·7 in. Given by C. J. Pocock, Esq., 1849. Found with nos. 257 and 259–263.

This and the following three numbers are probably more than a century earlier than no. 257.

**259.** PLATE FROM A BELT, gilt bronze, on one side in relief a nude male figure standing cross-legged and leaning with both hands on a staff. In the lower *r.* hand corner an animal resembling a panther and suggesting that the figure is intended for Bacchus. Pearled border; at the back broken studs for attachment.

L. 2·46 in. Given by C. J. Pocock, Esq., 1849. Found with nos. 257, 258, and 260–263.

**260.** SIMILAR PLATE, with a similar figure standing full face and holding a staff in his *l.* hand and a wreath (?) in his *r.* Pearled border; remains of studs at back.

L. 2·12 in. Given by C. J. Pocock, Esq., 1849. Found with nos. 257–259 and 261–263.

**261.** SQUARE PLATE of gilt bronze, with ornament on both sides in relief, and with a heavier pearled border. On one side to *r.* a male figure as before leaning on a staff, to *l.* a female figure moving away to *l.*; on the other, a male figure holding a staff in his *l.* hand and making an offering with his *r.* to a statue of Diana upon a rectangular pedestal before him.

*See* figure.

L. 2·32 in. Given by C. J. Pocock, Esq., 1849. Found with nos. 257–260 and 262–263.

**262, 263.** OBJECTS OF ROCK CRYSTAL like large beads, pierced and facetted; perhaps spindle-whorls.

> D. 1·25 in.　Given by C. J. Pocock, Esq., 1849.　Found with nos. 257–261.
> Similar examples have been discovered in Gaulish and Teutonic graves on the Continent as well as in England.　*See* e. g. Lindenschmit, *Altertümer unserer heidnischen Vorzeit*, vol. iii, Heft x, pl. vi, figs. 10 and 11 ; Moreau, *Album Caranda*, vol. iii, pl. 75 ; *Archaeologia*, vol. xxxviii, pl. iii, p. 97.

**264.** GOLD FIBULA, of the cross-bow type with fusiform bow, the stem hexagonal in section, and having down the front the inscription in niello + Θ̄Ȳ XAPIC.　The pin is missing.

> *Plate* IV.　*5th century.*
>
> L. ·73 in.　Franks Bequest, 1897.
> The same inscription (Θεοῦ χάρις) occurs on an exagium of the 6th or 7th century obtained in Corfu (*see* Schlumberger in *Gazette Arch.* 1883, p. 296, and pl. l, fig. 4), on another exagium found at Alexandretta, which has the further inscription AΓIA MAPIA BOHΘICON (*see* Papadopoulos Kerameus, Μουσεῖον καὶ βιβλιοθήκη τῆς Εὐαγγελικῆς Σχολῆς, vol. iii (Smyrna, 1880), p. 82, no. 1, and pl. vii, fig. 1) ; and on a necklace (*see* Garrucci, *Storia*, vol. vi, pl. 479, fig. 3).

**265.** GOLD, RECTANGULAR PLAQUE, with hinge at one end.　It is ornamented on one side with a conventional tree of pearled wire between four large pearls in raised and beaded circular settings.　The tree has two branches, each terminating in a trefoil set with pastes ; at their point of junction is a pearl in a raised setting.

> *Plate* IV.
> L. 1 in.　1897.

**266.** GOLD LOCKET, rectangular at base and arched at the top.　On each side is a design in cloisonné enamel, a lozenge between two vertical bars with trefoils in the angles.

> *Plate* IV.
> H. ·92 in.　Franks Bequest, 1897.

**267.** PAIR OF GOLD AND ENAMELLED LOOP-EARRINGS, the upper part a plain wire springing from a hollow sphere and terminating in another, the lower a segment of a circle filled on both side with cloisonné enamel in blue, green, and white. On one side are three birds, each holding a grape in its beak, on the other is a similar bird between scrolls.　The outside edge of each segment is ornamented with radiating pins with pearls, some of which are lost, alternating with pyramids of pellets ; to the inner edge is fixed in a vertical position a disc ornamented with similar enamel, and having on one side a bird with a branch, on the other a conventional flower.　Round the enamel have been threaded pearls, the loops for which alone remain.

> *Plate* IV.
> L. 1·8 in.　Franks Bequest, 1897.

**268.** PAIR OF GOLD EARRINGS in openwork, semicircular ; the design represents two birds confronted, and divided by a vertical bar with two V-shaped projections. Round the lower edge is a row of loops for a string of pearls or beads now missing.

> *Plate* V.
>
> L. 1·7 in.   Franks Bequest, 1897.

**269.** GOLD LOOP-EARRING, the lower part semicircular and of filigree wire, ornamented at intervals with bosses. In the central part are threaded two cylindrical beads of pink shell. Round the lower edge a string of glass and gold beads.

> *Plate* V.
>
> L. ·76 in.   Castellani Coll. 1872.

**270.** PAIR OF SEMICIRCULAR GOLD EARRINGS, in filigree studded with pellets. In the middle is a rounded arch filled with formal scrolls and separating two confronted birds. The rest is formal scroll work with a border formed of an involved maeander formerly edged with pearls or beads, the loops for which alone remain. One earring is imperfect at the top.

> *Plate* V.
>
> L. 2·34 in.   Franks Bequest, 1897.

**271.** GOLD FILIGREE EARRING, in shape resembling a padlock. The ornament consists of simple scrolls.

> L. 1·24 in.   Franks Bequest, 1897.

**272.** GOLD EARRING, a penannular loop to which is attached a hemispherical cage, the convex side formed of openwork scrolls, the flat side closed by a disc ornamented with two pearled concentric circles surrounded by pellets in groups of three. Across the disc is a wire on which a pearl has probably been threaded. At the bottom a loop.

> L. 1·5 in.   Franks Bequest, 1897.
>
> Cf. for very similar earrings, Riegl, *Die spätrömische Kunstindustrie*, p. 153, fig. 59 (Vienna, 1901) ; J. Hampel, *A Régibb Közerkor, &c.* (*Early Mediaeval Antiquities in Hungary between the 4th and 10th centuries*), vol. i, pl. lxxxv, figs. 7 and 12ª, cxvii, fig. 2ª, cxxv, figs. 1 and 3. (Buda Pesth, 1894.)   The type is found in Lombard tombs, but as it occurs in Egypt, an East-Roman attribution seems possible.

**273.** SIMILAR EARRING, smaller.

> L. 1·3 in.   Franks Bequest, 1897.

**274.** PAIR OF GOLD EARRINGS. Each is composed of a loop of penannular wire, to which is attached a thimble-shaped cage of filigree, the flat end of which is closed and has in the centre a raised setting, now empty ; at the opposite end is a disc of openwork.

> D. 2·1 in.   Franks Bequest, 1897.
>
> Cf. Riegl, as above, p. 153, figs. 59, 60.

**275.** GOLD LOOP-EARRING ; the lower part is crescent-shaped and in openwork, representing a bird enclosed in a circle surrounded by a foliate design. Round the lower edge are five large pellets.

> L. 1·4 in.   Franks Bequest, 1897.

**276.** PAIR OF GOLD LOOP-EARRINGS of similar shape. Each has a cross pattée inscribed within a circle between two peacocks confronted, and on the lower edge five pellets.

> *Plate* V.
>
> L. 1·5 in. Franks Bequest, 1897.
>
> Cf. two earrings from Pannonia in the National Museum at Buda-Pesth (Kondakov, *Geschichte und Denkmäler des Byzantinischen Emails*, p. 361 (Frankfurt, 1892)); and *see* Hampel, *as above*, vol. i, pl. xlv, figs. 3 and 4.

**277.** LOWER PART OF A LOOP-EARRING, gold, of similar work. Two peacocks confronted; on the lower edge three pellets.

> *Plate* V.
>
> L. 1·2 in. Franks Bequest, 1897. From Erythrae.

**278.** GOLD LOOP-EARRING, the lower part crescent-shaped and in openwork, the design taking the form of two lines of a plain twist. On the edges are loops for strings of pearls, now missing. The wire loop moves on a hinge fastening with a pin.

> *See* figure.
>
> L. 1·3 in. 1900.

**279.** GOLD BRACELET, the front opening on a hinge. The hoop is a band of openwork with plain tube edges. The design, beginning at the back of the hoop,

*a.*

consists of a pair of peacocks confronted and separated by a vase; on each side of them is a pair of confronted swans, and at each end a peacock looking towards

the front. All the birds are enclosed in scrolls issuing from a vase in the middle.
Above and below is a band of openwork lozenges
within a pearled band. The front is composed of
a circular medallion flanked on each side by an
oblong with two square settings, now empty. In
the centre of the medallion is a bust of the Virgin
in relief with both hands raised : round this are two
borders, the inner of lozenges, the outer scalloped.

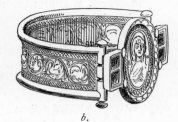

*See* figures *a* and *b*. Fig. *a* is from a cast. *b.*

D. 2·84 in. Franks Bequest, 1897.

This bracelet is one of a pair sold at Cairo, and once in the possession of Count Tyszkiewicz.
Garrucci, *Storia*, vol. vi, pl. 479, fig. 24. Said to have been found in Syria.

**280.** OVAL AND PYRAMIDAL BROOCH, gold, the truncated apex set with an onyx with
cameo inscription in three lines : ЄΥΤΥΧѠϹ | ΠΡΟΚΟΠΤЄ | Ο ΦΟΡѠΝ. The
sides are ornamented with concentric rings of pellets, the lowest stage having
loops on which pearls or beads have been threaded.

*Plate* V.

L. 1·32 in. Franks Bequest, 1897.

**281.** GOLD BROOCH, a solidus of Constantine V and Leo III, surrounded by a
pearled border and fitted at the back with a pin and catch.

L. 1 in. Castellani Coll. 1872.

**282.** GOLD NECKLACE, a thin wire chain with twenty pear-shaped pendants and one
cruciform. Four of the former are of larger size and arranged in two pairs,
one near each end ; they are ornamented with nude nielloed figures. At each
end is an openwork disc with pearled borders, to one of which is attached a
loop, and to the other a hook.

*Plate* V.

L. 16·8 in. 1856. From Sardinia. The rude workmanship of this object is in favour of
a comparatively late date.

**283.** GOLD, OVAL PENDANT, embossed with a figure of the Virgin (?) standing in the
attitude of an *orans* within a pearled border.

*Plate* V.

L. 1 in. Franks Bequest, 1897. Obtained in Alexandria.

**284.** GOLD RELIQUARY, octagonal, with hinged
loop for suspension. The front is divided
by a horizontal line into two parts, on the
upper of which is the Nativity, on the lower
the Adoration of the Magi, both engraved
and filled with niello and silver. In the
former scene the Virgin lies on a couch
with a back and ornamented in front with
a chequer pattern. At her feet is seated
Joseph, and behind lies the Child. Behind

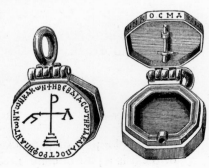

are seen the heads of the ox and the ass. In the lower zone the Virgin is seated in a chair on the *l.* with the Child in her arms: before her head is a star. Before her advance the three Magi in oriental costume, and on each side is a tree with double top. On the back is a monogrammatic cross raised on three steps and surrounded by the inscription ☩ H BEBAIA CωTHPIA KAI AΠOCTPOΦH ΠANTωN TωN KAKωN ; and round the edge of the lid : ☩ TωN AΓIωN KOCMA KAI ΔAMIANOY· Both cross and inscriptions are engraved and filled with niello. The reliquary is closed by a sliding pin inside.

*Plate* IV, and *see* figure. *10th or 11th century.*

L. ·44 in. Franks Bequest, 1897. Obtained in Constantinople.

**285.** GOLD PECTORAL CROSS, the limbs octagonal in section. Below the traverse and the lower limb are loops for pendants. At the top is a hinged loop for suspension, and in the centre a cup-shaped setting for a jewel now lost. The front is covered with an inscription engraved and filled with niello. EMOI ΔE MH ΓENOITO KAYXACΘAI EI MH EN Tω CTAYPω TY K̄Ȳ HMωN ῙȲ XY. (Galatians vi. 14.)

*Plate* IV.

L. 2·8 in. Franks Bequest, 1897.

**286.** GOLD PECTORAL CROSS ; on the front in low relief our Lord as crucified, bearded and wearing a long tunic. At the end of each of the limbs is a medallion containing a bust.

*Plate* V.

L. 2 in. Franks Bequest, 1897. From Alexandria. Very rude work.

**287.** GOLD PECTORAL CROSS engraved on one face with five partially nielloed figures. At the top is our Lord standing with his *r.* hand raised in the gesture of benediction ; in the centre is the Virgin standing in the attitude of an *orans*, to her *r.* and *l.* an adoring angel ; at the bottom stands a military saint (St. Theodore ?) supporting a shield with his *l.* hand and holding in his *r.* a spear with cruciform butt, with which he transfixes a serpent or dragon. On the back is engraved an inscription filled with niello : ☩ ΓEOPΓIOY|CKOΠEΛOY.

*Plate* IV.

L. 2·44 in. Castellani Coll. 1872.

Σκόπελος is most commonly a geographical name.

**288.** SILVER PECTORAL CROSS, with floriated ends. On the front the inscr. K̄Ē BOHΘH Tω ΦωP | TOTON (Κύριε βοήθει τῷ φοροῦντι τοῦτον τὸν σταυρόν).

*Plate* V.

L. 1·3 in. Franks Bequest, 1897.

# III. IVORY CARVINGS.

## A. From Italy.

**289.** IVORY BOX (*pyxis*), with carvings in relief, oval, and cut from the solid : in front is a plain square panel with four holes, and behind two vertical raised bands, for lock and hinges respectively.

To *r*. of the lock are two seated goatherds, one, to *l.*, playing on a pipe, the other on a circular drum or cymbal; between them is a seated goat, behind them is a hut. To *l.* of the lock stand two shepherdesses in long tunics and veils, one, to *l.*, holding in her *l.* hand a basket of fruit and with her *r*. extending a crook (*pedum*) over two sheep, the other playing on a pipe. Below the lock is a sheep ; below the hinges is a goat standing before two trees or bushes.

*See* figure. *4th century.*

L. 5·25 in. Franks Coll. 1866.

*See* H. Graeven, *Pyxide en Os représentant la Naissance d'Apollon, Mon. Piot*, vol. vi (1900), p. 160 (no. v), and p. 163. This box, the designs on which are purely secular, was originally made as a jewel-case. Its use for any other purpose is not certain; but as similar objects were used by the early church as reliquaries or pyxes, and most of the surviving examples owe their preservation to this fact, it has been thought desirable to include it in the catalogue. On the subject of these ivory boxes *see* Graeven as above. Round the edges are pierced eight holes. The lid and bottom are lost.

**290.** FRAGMENT, from the top of a diptych, in the form of a pierced disc between two open scrolls.

L. 4 in.

Said to be from the Catacombs. To the back adheres a quantity of the plaster in which it has been imbedded. Cf. the top of the panel, commonly known as the Apotheosis of Romulus in the British Museum (Molinier, *Ivoires*, no. 40, p. 36).

**291.** FOUR PANELS FROM A CASKET. (*a*) *The Judgement and the Denial of St. Peter.* To *l.*, Pilate wearing a mantle fastened on the *r.* shoulder is seated on a raised throne with high back, his hands over a basin into which an attendant to *l.* pours water from a ewer. In the middle our Lord, young and beardless and without the nimbus, carries his cross on his *l.* shoulder as he moves to *r.*, urged forward by a soldier. To *r.* St. Peter is seated on the ground before a small brazier: above him on a bracket is a cock, and behind him the female servant pointing at him with her *r.* hand while her *l.* is raised to her face.

In this scene the carrying of the cross by our Lord himself is exceptional, *see* Wiegand, *Das altchristliche Hauptportal an der Kirche der heiligen Sabina*, p. 41 (Trier, 1900).

(*b*) *The Death of Judas and the Crucifixion.* To *l.* Judas, in tunic and pallium, hangs from a tree; below him is the purse, from the mouth of which fall the pieces of silver. To *r.* is our Lord nailed by the hands only to a cross with expanding ends. His feet are side by side and unsupported by any *suppedaneum*; round his loins is a narrow loincloth, and at the back of his head an engraved nimbus. On the border of the panel above his head is a *titulus* with the inscr. REX IVD. To *r.* stands a soldier (Longinus) in the act of piercing our Lord's left side with a spear; on the *l.* stand the Virgin and St. John.

(*c*) *The Maries at the Sepulchre.* In the middle the sepulchre, a quadrangular building with columns at the corners and surmounted by a cupola with a domed roof and round-headed windows. The folding doors are open, disclosing part of a sarcophagus ornamented with strigils. The door to *r.* has a handle in the shape of a lion's head with a ring in its mouth; on its upper panel is carved the scene of the Raising of Lazarus, on the lower, a seated female figure (Mary). On the corresponding lower panel of the other door, which is broken, is a similar figure of Martha. To *r.* and *l.* are seated sleeping soldiers reclining upon their shields, and holding spears in their *l.* hands. Above them are seated the two Maries, their heads resting on their *l.* hands in an attitude of grief.

(*d*) *The Incredulity of Thomas.* In the middle our Lord, young and beardless as before, with engraved nimbus, stands on a low step, his *l.* hand raised as if in discourse with four disciples, three of whom have beards, while the fourth, to *r.*, is beardless. On the *r.* is Thomas, who extends the forefinger of his *r.* hand towards the *r.* side of our Lord.

Upon these panels the costume of our Lord and the apostles is the tunic and pallium with sandals, that of the soldiers an Oriental dress commonly given to Jews in Early Christian art, and consisting of a tunic, closely fitting trousers, mantle fastening on the *r.* shoulder, and flat-topped cap. The women wear a long mantle drawn over the head like a hood. In the Crucifixion scene the narrow loincloth worn by our Lord points to a period anterior to the 6th century. As on the doors of St. Sabina at Rome, the nimbus is not given to our Lord throughout.

*Plate* VI. *Early 5th century.*

L. of panels, 3·92 in. Maskell Coll. 1856.

All four panels. Garrucci, *Storia*, pl. 446, figs. 1–4; Rohault de Fleury, *L'Evangile*, vol. ii, pl. 86, fig. 1; 87, fig. 2; 92, fig. 3; 96, fig. 2; Kraus, *Geschichte der chr. Kunst*, vol. i, pp. 174, 505–6; Venturi, *Storia dell' Arte Italiana*, vol. i, pp. 435–439 (Milan, 1901). Photo: Simielli, no. 20-b.; Philpot and Jackson, no. 2646 f.; Graeven, *Elfenbeinwerke*, series i, nos. 24 and 25.

    *a* and *b* only. Lübke-Semrau, *Grundriss der Kunstgeschichte*, vol. ii, p. 53 (Stuttgart, 1901).

    *a* and *c* only. Westwood, *Fictile Ivories*, p. 44.

    *b* and *c* only. Smirnoff in 'A Syrian Silver Dish found in Perm,' *Mat. Russ. Arch.*, pp. 16 and 19, St. Petersburg, 1899 (Russian).

    *b* only. Wiegand, *Das altchristliche Hauptportal an der Kirche der heiligen Sabina*, p. 24 (Trier, 1900); Detzel, *Christl. Ikonographie*, vol. i, p. 575, fig. 219; Kraus, *Über Begriff*, &c., p. 26, and *Real-Encyklopädie*, vol. ii, p. 75, fig. 52; Dobbert, *Jahrb. der k. Preuss. Kunst-Samml.*, vol. i (1880), p. 46; De Waal, *Das Kleid des Herrn auf den frühchristl. Denkmälern der christl. Arch.* p. 20, fig. 15; Forrer and Müller, *Kreuz und Kreuzigung Christi*, &c., pl. iii, fig. 2; and *see* Dobbert, as above, pp. 46–49; Bode, *Geschichte der deutschen Plastik*, p. 14; Wiegand, as above, pp. 24 and 120; Kraus, *Geschichte*, vol. i. 505 f.; Molinier, *Ivoires*, p. 64; V. Schultze, *Arch. der altchr. Kunst*, p. 334; Stuhlfauth, *Altchr. Elfenbein-Plastik*, p. 32; Graeven in *Göttingische Gelehrte Anzeigen*, 1897, pp. 72 and 75; Kondakoff, *Geschichte der Byzantinischen Kunst und Ikonographie*, p. 78; Engels, *Die Kreuzigung*, &c., pl. viii, fig. 9 (1899).

These panels are probably of Roman origin. Their style may be compared with that of the Roman sarcophagi of the 4th and early 5th centuries, and with that of the leaf of a diptych of the Trivulzi Coll. at Milan (Garrucci, *Storia*, 450; but better Molinier, pl. vi). The representation of the Crucifixion is marked by an absence of realism, and is one of the earliest known; it should be compared with that upon the doors of St. Sabina at Rome (Wiegand, *Das altchristliche Hauptportal*, &c., pl. iv). On the ground of the latter resemblance Molinier is inclined to ascribe the panels to an early Byzantine period (5th century); but as the Trivulzi ivory has points of resemblance with the diptych of Rufius Probianus at Berlin (W. Meyer, *Zwei antike Elfenbeintafeln*, &c., pl. ii; Molinier, pl. iv), which must be of Western origin, and probably dates from the late 4th century, it is more natural to suppose that the whole group, including the panels from the casket, was produced at Rome. For other early representations of the Crucifixion *see* no. 43, note.

In *b* the middle section of the tree is a restoration, and the spear of Longinus is broken; in *c* one of the doors of the sepulchre and the upper parts of both the soldiers' spears are broken. In *d* the two semicircular excisions in the upper edge mark the places where the hinges of the casket were fixed. The absence of the nimbus in *a*, and the fact that in *b* and *d* it is merely an engraved line, suggest that it may possibly be a later addition.

**292.** THREE PANELS AND TWO FRAGMENTS FROM A CASKET. (*a*) *Moses striking the Rock.* In the middle Moses stands to *r.* holding out a rod in his *r.* hand. To *r.* are two Israelites in Oriental costume, one standing and extending both hands towards the rock, from which a stream of water issues, the other almost prostrate and in the act of drinking. To *l.*, at a rounded archway, stands a figure holding a roll in both hands. (Aaron, or a second representation of Moses.)

    (*b*) *The Raising of Tabitha.* In the middle, on a bed having sloping back with posts in the shape of dolphins, and furnished with cushion and coverlet, is Tabitha in a sitting posture to *r.*, her *r.* hand extended and grasped by St. Peter, who stands at the foot of the bed. Behind him is a male figure (a disciple), similarly clothed and in exactly the same attitude, and at his feet in front of the bed is a prostrate female figure (a mourning woman?) At the head of the bed another woman with long hair and hands raised in wonder moves away to *l.*

    (*c*) *St. Paul conversing with Thecla* (*l.*); *the Stoning of St. Paul* (*r.*), the two scenes divided by half a rounded arch. In the first scene Thecla appears behind the wall of a building terminating in a round tower and having a round gateway with half opened folding doors; she rests her *l.* elbow on the wall and supports her head on her hand. On the *r.* St. Paul is seated to *l.* and holds an open roll in both hands. In the second scene a man stands in the act of throwing a large stone, while his *l.* holds other stones in the fold of his mantle. To *r.* St. Paul has fallen to the ground and raises his *r.* hand in self-defence. The above three panels are all enclosed in a stiff border of leaves. The principal figures throughout wear the tunic and pallium.

(*d*) and (*e*) Two antique fragments carved with conventional floral scrolls, and fitted together to form the fourth side of the casket.

*Plate* VII. *Late 4th or early 5th century.*

L. of panels, 3·92 in. Maskell Coll. 1856.

Garrucci, *Storia*, pl. 446, figs. 9–11. Photo.: Graeven, *Elfenbeinwerke*, series i, no. 26. *See also* Ficker, *Die Darstellung der Apostel*, p. 146 ff.; Stuhlfauth, *Elfenbeinplastik*, p. 40; Westwood, *Fictile Ivories*, nos. 241–243; Strzygowski, *Byzantinische Denkmäler*, vol. i, p. 7.

Strzygowski would appear to assign these panels to the early Byzantine period, Stuhlfauth to a Roman school of the first half of the 5th century, especially comparing them with the Reliquary in the Museo Civico at Brescia (Garrucci, *Storia*, pl. 441–445). The question of the origin of these and other ivories of a similar period is one of extreme difficulty, as the work produced in Egypt and Syria has only recently attracted the attention it deserves. The influence of the Christian Orient on the art of the ivory carver was clearly an important one; but in the present case a comparison with the Roman sarcophagi makes the Roman origin seem more probable.

**293.** PANEL. *The Disputation with the Doctors in the Temple, and the Baptism.* In the first scene our Lord, in tunic and pallium and without the nimbus, stands

to *l.* on a stool in the centre, his *r.* hand holding a book. Before him stands a bearded doctor, his hands also held as if in discourse, and apparently wearing a *planeta* over a long tunic. In the background are two rounded arches of brickwork draped with curtains, from the further of which issues another doctor, beardless, in tunic and pallium, and holding a book in his *l.*   To the extreme *r.* are four steps, perhaps of a pulpit.   In the second scene, which is flanked by two candelabra (*ceriolaria*), our Lord stands as a juvenile nude figure with plain nimbus in the centre, the water of the Jordan being conventionally represented at his feet.   To *r.* stands St. John the Baptist with short beard, and wearing a tunic which leaves the arms bare ; his *l.* hand points to our Lord's head, his *r.* rests upon it.   Above is visible the head of a dove, from which rays of light (?) like a stream of water descend upon the head of our Lord.   To *l.* stands a winged bearded figure (of an angel) in a tunic and pallium and wearing sandals ; his *r.* hand, which is held over his breast, forms the Latin gesture of benediction. The background to *l.* shows part of a brick arch draped by curtains as in the first scene.   The treatment is very unusual.

> *See* figure.   *5th century.*
> L. 6·9 in.   Maskell Coll. 1856.

> Torr, *On Portraits of Christ in the British Museum*, fig. 4, p. 13 (London, 1898), and *Berliner Philologische Wochenschrift*, 1898, pp. 779 ff. and 1086-7.   Photo.: Graeven, *Elfenbeinwerke*, series i, no. 22.   *See* also Westwood, *Fictile Ivories*, no. 154, pp. 68 and 69.   Cf. the Quintuple Book Cover in Milan Cathedral (Garrucci, *Storia*, pl. 454), and the Werden Casket in the Victoria and Albert Museum (Garrucci, *Storia*, pl. 447).

> On *ceriolaria* and their use in Christian art as representing Paradise *see* de Rossi, *Bullettino*, 1887, pp. 122–128, pl. viii, and 1894, p. 42, and pl. iv ; cf. also Garrucci, *Storia*, pl. 101, 1 and 2 ; 102, 2 ; 104, 2 ; *Recueil de Notices de la Société de Constantine*, vol. xiv (1870), pl. ix.

> For the rays of light round the dove cf. Strzygowski, *Ikonographie der Taufe Christi*, pl. i, fig. 15, and pl. ii, fig. 9 (mosaic from St. Maria in Cosmedin, and miniature from the MS. of Rabula).   With the bearded winged figure cf. the scene of Pharaoh's Dream on the chair of Maximianus at Ravenna (Garrucci, *Storia*, pl. 421–2), and on the subject of bearded angels *see* V. Schultze, *Studien*, 150 ff., and *Arch. der altchristl. Kunst*, p. 350; Stuhlfauth, *Die Engel*, &c., p. 247 ff.; Kraus, *Real-Encykl.* vol. i, p. 417, article *Engelbilder*.

**294.** PANEL ; THE BAPTISM.   Our Lord, young and beardless, with curly hair, stands full face, with his hands by his sides, up to the waist in water.   To *l.* is St. John the Baptist, bearded and with long hair, and wearing tunic and pallium and sandals.   He stands leaning forward upon a rock, his *l.* foot on a higher level than his *r.*, and his *l.* forearm supported on his knee ; his *r.* arm is extended, the hand resting upon our Lord's head.   Above is the hand of the Almighty with rays of light, and issuing from it the dove, which holds a shallow bowl in its beak.   In the background to *r.* stands an angel, perhaps holding a garment ; in the foreground on the same side reclines a draped and bearded figure (the River Jordan) crowned with reeds, his *r.* hand raised as if in amazement.   To *r.* and *l.* in the upper part are portions of trees.   The figures of the Angel and the River Jordan are incomplete owing to the panel being imperfect on both sides.   To *l.* of the hand of the Almighty is a circular perforation. At top and bottom, a raised border.

> *Plate* VII.   *6th century.*
> L. 6·5 in.   1896.
> Photo.: Graeven, *Elfenbeinwerke*, series i, no. 28.

This style of the panel resembles that of one with the same subject in the back of the episcopal chair of Maximianus at Ravenna (Garrucci, *Storia*, pl. 4, and Rohault de Fleury, *L'Evangile*, vol. i, pl. 32, fig. 2), *see* H. Graeven in *Bonner Jahrbücher*, Heft 105 (1900), p. 152. It is interesting as an early example of the introduction of angels into the scene of the Baptism, on which subject see Strzygowski, *Ikonographie der Taufe Christi*, p. 16. The association of a shallow bowl with the dove is also curious, but examples of the dove holding a jug in its beak occur in early Italian art at a slightly later period, e. g. in the Lunette of the larger portal of S. Giovanni in Fonte at Monza (about 700 A.D.), and on an ivory in the Berlin Museum, Strzygowski, as above, p. 36, and pl. viii, figs. 1 and 3. On the same subject *see also* de Rossi, *Bullettino*, 1876, pp. 10 and 11. There seems good reason to believe that the chair of Maximianus was made in Egypt, and it is possible that this panel was also produced in the Christian East; but as the execution is rude, the work may have been produced in Northern Italy, possibly from an Oriental model.

## B. From the Christian East.

**295.** HALF OF A DIPTYCH. The archangel Michael standing at the top of a flight of six steps under a round arch carved with acanthus ornament and supported by fluted columns. Within the arch is a scallop, before which is a wreath bound with ribbons and containing a cross: in the spandrils are rosettes and acanthus leaves, and above these a tablet with the inscr. + ΔЄΧΟΥ ΠΑΡΟΝΤΑ | ΚΑΙ ΜΑΘΩΝ ΤΗΝ ΑΙΤΙΑΝ. The archangel, wearing a tunic and mantle, with sandals on his feet, holds in his *r*. hand an orb surmounted by a jewelled cross; in his *l*. a staff with a ball at each end. He has no nimbus.

*Plate* VIII. *Byzantine. 4th century.*

L. 16·26 in. B. 5·75 in.

Garrucci, *Storia*, pl. 457, fig. 1; Labarte, *Hist. des Arts Industriels*, vol. i, pl. iii; Didron, *Annales Archéologiques*, vol. xviii (1858), p. 33; Molinier, *Ivoires*, pl. v; Bayet, *L'Art Byzantin*, p. 91; Lacroix, *Vie militaire et religieuse au moyen âge*, p. 271 (Paris, 1873); Stuhlfauth, *Die Engel*, frontispiece; Venturi, *Storia dell' Arte Italiana*, vol. i, p. 434, fig. 396 (Milan, 1901).

Photo.: British Museum Photos. Simelli, no. 123. Philpot and Jackson, no. 2659. Cast: Arundel Society's series, class iii[a] (Oldfield, *Cat.* p. 10 (1855)). *See also* Bayet, as above; Didron, as above, pp. 39 and 40; Kraus, *Real-Encykl.*, p. 410[a]; Labarte, as above, vol. i, p. 31 ff.; Molinier, as above, p. 60: Barbier de Montault, Cat. of Simelli's Photos, no. 123; Riegl, *Die spätrömische Kunstindustrie*, p. 122 note; Schaefer, *Die Denkmäler der Elfenbeinplastik des grossherzoglichen Museums zu Darmstadt*, p. 28 (Darmst. 1872); Strzygowski, *Byzantinische Denkmäler*, vol. i, p. 10; Stuhlfauth, as above, p. 179, and *Elfenbeinplastik*, p. 174 ff. (Freiburg, 1896); Venturi, as above, p. 506; Wyatt, *Notices of Sculpture in Ivory*, p. 7 (London, 1856).

This figure, remarkable for its dignity and the general excellence of its style, belongs to that early period of Byzantine art in which the reigns of Theodosius and Justinian stand out so conspicuously. Opinions differ as to the part of this period to which it should be ascribed, some authorities preferring the earlier, others the later limit. The almost classical treatment favours the attribution to the 4th century, while on the other hand some of its defects, e. g. the heavy modelling, particularly of the neck, find parallels in sculpture of the time of Justinian, *see* Strzygowski, *Die Byzantinische Kunst der Blütezeit*, in *Byz. Zeitschr.* vol. i (1892), esp. p. 589. The effect is indeed somewhat marred by faults of proportion and in the treatment of the drapery; the position of the feet, which appear to slide rather than to stand upon three steps at once, is also an unnatural feature (*see* Riegl, as above). The panel formed the first half of a diptych, as is evident from the holes along the *l*. side. The general opinion is that the subject of the second leaf was an emperor, to whom the archangel offers the orb as a sign of sovereignty, and to whom the words of the inscription: 'Receive these gifts, and having learnt the cause . . .' are addressed. It has been argued that the second leaf contained a figure of the Virgin, and an alternative translation of the inscription has been suggested (Stuhlfauth, *Die Engel*, p. 180, and *Elfenbeinplastik*, p. 174). Another view is that the angel is presenting the orb as the fruit of conquest to a crowd of worshippers (Venturi, as above 506). Along the top are three perforations, on the *l.* side three, and at the bottom one. On the back, which is sunk with a border ·6 in. in width, is a palimpsest inscription written in ink in a hand of the 7th century, beginning: + παρακαλῶ σὲ δέσποτα ἐπει . . . , probably part of a liturgy. The letters are much effaced, parts of words being decipherable at the beginnings of the lines only. On St. Michael in Byzantine art *see* F. Wiegand, *Der Erzengel Michael in der Bildenden Kunst*, pp. 6–16 (Stuttgart, 1886).

**296.** IVORY PANEL ; THE RAISING OF LAZARUS. Our Lord with cruciferous nimbus, wearing tunic and pallium with sandals, advances to *r.* with his *r.* hand raised with the first finger extended as if in discourse; in his *l.* he carries a staff. Behind him walks a bearded apostle with his *r.* hand in the fold of his mantle ; before him are Mary and Martha, wearing long-sleeved tunics with ornamented stripes, and fringed mantles drawn over their heads like hoods, one standing in a listening attitude, the other kneeling on one knee with her hands extended in supplication. Behind them to *r.* is an *aedicula* with cupola, in which is placed in an erect posture the swathed body of Lazarus. In the background the buildings of Bethany.

> *Plate* XI. *6th century.*
>
> L. 7⅝ in. 1856. Formerly in the church of St. Andrew at Amalfi.
> Gori, *Thesaurus Diptychorum*, vol. iii, pl. xiii. Photo.: Graeven, *Elfenbeinwerke*, series i, no. 29.
> This panel, which was perhaps made in Egypt, is identical in style with six others in the Museo Archeologico at Milan, representing the story of St. Mark in the Pentapolis, and to be ascribed with some probability to the chair of St. Mark at Grado. This chair was presented to the Church at Grado by the Emperor Heraclius and remained there until 1521, but had disappeared in 1659 (*see* Graeven in *Römische Quartalschrift*, vol. xiii (1899), p. 109 ff.; *Bonner Jahrbücher*, Heft 105, p. 151, and *Elfenbeinwerke*, series ii, nos. 42–48). Our panel may have also belonged to this chair, but it has no projecting flange at the sides like the others. For other carvings probably belonging to the same group, *see also* Strzygowski, *Orient oder Rom*, pp. 65–89 (Leipzig, 1901).

**297.** IVORY BOX (*pyxis*), oval, and cut from the solid, with provision for a hinge and lock, as in the case of no. 289. The sides are carved with scenes representing the martyrdom and the sanctuary of St. Menas of Alexandria. On one side (*a* and *b*) a Roman official in tunic and mantle is seated to *r.* as judge upon a stool with cushion, his feet resting on a footstool ; his *r.* hand is raised as if in discourse, and in his *l.* is a staff or wand. Behind him is a guard with helmet, spear, and oval shield ornamented with a foliate design, and holding up his *r.* hand in a gesture of surprise ; beyond is a basket beneath the space formerly covered by the lock. Before him is a table covered with a cloth, upon which is an inkpot. Behind the table stands a man wearing a chlamys with the rectangular patch (*tablion*) over the breast ; in his *l.* hand he holds a diptych, while his *r.* is extended over the table. Behind is a veiled doorway, perhaps representing the entrance to the praetorium. Before the table St. Menas, a beardless figure wearing only a loincloth, and with his hands bound behind his back, has fallen upon his *l.* knee ; an executioner wearing long trousers and a girded tunic ornamented with stripes grasps him by the hair with his *l.*, while in his *r.* he brandishes a sword. Behind him is seen an angel flying down to *l.*, his hands extended beneath his mantle as if to receive the soul of the saint. On the other side (*c* and *d*), beneath an arch supported by two twisted columns, stands St. Menas wearing a short tunic, closely fitting trousers, and a chlamys with the *tablion* ; his hands are raised in the attitude of an *orans*, and he now has the nimbus. On each side of the sanctuary is seen the head of a recumbent camel, and from each direction approach two worshippers with extended hands— on the *r.* two men, one wearing a striped tunic and mantle, the other a *paenula* ; on the *l.* two female figures, behind whom and occupying the space between the hinges is a tree. The more important figures appear to have their hair bound with fillets.

    *Plate* IX. *6th century.* Probably made in Egypt.

    L. 4·85 in. 1879. Formerly in the Collection of Mr. Nesbitt, who obtained it in Rome.

    *Archaeologia*, vol. xliv (1873), pp. 322 and 324: Garrucci, *Storia*, pl. 446, fig. 3 ; *Bonner Jahrbücher*, Heft 105 (1900), pl. xix, fig. 2 (Judgement scene only).

    Photo.: Parker, nos. 1780-1783 ; Graeven, series i, nos. 14-17. *See also* Westwood, *Fictile Ivories*, p. 274 ; Stuhlfauth, *Elfenbeinplastik*, p. 92, and *Die Engel*, p. 178.

    The carving upon this pyxis resembles in style that of the chair of Maximianus at Ravenna, and is probably of the same school. *See* Strzygowski in *Römische Quartalschrift*, 1897, p 40 ; Graeven in *Bonner Jahrbücher*, Heft 105, p. 158.

    On the story of St. Menas *see* E. Michon, *La Collection d'Ampoules à Eulogie*, &c., in *Mélanges G. B. de Rossi*, supplement to *Mélanges d'Archéologie et d'Histoire* (*École française de Rome*), Paris-Rome, 1892.

    For the scene of a tribunal cf. Gebhardt und Harnack, *Codex Rossanensis*, pl. xvi (and Haseloff's edition of the same Codex, 1899) ; E. Le Blant in *Rev. Arch.* 1889, pt. i, p. 23 ff ; Molinier, *Ivoires*, vol. i, pl. iv (Diptych of Probianus) ; and especially for the trial of St. Menas, Albani, *Menologium Graecorum*, &c., Dec. 10th. For St. Menas standing in the sanctuary between two camels, cf. an ivory panel at Milan (Graeven, *Elfenbeinwerke*, series ii, no. 47). Cf. also no. 860 ff., below.

**298.** IVORY BOX (*pyxis*), formerly with a locked cover, now wanting. On one side (*a* and *b*) Daniel, a youthful figure in oriental costume, cap, tunic, mantle, and closely fitting trousers, stands full face with hands raised in the attitude of an *orans* beneath a canopy supported by four square columns. To *r.* stands a man (a guard) in tunic, mantle, and trousers, holding a staff or spear in his *l.*, and raising his *r.* above the canopy as if in astonishment. From the *l.* approaches a flying angel, leading by the hair a youthful figure (Habbakuk) in a mantle, bearing in both hands a bowl of bread and pottage for the prophet (*History of the Destruction of Bel and the Dragon*, v. 33 to 39). On the ground beneath is a basket. On the other side (*c* and *d*) an angel, walking to *r.*, points to a ram which stands near a palm tree ; behind the angel, a female figure in a mantle moves to *l.* with head turned back ; before her is the rectangular space left by the lock, below which is a cross between two swans.

    *Plate* X. *6th or 7th century.* Made in Egypt.

D. 4·15 in.   1877.   Formerly in the Garthe Coll., Cologne.

Stuhlfauth, *Elfenbeinplastik*, p. 189 (from a cast) ; Strzygowski, *Orient oder Rom*, p. 93 (*a* only) ; Lübke-Semrau, *Grundriss der Kunstgeschichte*, vol. ii, p. 55, fig. 50 (*a* and *b*, after Graeven's photographs) ; Graeven, *Elfenbeinwerke*, series i, nos. 18–21.   *See also* Strzygowski, *Orient oder Rom*, p. 94 ; *Byz. Zeitschr.* vol. viii, p. 681.

Cf. a pyxis with similar subjects from Nocera Umbra, in the Museo Nazionale delle Terme Diocleziane, to be figd. *L'Arte*, 1901 ; one side reproduced by Strzygowski, as above, p. 94, fig. 40 ; the other by Venturi, *Storia dell' Arte Italiana*, vol. i, p. 447, fig. 406 ; and the book cover from Murano in the Museum at Ravenna (Garrucci, *Storia*, pl. 456, and Rohault de Fleury, *La Messe*, vol. ii, pl. 156).

The scene *d*, which has been interpreted as part of the sacrifice of Isaac, may be a symbolic representation, the lamb, like Daniel, being a type of Christ, but the meaning of the figure near the lock is obscure.   Strzygowski, as above, thinks that the scene is the same as that on the doors of St. Sabina, Rome (Garrucci, *Storia*, pl. 499. 8 ; Wiegand, *Das altchristliche Hauptportal*, &c., pl. xix).   The pyxis has been broken into two pieces and roughly nailed to a wooden cylinder.

**299.** PANEL ; THE DESCENT OF OUR LORD INTO HELL (*Anastasis*).   To *r*., in a glory (*mandorla*), our Lord with cruciferous nimbus, wearing tunic, pallium, and sandals, supported upon a rainbow and resting his feet upon a carved footstool.   His *r*. hand is extended in the gesture of benediction (Greek form) ; in his *l*. is a jewelled book of the gospel ; behind him is a group of eight angels with curly hair.   To *l*. stands a tall figure similarly clothed but with plain nimbus (St. John the Baptist), his *r*. hand extended in the gesture of benediction above the heads of three small nude figures with curly hair emerging from a rectangular tomb.   Behind, upon a basement of masonry, a building (part of the city of Hades) with two gables, each supported on two columns, below which are seen two windows and a closed door.   Above the gables is the inscr. TOTE O X̄C̄ ΔHA TY ꝑ HNECCEN TA OCTA (Τότε ὁ Χριστὸς διὰ τοῦ Προδρόμου ἀνέστησεν τὰ ὀστᾶ).

*Plate XI.   Byzantine.   9th century.*

L. 5·8 in.   Given by Felix Slade, Esq.   1856.   Round the rim are seven holes, in one of which is a bone peg.

H. Graeven, *Jahrbuch der kunsthist. Samml. des allerh. Kaiserhauses*, vol. xx (1899), p. 11, fig. 4.

Photo. : Graeven, series i, no. 45.   *See also* Maskell, *Ivories in the South Kensington Museum*, p. 152, no. 11.   Cf. Stuhlfauth, *Elfenbeinplastik*, pl. iv, fig. 3 ; Graeven, *Elfenbeinwerke*, series ii, no. 2 ; Bode und von Tschudi, *Beschreibung der Bildwerke* (1888), pl. lxii, no. 442, and 2nd ed. by Vöge (1900), no. 11.

The interpretation of the scene will be found in Graeven, *Jahrbuch*, as above.   This panel is interesting as an early example of the Anastasis, but especially for the introduction of St. John the Baptist, who was formerly supposed to appear first in this scene in the year 1037 (*see* Millet in *Mon. Piot*, vol. ii, p. 209, and Diehl, *ibid.*, vol. iii, p. 232).   With the peculiar style of the angels and the small figures, probably due to the copying of more ancient work in silver, cf. nos. 104 and 301 ; and *see* Graeven, as above, p. 5 ff.

**300.** PANEL ; THE NATIVITY AND WASHING OF THE INFANT JESUS.   In the middle the Virgin reclines on a couch, while behind her in a manger of masonry lies the Child wrapped in swaddling clothes.   Beyond the manger are seen the heads of the ox and the ass, and above these a group of seven angels, of whom the foremost on the *r.* leans over with outstretched hand addressing two herdsmen holding staves and wearing tunics and high boots, who stand below to *r.* of the manger. Below the herdsmen are three goats. In the foreground to *l.* is seated Joseph, resting his head on his *l.* hand, while to *r.* a kneeling nurse immerses the Child in a large two-handled vase, beside which stands a ewer, the spout of which has the form of a bird's head. The Angels, the Virgin, and Joseph have the plain nimbus; the Child, the cruciferous nimbus. In the field the inscr. Η ΓΕΝΝΗϹΙϹ.

*Plate* XI. *Byzantine. 9th century.*

L. 4·6 in. Rohde Hawkins Coll. 1885.

H. Graeven in *Jahrbuch der kunsthistor. Samml. des allerh. Kaiserhauses,* vol. xx (1899), p. 12, fig. 5.

Photo.: Graeven, *Elfenbeinwerke,* series i, no. 44. The panel has raised borders, with four holes for pegs in the rim. The rim of the *l.* hand lower corner and the *r.* hand lower corner are restored.

Cf. for the scene of the washing of the new-born Infant the Ivory Book Cover at Ravenna (Rohault de Fleury, *L'Evangile,* vol. i, pl. xii, fig. 1); and the *Menologium of Basil,* Albani's ed., pt. i, p. 24, Sept. 8th (Nativity of the Virgin), where the ewer is identical with that here seen.

**301.** TWO SIDES OF A CASKET, bone plates backed with wood, with hunting and dancing scenes within borders of formal rosettes. (*a*) To *l.* a nude hunter, with pointed cap, holding a spear and accompanied by a large dog, approaches a hare of exaggerated size nibbling a bush near a tree. In the centre a similar hunter, with scarf or mantle flying in the wind, is shooting with a bow at a stag which is attacked by two dogs. To *r.* a leopard and a wolf are fighting or playing together. (*b*) is divided into two compartments by an indeterminate rectangular object. To *l.* a man dances with a mantle or scarf, another poised in the air blows a horn, while beneath him a third, in a similar attitude, holds out a rectangular object with four small globes at the top towards two dancers, one of whom holds two wreaths, while the other plays a tambourine. In the *r.* hand compartment are five figures: to *l.* a man dances with a mantle or scarf, in the middle two figures, one poised in the air holds a loop or skipping-rope, in the centre of which a fourth figure is dancing with a garland and scarf; to *r.* a fifth figure blows a horn and holds a garland in his *r.* hand.

*Plate* XII. *Byzantine. 9th century.*

L. 13 in. and 12 in. Rohde Hawkins Coll. 1885.

Photo.: Graeven, *Elfenbeinwerke,* series i, nos. 46 and 47. *See also* Nesbitt in *Arch. Journ.* vol. xxiv (1867), p. 283; Graeven in *Jahrbuch der kunsthistor. Samml. des allerh. Kaiserhauses,* 1899, p. 25, and p. 26, no. 12.

Cf. the casket from the cathedral of Veroli in the Victoria and Albert Museum, no. 216-'65 (Maskell, *Description of the Ivories,* &c., p. 47), and nos. 104, 299, and 300 above; and *see* Graeven, as above, pp. 5–29. With the hunting scenes cf. miniature in a 10th-century MS. of the Gospels in the Bibliothèque Nationale (Bordier, *Description des Peintures,* &c., p. 104). The figures on these caskets, with their pseudo-antique style, exaggerated muscles, and conventionally curled hair, are characteristic of the iconoclastic period, and are probably copied from antique Roman silver plate.

**302.** PANEL FROM A CASKET. The archangel Michael advancing to *r.*, holding a rod in his *l.* hand and raising his *r.* in discourse. Above, MIX(AHΛ) with traces of red pigment in the letters.

> *See* figure. *Byzantine.* 10*th*–12*th century.*

> L. 2·66 in. Rohde Hawkins Coll. 1885.
> Part of the scene of the expulsion of Adam and Eve from Paradise. Graeven in *L'Arte,* 1899, *Adamo ed Eva sui cofanetti d'avorio Bizantini,* fig. 10ᵃ; Graeven in *Jahrbuch der kunst-histor. Sammlungen des allerh. Kaiserhauses,* xxi (1900), p. 107 (*Typen der Wiener Genesis auf Byzantinischen Denkmälern*); Schlumberger, *L'Épopée Byzantine à la Fin du Xᵐᵉ Siècle,* Pt. ii, Basile II, p. 105.
> Photo.: Graeven, *Elfenbeinwerke,* series i, no. 23.
> This panel is related in style to the following number, 302 *a.*

**302** *a.* PANEL FROM A CASKET, with two scenes from the history of Joseph; *Jacob blessing Ephraim and Manasseh* (Gen. lxviii), and *The death of Jacob.* In the *first scene,* which is on the *l.,* the Patriarch is seated on a cushioned chair without a back and with reel-moulded legs. He has long hair and beard, and wears a long garment falling to his feet, which rest upon a stool. His arms are crossed

before him, the *r.* and *l.* hands resting upon the heads of the two boys, who stand by his knees. In the background stand four of his sons. In the *second scene* the corpse of the Patriarch lies on a high table or bier, the legs of which are moulded like those of the chair in the scene of the blesssing. At the head stands Joseph in a long robe, and wearing on his head a diadem surmounted by the Uraeus; at the feet and behind the bier four of Joseph's brothers; beneath the top of the bier is a square box-like object ornamented with circles.

The costumes of all the figures except Joseph and Jacob consist of a tunic reaching to the knees, widely opened at the neck and with rolled-up sleeves, and high boots. The head-dresses of Joseph's brothers, which appear to be oriental in character, are worthy of remark. Jacob, Joseph, and the figure at the foot of the bier are drawn on a larger scale than the others, and the feet of the figures in the background are not shown except in one instance, where the position of the leg would seem to be a distortion.

Of the border above and below a small part only remains, especially in the case of the latter; the former appears to have been of an acanthus pattern, and is pierced with four holes.

*See* figure. *Byzantine.* 10*th–12th century.*

L. 7·25 in. H. 3·5 in. 1901. The border at the two ends is modern, and the whole panel has been backed with an ivory plate in recent times. A circular hole near the head of the bier has also a modern plug. The higher parts of the relief, e. g. the heads of the two boys, are much worn.

This panel was let into the cover of a 13th century MS. of the romance of Parceval le Galois belonging to the Barrois Collection, bought by the Earl of Ashburnham, and sold at Sotheby's in June, 1901 (Lot 463). It forms part of the same series illustrating the Story of Joseph, to which belong the two panels in the Royal Museum at Berlin (Bode und Von Tschudi, *Beschreibung der Bildwerke* (1888), nos. 434, 435, pl. lv, and Vöge, *Beschreibung,* &c. (1900), nos. 13 and 14). It may be compared in style with several other ivories, especially with three small panels from the Pulszky and Oppenheim Collections (Molinier, *Ivoires,* pl. ix, figs. 2 and 3); two panels in the Museo Olivieri, Pesaro (Graeven, *Elfenbeinwerke,* series ii, nos. 49 and 50, and a panel in the Museo Civico, Bologna, *ibid.* no. 3). Cf. also no. 302 above.

**302** *b.* PANEL; the entry into Jerusalem. Our Lord is seated sideways upon the ass, which advances to *r.* He wears the tunic and pallium, and makes with his *r.* hand the gesture of benediction, while he holds a scroll in his *l.* A boy is spreading a tunic in the way, while behind him a man is leading another child by the hand. In the background is a crenelated tower, and by the side of it a palm-tree, into the branches of which a

boy has climbed.   Behind our Lord follow four apostles in tunic and pallium, and from the upper *r.* and *l.* corners descend two angels.

*See* figure.   10*th–*12*th century.*

L. 4·1 in.   Maskell Coll. 1856.   The panel has raised borders, which are pierced with four holes at the top and two at the bottom.

**303.** SIDE LEAF OF A TRIPTYCH.   Two saints.   Above, in a medallion, a bust of St. John the Baptist in a mantle fastening over the breast.   Below, a bishop in episcopal vestments, with his *r.* hand in the gesture of benediction, and a maniple over his *l.,* which holds a book.   The sides are ornamented with an undulating raised border with serrated edges of acanthus pattern. The back has a cross with a rosette in the centre and at the end of each of the limbs ; and down one side is a band of zigzag ornament.

*See* figure.   *Byzantine.*   12*th century.*

L. 4·7 in.   1890.   At the top are two holes.

Photo. : Graeven, *Elfenbeinwerke,* series i, no. 23.

With the bust of St. John cf. an ivory at Liverpool, Graeven, *ibid.,* no. 10, and Cat. of the Mayer Museum (1882), pt. iii, no. 28.

# IV. SILVER TREASURES.

## I. The Esquiline Treasure.

### (Nos. 304–345 with nos. 227–241.)

Found in 1793 on the Esquiline Hill, Rome, near the church of Saints Silvester and
Martin. The miscellaneous nature of the objects which comprise this treasure
suggests that it was buried at some time of danger, such as a barbaric invasion.
*4th–5th century.*

Formerly in the Collections of Baron von Schellersheim and the Duc de Blacas. Acquired
1866.

*See* Visconti, *Lettera su di una antica argenteria nuovamente scoperta in Roma* (Rome, 1793);
the same, *Lettera intorno ad una antica supellettile d'argento*, &c., a reprint with plates, edited
by Montagnani (Rome, 1827); the same, *Opere Varie*, edited by G. Labus, vol. i, pp. 210–235,
pl. xvii and xviii (Milan, 1827); d'Agincourt, *Histoire de l'art par les monuments, Sculpture,*
pl. ix (Paris, 1823); Böttiger, *Sabina, oder Morgenszenen im Putzzimmer einer reichen*
*Römerin*, vol. i, p. 63 ff. (Leipzig, 1806); C. T. Newton, *Guide to the Blacas Coll. of Antiquities,*
*British Museum*, 1867. In the following description, where the name Visconti is given alone,
the reference is to the second edition of the *Lettera*, edited by Montagnani.

**304.** Oblong casket known as the casket of Projecta, embossed and partly
gilt, the lid in the form of a truncated pyramid, the body of corresponding shape.

It has three hinges at the back and a swing handle at each end, and is without lock or fastening. The gilding is applied to the drapery of the figures and to other accessories, which are also ornamented with lines of punched dots, circles, &c. *Plate* XIII.

THE LID. *See* figure, p. 61.

*The Top.*

Within a wreath supported on either side by a genius with a gilded band across the shoulders are the half-length full-face figures of a husband and wife. The former wears a chlamys fastened over the *r.* shoulder by a fibula with vertical stem, and dotted with small pounced rings in groups of three, and small pounced circles. The latter has the hair dressed high at the top of her head, and wears a broad jewelled collar over a mantle diapered with small circles of punched dots ; she holds with both hands a roll, perhaps the *volumen nuptiale*. *Plate* XIV.

*Front Panel.*

In the centre Venus seated in a shell dressing her hair. A dotted gilded band runs round her neck and is continued down the body as far as the navel. The shell is supported on either side by a Triton, one of whom holds up a mirror before the goddess, in which her face is reflected. On the back of each Triton is a genius, one holding a basket of fruit, the other a box. *Plate* XV. Cf. *Bull. della Commissione Arch. Comunale di Roma*, pl. xiv and xv (Rome 1877).

*End Right Hand Panel.*

A nereid partially draped seated on a hippocamp to *l.* Behind her are a genius and a dolphin ; before her face a duck. *Plate* XVII.

*End Left Hand Panel.*

A nereid riding a sea monster, her veil twisted round her arms and blown into an arch above her head. She holds a garland before her with both hands. Behind is a genius, in front swim two dolphins. *Plate* XVIII.

*Back Panel.*

The *deductio* of the bride. In the centre is a palace crowned by a large central dome flanked by domes of smaller size : the façade is supported by two twisted columns and two piers ; the upper part is pierced with four arches, while the *l.* side is formed of one large arch. To the *l.* of the building the bride approaches, conducted by a boy (*puer patrimus et matrimus*), and followed by a girl carrying a large oval box. From the *r.* come three persons bringing nuptial gifts. In the centre is a woman carrying in both arms a large rectangular box, conducted by a girl bearing a candelabrum, and followed by another with a ewer and a patera with a handle. On the ground behind is a bucket or basket. The background consists of an arcade with twisted columns and floriated capitals. *Plate* XVI.

These five panels are separated by formal foliated bands, the leaves arranged herring-bone fashion and gilded in alternate sections of about one inch in length.

The bottom of the lid is a flat ledge, along the front of which is punched the inscription ✝SECVNDE ET PROIECTA VIVATIS IN CHRI(STO) (*see* figure, p. 61), and on the flange in front are pounced figures indicating the weight, which is twenty-two pounds, three and a half ounces. (*see Plate* XIII, and Visconti, Pl. V.)

Dr. O. Pelka (*Altchristliche Ehedenkmäler*, p. 117, Strasburg, 1901) suggests that the cupolas are really arches at the back of the inner court of the house. The finials upon three of them are against this view. *See* note on next page.

THE BODY.

The decoration of the sides consists of an arcade of round and pointed arches alternating and draped with curtains, each arch occupied by a human figure, except at the ends of the sides, where there are peacocks. Both sides and ends are enclosed in a border ornamented with meandering vine scrolls.

*The Front.*

In the middle is the bride seated full face upon a cushioned chair with high back: in her *r.* hand she holds a fillet for her hair, in her *l.* a cylindrical unguent box. To *r.* stands an attendant holding up a mirror in her *r.* hand, to *l.* another attendant holding in both hands a rectangular box. At each end is a peacock. In the spandrils are two rosettes, two doves, and two baskets filled with fruit. *Plate* XV.

*Right End.*

In the middle is an attendant holding a pillow (?) before her breast with both hands. To the *l.* is a girl with a ewer in her *r.* hand and a patera in her *l.*; to the right another, holding in her *r.* a bucket. In the spandrils are two ducks. *Plate* XVII.

*Left End.*

In the centre a female figure holding a box (?) in both hands. To *r.* and *l.* two long-haired youths (?) holding a torch in the *l.* and *r.* hand respectively; they wear long tunics with gilded vertical stripes down the breast and circular ornaments (*orbiculi*) at the bottom in front, similar to those seen on tunics from Achmîm-Panopolis in Egypt (cf. no. 951). In the spandrils two birds and two rosettes. *Plate* XVIII.

*The Back.*

In the middle a female figure holding in her *l.* a cylindrical casket with pyramidal cover suspended by three chains (cf. no. 305). To *r.* a similar figure holding a shallow basin in both hands, to *l.* a third holding a box (?), while on the ground at her feet is a vase (cf. no. 306). At the ends are peacocks, and in the spandrils a pair of filled baskets, a pair of birds, a rosette, and a disc. The three riveted hinges are ornamented with a design of quatrefoils and dots. *Plate* XVI.

The bottom of the casket seen from the interior is filled by a large embossed lozenge upon a raised rectangle. The swing handles at the ends are semicircular and fluted, and one has been restored. The hinges are very clumsy, and can hardly have been applied by the maker of the casket. The metal is in places much decayed, and has been strengthened inside with numerous plates, but the actual restoration of any of the ornamental parts is very slight. Of the inscription, the left side of the monogram, the lower halves of the third and fourth letters in **VIVATIS**, the lower part of the **I** and the last three letters in **CHRISTO** are restored.

L. 21·7 in.   H. 11 in.   W. 17 in.   Weight, 125,620 grains (over 21¾ lb.).

Visconti, *Lettera*, &c., pl. i–vi, and *Opere Varie*, vol. i, pl. xvii ; Böttiger, *Sabina*, vol. i, pl. iii ; Sanclementi, *Numism. Selecta*, vol. iii, p. 203 ff. ; Mozzoni, *Tavole cronologiche della Storia della Chiesa*, &c., Secolo iv, p. 47 (Venice, 1857) ; Du Sommerard, *Les arts au moyen âge*, Album, Iʳᵉ série, pl. ii, fig. 3 ; Kraus, *Geschichte der christlichen Kunst*, vol. i, p. 216, fig. 178 ; O. Pelka, *Altchristliche Ehedenkmäler*, pl. ii–iv (Strasburg, 1901). *See also* Piper, *Mythologie und Symbolik der christl. Kunst*, vol. i, pp. 20 and 188 ff. ; Raoul Rochette, in *Journal des Savants*, 1830, p. 626 ff. ; Kraus, *Die christl. Kunst in ihren frühesten Anfängen*, p. 214 (Leipzig, 1872), *Roma Sotterranea*, pp. 232, 233 (Freiburg, 1879), *Real-Encykl.* vol. i, p. 384 ; V. Schultze, *Arch. Studien*, p. 110, *Die Katakomben*, p. 215 (Leipzig, 1882), *Arch. der altchristl. Kunst*, p. 278 ; E. Le Blant, *Mélanges d'Arch. et d'Histoire*, vol. iii (1883), p. 441, and *Cat. des Mon. chrét. du Musée de Marseille*, p. 24 (Paris, 1894).

The early representations of the casket are misleading, as they unite the front of the lid with the back of the body, and show the former in an imperfect condition.

This casket, which was a wedding gift, should be compared with the sarcophagi of the late 4th and early 5th centuries, in many of which portraits of husbands and wives in medallions, and a similar disposition of figures under arcades, will be found. It is of especial value in the illustration which it affords of contemporary costume, and in this it may be compared with the gilded glasses of the same period (cf. nos. 608 ff.). It has been often quoted as an example of the syncretistic spirit which prevailed among many Christians at this time, the pagan subjects upon the lid scarcely according with the sacred monogram beneath them. But in this respect it has numerous parallels, and it is not necessary to suppose that the inscription with the Christian monogram is later than the casket itself. It may be remarked that the domes of the buildings upon the back of the cover suggest oriental influences, and the finials upon some of them may be compared with those seen on ivory carvings and MSS. from Egypt and Syria (*see* Strzygowski, *Orient oder Rom*, pp. 33, 34). The circumstances of the discovery and the relation to Roman sarcophagi make it probable that the casket was executed in the Capital ; but this need not necessarily have been the case, as there exist fragments of an ivory casket found in Egypt, and now in the Gizeh Museum, which present close similarities of style and subject, and there can be little doubt that work of this kind might equally well have been produced, for instance, in Alexandria. Projecta must have been the wife of some member of the great family of the Asterii, perhaps of L. Turcius Rufius Apronianus Asterius, Prefect of Rome in 363 ; though inscriptions show that this family did not embrace Christianity till quite late in the 4th century. (*See C. I. L.* vol. vi, 1768–9 and 1772–3, and V. Schultze, *Arch. Studien*, p. 112.)

**305.** CASKET, with embossed ornament and domed cover with hinge fastened by a hasp ; it is suspended by three chains uniting in a large ring. The dome and sides are shaped alternately as broad flutes and flat panels. On the cover the flutes are plain, and the panels ornamented with a vine scroll growing from a vase and enclosing a bird. On the top is a medallion with a female figure seated on a folding stool beneath a tree, and holding a garland to which she is adding from a basket ; behind her is a parrot (*see* fig. *a*). In the flutes on the sides stand figures of eight Muses, beneath arches, supported by fluted columns. To *r.* of the lock is Urania, in a long tunic and mantle. She stands with crossed legs, her *l.* arm supported on a column, her *r.* hand, which holds a rod, resting upon a globe (*see* fig. *b*). Next is Melpomene, in a girded tunic, with

(b) URANIA.

(c) MELPOMENE.

(d) CLIO.

(e) POLYHYMNIA.

(a)

(f) TERPSICHORE.

(g) EUTERPE.

(h) THALIA.

(i) CALLIOPE.

K

her *l.* foot raised; in her *l.* hand she holds a tragic mask, in her *r.* a club. Near her upon the ground is an open scroll (*see* fig. *c*). To her *r.* is Clio, holding in her *l.* hand an open roll; on the ground at her side is a *scrinium* containing other rolls (*see* fig. *d*). Polyhymnia follows, holding out a mask in her *l.* hand; in her *r.* she holds the end of a veil or mantle passing over her *l.* shoulder (*see* fig. *e*). Next comes Terpsichore, in a girded tunic and mantle; she holds in her *r.* hand a plectrum, while her *l.* is covered by the plate of the ring to which one of the chains is attached (*see* fig. *f*). Euterpe, who follows, holds a flute in each hand (*see* fig. *g*). Thalia has a *pedum* in her *r.* hand and a comic mask in her left (*see* fig. *h*). The last in order is Calliope, wearing a mantle over both shoulders and holding a scroll in both hands; on a column at her side is a vase (*see* fig. *i*). All the Muses have a feather in their hair, in allusion to their victory over the Sirens. Of the alternate flat

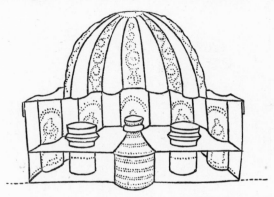

panels, that containing the lock has a wreath, below which are two doves; the others all have a similar design, a vase from which rises a conventional plant, forming a symmetrical scroll-design between two birds. Within is a thin bronze plate with five circular holes, the largest in the centre. In the four outer holes are cylindrical silver boxes with lids, and engraved with horizontal lines; in the centre hole is a narrow necked flask of similar workmanship (*see* figure). *Plate* XIX.

H. 10 in.   D. 13·1 in.   Weight 75,660 grains (over 13 lb.).

Visconti, pl. vii–xi; d'Agincourt, *Sculpt.* pl. ix, fig. 9 and 10; Böttiger, *Sabina*, vol. i, pl. iv.

Visconti's description of fig. *a* as the Muse Erato is doubtful, as this figure has not the proper attributes, and is without the feather in the hair. On the Muses and their attributes in late Roman art *see* O. Bie, *Die Musen in der antiken Kunst*. It will be noticed that the central figure on the back of the Casket of Projecta, pl. xvi (lower panel), carries a casket suspended by chains in a similar manner to the present example. The bronze plate has been broken and mended with rivets between one of the smaller holes and the edge. The interior has been strengthened with plates and a modern lock and key added.

**306.** FLASK of elegant outline, with embossed ornament consisting of six zones of spiral scrolls, diminishing in size towards top and bottom. The larger contain:

*a.* A genius riding a kicking ass to *l.* ; beneath, a basket of grapes overturned ; *b.*
a genius seated on a basket plucking grapes while a goat stands with its forefoot
on his *r.* knee ; *c.* a genius standing to *r.* picking grapes over a bowl or basket to
which a bird is flying down from *r.* ; *d.* a genius walking to *r.* holding a basket
of grapes upon his head while a hare rises on its hind legs before him.   The

remaining zones and interspaces contain single animals, in several cases repeated
more than once ; they are the goat, ram, lamb, hare, and numerous birds.   In
one instance (*d*) a grasshopper occurs, and in another a bird with a snake.

H. 13·5 in.   Weight 11,040 grains (nearly 2 lb.).
Visconti, pl. xv, fig. 2 ; d'Agincourt, *Sculpt.* pl. ix, fig. 13.
The neck has been broken and mended, and the foot restored.

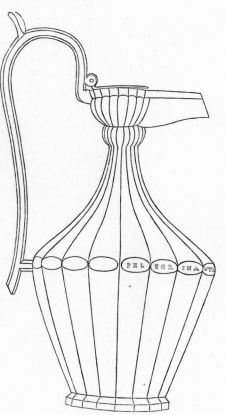

**307**. EWER, with facetted sides, slender handle of octagonal section, and long horizontal spout with hinge for a lid, which is missing. Round the shoulders a sunk oval occupies the width of each facet, on six of which, in front, is an inscription filled with niello (*see* figure) PELEGRINA VTERE FELIX.

*See* figure.

H. 13·7 in. Weight, 24,360 grains (nearly 4¼ lb.), Visconti, pl. xv, fig. 1 ; d'Agincourt, *Sculpt.* pl. ix, fig. 12.

Many of the letters of the inscription, especially the last four, are almost totally effaced.

PEL    EGR    INA    VTE    REF    ELI    X

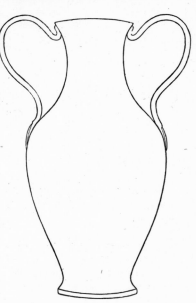

**308**. AMPHORA, with plain handles of stout wire.
See figure.

H. 7·9 in. Weight, 9,280 grains (over 1½ lb.). Visconti, pl. xv.

**309**. AMPHORA matching no. 308. H. ·8 in.

**310.** LARGE CIRCULAR DISH, with foot-rim and twelve radiating flutes terminating · in scallops, the spaces between which are engraved with formal foliated bands in pairs. The circular centre contains a square diapered with quatrefoils ; in

the space unoccupied by the square are formal foliated designs.
*See* figure.

D. 22·5 in. Weight, 42,360 grains (7 lb. 4 oz. 5 dwt.). Visconti, pl. xvii.
The dish has been broken, and is strengthened by plates at the back.

**311.** FLAT CIRCULAR DISH, with upright scalloped rim.  The background represents a rectangular trellis with a large circular medallion, containing a rosette at each point of junction.  In the centre is a medallion engraved with a beardless emperor (?) holding a roll in his *l.* and sacrificing before an altar.  The design has been outlined in gold, a small part of which remains.  The surface is

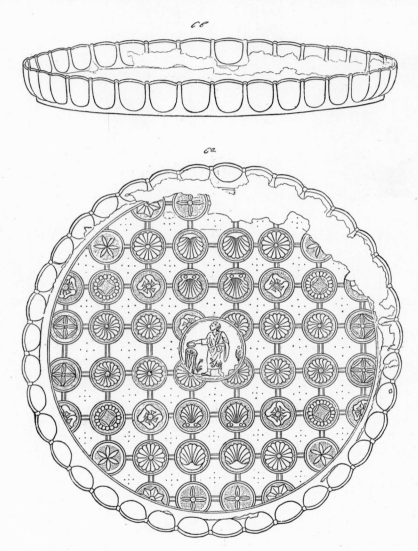

much decayed ; in parts the silver has entirely disappeared, and is roughly strengthened by a modern silver plate.

*See* figure.

D. 10 in.   Visconti, pl. xxi.

**312.** RECTANGULAR SHALLOW DISH, with foot-rim. The border is pierced with crescent-shaped openings with incurved ends, and at each corner is a projecting leaf. In the centre a monogram (*see* fig. *b*) within a laurel wreath in gold with nielloed outline (*see* fig.).

**313.** IDENTICAL DISH.

**314.** ANOTHER.

**315** ANOTHER.

    L. 7 in. Visconti, pl. xiii; d'Agincourt, *Sculpt.* pl. ix, fig. 11.
    The monogram is read by Visconti as **PROIECTA TVRCI.**
    The weight of the four dishes is 29,020 grains (over $5\frac{3}{4}$ lb).

**316.** FLAT CIRCULAR DISH, with foot-rim; in the centre the same monogram in gold and niello within an identical wreath. On the under side near the rim the indication of weight: $S\overline{CV}T.$ IIII. P.V. (*see* figure).

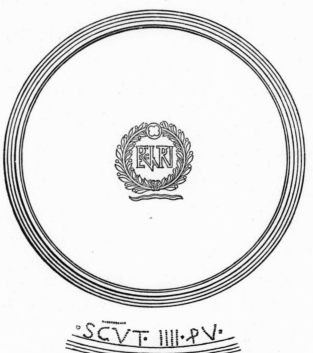

**317.** IDENTICAL DISH, without indication of weight.

**318.** ANOTHER.

**319.** ANOTHER.

> D. 6·3 in.  Visconti, pl. xiv.
> The inscription on no. 316 reads *Scutellae quattuor pondo quinque*, meaning that the four dishes together weighed five Roman pounds, *see* Visconti, p. 26.  The actual weight is 25,220 grains (a little under 4½ lb.).

**320.** CIRCULAR DISH, with foot-rim.  In turning the piece on the lathe the edge has been ribbed and simple concentric circles produced in the bottom.

> D. 9·45 in.  Weight, 9,760 grains (over 1½ lb.).  Visconti, pl. xviii.

**321.** CIRCULAR BOWL, on low foot-rim, the outside vertically fluted.
  *See* figure.
  D. 4·72 in.  Visconti, pl. xv.

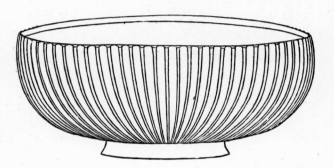

**322.** SPOON, with a pear-shaped bowl ending in a vertical disc, on the upper edge of which is fixed a tapering handle of octagonal section.  On the upper part of the handle nearest the bowl is engraved: IVNONI LANVMVINAE SPS SVLP

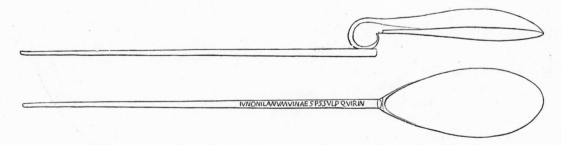

QVIRIN (*Junoni Lanuvinae sua pecunia Servius Sulpicius Quirinus* (*dono dedit*)).
  *See* figure.

> L. 7·9 in.  Visconti, pl. xvi, fig. 3.
> This spoon had perhaps at one time formed part of the treasure of the Temple of Juno Sospita at Lanuvium.

**323.** SPOON, with narrow pear-shaped bowl ending in a stout vertical spiral, upon the upper edge of which is fixed a tapering fluted handle. In the bowl is engraved a monogram.

> L. 8·74 in. Visconti, pl. xvi, fig. 1.

**324.** SPOON, with similar bowl ending in a stout scroll, to the upper edge of which is fixed a straight tapering handle of octagonal section.

> L. 7·9 in. Visconti, pl. xvi, fig. 2.

**325.** SPOON, with pear-shaped bowl ending in a pierced vertical disc, upon the upper edge of which is fixed a plain tapering handle. Upon one side of the disc are the letters M A, deeply cut and probably once filled with niello.

> L. 7·44 in. Visconti, pl. xvi, fig. 4.

**326.** SPOON, with similar bowl, the bottom modelled to imitate a leaf and ending in a stout scroll, to the top of which is fixed a tapering fluted handle.

> L. 8·2 in.

**327.** SPOON, with shallow oval bowl; the handle, which is octagonal in section, rises at an angle and expands to a spatulate end, engraved with a simple geometrical design.

> L. 6 in. Visconti, pl. xvi, fig. 6.

**328.** SPOON, with fiddle-shaped bowl ending in a stout scroll, from the end of which

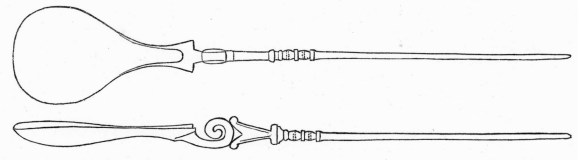

issues the straight handle, pierced and moulded at the upper part and tapering to the end.

> L. 5·86 in. Visconti, pl. xvi, fig. 7.

**329.** SPOON, with fiddle-shaped bowl and handle of octagonal section, terminating in a conical knob.

> L. 5·7 in. Visconti, pl. xvi, fig. 8.

**330.** SPOON, with straight tapering handle and shallow circular bowl, in which are scratched the letters ЄΥΧЄ (?).

> L. 3·9 in. Visconti, pl. xvi, fig. 5. Part of the bowl is missing.

**331.** HANDLE OF A KNIFE, octagonal in section, the surface covered with engraving.

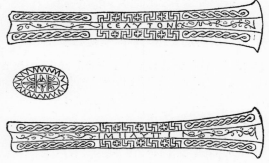

At each end are longitudinal bands of guilloche, and scrolls partly inlaid with gold ; in the middle, bands of fret pattern with inlaid gold crosses. Between the fretted bands there are on opposite sides two plain bands, on one of which is engraved MH ΛΥΠΙ, and on the other CEΑΥΤΟΝ (Μὴ λύπει σεαυτόν). On the butt are traces of engraving and gold inlay.

*See* figure.

L. 2·7 in.

**332.** ORNAMENT, partly gilt, for the end of the pole of a *sedia gestatoria*, or for the cross-piece of a chair. It consists of a rectangular socket, on the end of which is seated a female figure, the *Tyche* of Rome, wearing a girded tunic and mantle, and a crested helmet. In her *r.* hand she holds a spear, in her *l.* a

circular shield. Two *clavi* upon the tunic are represented by bands of pounced dots, and the mantle is diapered with similar dots in groups of three. Below the socket in front is a leaf-shaped pendant, the veins of which are indicated by pounced lines. The socket is pierced with two holes, through which passes a pin to hold the ornament in position.

*Plate* XX.

H. 5·4 in. Weight, 11,340 grains (nearly 2 lb.). Visconti, pl. xix, fig. i ; d'Agincourt, *Sculpt.* pl. ix, fig. 17 ; P. Gardner in *Journ. of Hellenic Studies*, vol. ix (1888), pl. v.

On personifications of towns *see* Gardner, *l. c.*, pp. 77–8 ; Strzygowski, *Die Kalenderbilder des Chronographen*, in *Jahrbuch des kaiserlich-deutschen Arch. Instituts*, Ergänzungsheft I, Berlin, 1888. Cf. also for Rome and Constantinople various consular Diptychs (esp. two at Vienna, Westwood, *Fictile Ivories*, nos. 79 and 80), and gilded glasses, Garrucci, *Vetri ornati di figure in oro*, pl. xxxvi, fig. 1.

**333.** SIMILAR ORNAMENT. The female figure, which represents Constantinople, is draped in a similar manner, but wears an armlet and a bracelet on the *r.* arm. In her *r.*

hand she holds a *patera*, and in her *l.* a *cornucopiae*. The chain and pin for fastening the socket are missing.

*Plate* XX ; and *see* figure.

H. 5·4 in.  Weight, 11,340 grains (nearly 2 lb.).  Visconti, pl. xix, 2 ; d'Agincourt, *Sculpt.* pl. ix, 18 ; Gardner, as above, pl. v.  *See also* Strzygowski, *Analecta Graeciensia, Festschrift zur* 420. *Versammlung Deutscher Philologen in Wien*, 1893, p. 148 (Graz. 1893) ; and for the type of the *Tyche* of Constantinople in general, *ibid.*, pp. 143-153.

**334.** ANOTHER.  The figure, representing the City of Antioch, wears a turreted crown, and holds in her *r.* hand flowers and ears of corn.  Beneath her feet is a nude half-length figure representing the River Orontes.  The pin and chain for fastening the socket are missing.

*Plate* XX.

H. 5·2 in.  Weight, 11,340 grains (nearly 2 lb.).  Visconti, pl. xx, 2 ; d'Agincourt, *Sculpt.* pl. ix, 19 ; Gardner, as above, pl. v.  This figure is probably a copy of the statue of Eutychides ; *see* Gardner, as above, p. 78.

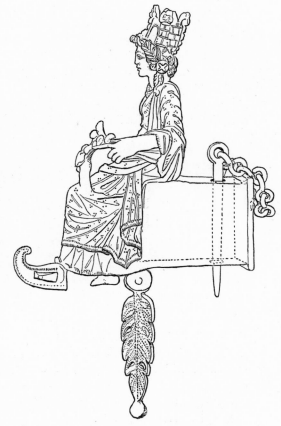

**335.** ANOTHER.  The female figure, here representing Alexandria, wears a turreted crown, and holds in her hands fruits and ears of corn, while beneath her *l.* foot is the prow of a ship.  The socket is fitted with a pin and chain for attachment.

*Plate* XX ; and *see* figure.

H. 5.4 in.  Weight, 11,100 grains (nearly 2 lb.).  Visconti, pl. xx, 1 ; d'Agincourt, *Sculpt.* pl. ix, 16 ; Gardner, as above, pl. v.

**336.** ORNAMENT from a chair, partly gilt, in the shape of a right forearm holding a vertical cylinder surmounted by a conventional pomegranate. On the wrist is a twisted bracelet.

*See* figure.

**337.** ORNAMENT to match the last ; a *l.* arm.

H. 13 in.    Weight of each, 17,360 grains.

**338.** HORSE-TRAPPINGS (*phalerae*), partly gilt, formed of nine plates, and a buckle to *l.*   The plates are of two different designs, the first, four in number, are circular and embossed with three lions' heads and an eagle respectively.   Each has a leaf-shaped projection at the top and a pendant at the bottom, that below

the eagle being an inverted crescent. The plates of the second type alternate with the others : each is a broad oval, consisting of two pelta-like ornaments, the curves of which form the outer edges, and having an applied quatrefoil in the centre.

*See* figure.

L. 25 in.   Visconti, pl. xxiv.

**339.** SIMILAR PHALERAE.

> L. 25 in.

**340.** OTHERS, similar ; buckle to *r*.

> L. 25 in.

**341.** OTHERS, similar.

> L. 25 in.

**342.** OTHERS, incomplete ; buckle and two plates, one pelta-shaped, the other with lion's head.

**343.** OTHERS, incomplete ; buckle and four plates, two pelta-shaped alternating with two others, one with lion's head and one with eagle.

**344.** HANDLE OF A JUG, fluted, at the bottom is a leaf with engraved veins. The upper part is ornamented with scrolls in openwork and is semicircular, fitting the lip of the jug. Its upper surface has an ornament of punched dots large and small, the latter forming scroll designs.

> H. 7·6 in.

**345.** PAIR OF SWING-HANDLES, semicircular, with recurved ends shaped like swans' heads, from each of which a flat leaf-like tab hangs by a hook of the same bird-shaped pattern.

> H. 5·6 in. Probably from a casket.

## II. Roman Silver Spoons of the Fifth Century.

**346.** SPOON, with pear-shaped bowl ending in a vertical disc, from the upper end of which issues a tapering fluted handle. On the upper part of the handle nearest the bowl is ✝ ALEXANDER engraved and filled with niello. On one side of the disc the number III.

> L. 8·32 in. Castellani Coll. 1872. Weight, 563 grains.
> This spoon with the following six nos. was found somewhere in the neighbourhood of Rome in 1886.
> De Rossi, *Bullettino*, 1868, pl. opposite p. 78, fig. 2 ; and *see ibid.*, pp. 79–84 ; Fortnum in *Arch. Journ.* xxviii, 1871, p. 285–6 ; and cf. Le Blant, *Inscr. Chrétiennes de la Gaule*, vol. ii, p. 370, no. 583.

**347.** SIMILAR SPOON, with name ✝ QVADRAGISIMA and the number II.

> L. 9 in. Castellani Coll. 1872. Weight, 640 grains.
> De Rossi, as above, fig. 3. Bowl imperfect.

**348**. SPOON OF SIMILAR SHAPE ; on one side of the disc, connecting the handle with the bowl, is engraved a monogram RSE, on the other a Latin cross in niello.

> L. 8·4 in.   Castellani Coll. 1872.   Weight, 506 grains.
> De Rossi, as above, fig. 4.   The name represented by the monogram is conjectured by de Rossi to be *Ireneus*.

**349**. SIMILAR SPOON, with the name + FAVSTVS and the number VII.

> L. 8·88.   Castellani Coll. 1872.   Weight, 600 grains.
> De Rossi, as above, fig. 6.
> A silver ring in the Fortnum Collection at Oxford, said to have been found in the same place, is engraved with the same name.   *See* Fortnum, *Arch. Journ.* vol. xxviii (1871), p. 285.

**350**. SIMILAR SPOON, with the same monogram but without the cross.

> L. 8·7 in.   Castellani Coll. 1872.   Weight, 562 grains.

**351**. SPOON OF SIMILAR SHAPE, without inscriptions.

> L. 9·14 in.   Castellani Coll. 1872.   Weight, 647 grains.

**352**. SIMILAR SPOON ; the bowl imperfect.

> L. 8·3 in.   Castellani Coll. 1872.   Weight, 525 grains.

**353**. SPOON, with pear-shaped bowl terminating in a vertical disc continued under the bowl in a keel-like ridge, and having fixed to its upper edge a tapering handle of round section.   On one side of the disc is the *crux monogrammatica* (☧) with the extremities pattées, on the other a bunch of grapes, both engraved and filled with niello.

> L. 8·8 in.   Weight, 480 grains (1 oz).   Franks Bequest, 1897.   Said to have been found in the Seine near Paris.

**354**. SIMILAR SPOON.   On one side of the disc is engraved a monogram formerly nielloed, on the other a Latin cross pattée, in which the niello still remains.
   *See* figure.

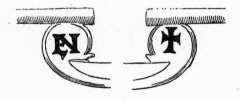

> L. 8·9 in.   Franks Bequest, 1897.   Found at Metz.

**355**. SIMILAR SPOON, with fluted handle.   On each side of the disc is engraved a Latin cross, probably once nielloed.

> L. 8·9 in.   Weight, 720 grains (1½ oz.).   Franks Bequest, 1897.   Found near Augsburg.

### III. Carthage Treasure.

(Nos. 356–375, with nos. 242–248.)          Franks Bequest, 1897.

Found on the Hill of St. Louis, Carthage.
*4th and early 5th centuries.*

**356.** HEMISPHERICAL BOWL, with foot-rim and broad flat edge ornamented with four pastoral groups chased in relief, each representing a shepherd with dogs, sheep, goats, &c. The groups are separated by four profile masks, male and female alternately. The circumference is bordered by an edging of large pellets. In the bottom on a circular medallion is a shepherd standing between a ram and a dog.
 *See* figure.

 D. 6·9 in.   H. 2·25 in.   Weight, 6,000 grains (12½ oz.).

**357.** SIMILAR BOWL, with narrower edge, having a beaded line round the inner side. The edge is divided into four groups chased in relief and divided by four masks male and female alternately; with the male are associated the *pedum, syrinx,* and altar, with the female, *tympana.* Of the groups, two are pastoral, representing shepherds with cattle, horses, &c. ; of the remaining two one shows a hind chased by a lion, the other the same animal pursued by a leopard. In the bottom is engraved an eightfoil.

 D. 6·6 in.   H. 2 in.   Weight, 5,040 grains (10½ oz.).

**358.** IDENTICAL DISH, but with the inscription : **D· D· ICRESCONI CLARENT.**
 *Plate* XXI.

 D. 5·4 in.   H. 1·25 in.   Weight, 2,400 grains (5 oz.).
 The Cresconii were a well-known family in N. Africa in the 4th and 5th centuries. *See* de Vit, *Onomasticon, s. v.* ; *C. I. L. Africa*, pt. i (1881), nos. 2,403, 4,354, 10,891 ; Mommsen, *Ephemeris Epigraphica*, vol. iii, 1871, p. 78.

**359.** DISH WITH FOOT-RIM. In the centre, within concentric circles turned and gilt, the inscription **LOQVERE FELICITER**, preceded by the sacred monogram ☧ flanked by Λ and ω. Round this is a broad band of engraved flutings within a gilt band. The steep sides are vertically fluted and gilt round the edge.

*Plate* XXI.

D. 5·4 in.  H. 1·25 in.  Weight, 2,400 grains (5 oz.).

**360.** SHALLOW BOWL, with foot-rim and horizontal handle. The centre is convex and embossed with a frog in high relief within a circle, the spots on the body being represented by circles of pounced dots. The handle is ornamented by four rows of drop-shaped bosses.

*Plate* XXI.

L. 9·8 in.  D. 6·2 in.  H. 1·9 in.  Weight, 4,800 grains (10 oz.).

The frog, which is sometimes found upon pottery lamps from Egypt, is emblematic of the Resurrection, and sometimes supposed to signify a heretical sect (*see* note on no. 819). It is uncertain whether it has any such meaning here.

**361.** LOW HEMISPHERICAL BOWL on a high foot, the outside ornamented with broad vertical hammered facets. Flat saucer-shaped cover, similarly ornamented, and having in the centre a high rim like that beneath the bowl, to serve as a foot-rim when the cover was used as a dish.

*See* figure.

H. (with cover) 4·5 in.  H. of cover, 1·3 in. D. 4·9 in.  Weight, 6,880 grains (14¾ oz.).

**362.** IDENTICAL BOWL, without cover.

Weight, 4,680 grains (9¾ oz.).

**363.** ANOTHER.

**364.** SPOON, with deep circular bowl and short handle of octagonal section terminating in a knob. At the juncture of the bowl and handle is a square panel with a curved continuation on each side; on the panel is a cross between two scrolls, all inlaid with niello.

*See* figure.

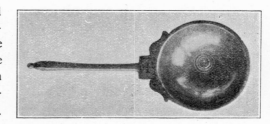

L. 6 in.  D. of bowl, 2·56 in.  Weight, 960 grains (2 oz.).

**365–370.** SIX IDENTICAL SPOONS.

The bowls of some of these spoons are coated inside with an incrustation of pale buff soil, traces of which were found in nos. 361–363.

**371.** SPOON, with pear-shaped bowl, modelled on the under side to imitate a leaf, the interior ornamented with traverse flutings on either side of a plain median band. The bowl terminates in a stout pierced vertical scroll, to the upper edge of which is fixed a fluted handle.

*Plate* XXI.

L. 6·9 in.   Weight, 600 grains (1¼ oz.).

**372.** SIMILAR SPOON, imperfect.

L. 5·8 in.

**373.** SIMILAR SPOON, the interior of the bowl plain.

L. 6·4 in.   Weight, 480 grains (1 oz.).

**374.** ANOTHER.

L. 7·36 in.   Weight, 1 oz.

**375.** SPOON, with shallow circular bowl connected with a fluted tapering handle by a stout pierced vertical scroll.   Within the bowl is engraved the sacred monogram (☧) between ⍺ and ⍵.

*Plate* XXI.

L. 6·72 in.   D. of bowl, 1·6 in.   Weight, 240 grains (½ oz.).

## IV. Lampsacus Treasure.

### (Nos. 376–396, with nos. 249 and 250.)

Found at Lampsacus on the Hellespont.

*6th—7th century.*

The greater part was given by Earl Cowley in 1848; the rest was partly acquired in 1886, and partly bequeathed by Sir A. Wollaston Franks, K.C.B., 1897.

**376.** TRIPOD LAMP-STAND, resembling a pricket candlestick, with square spike rising from a disc on a baluster-moulded stem with hexagonal expanding base, having three hollow feet.   Beneath are two impressions of a cruciform stamp, both imperfect, but containing the letters of a name—CECTOC.

*Plate* XXII ; and *see* figure.

H. 8·3 in.   Weight, 5,040 grains (10½ lbs.).   Given by Earl Cowley, 1848.

With the stamp cf. those on nos. 379, 397, and 399, and *see* the references there given.

**377.** CYLINDRICAL VESSEL, raised on a small, low circular foot.   Possibly a chalice.
*Plate* XXII.

H. 3·88 in.   D. at top, 4·9 in.   Weight, 3,840 grains (8 oz.).   Given by Earl Cowley, 1848.
It is worthy of note that this piece has not been put on the lathe either inside or out.   The finish is very rough, and hammer-marks show clearly over the whole surface.   It is imperfect, one side being broken away.

**378.** SHALLOW DISH, round at the bottom.   Inside, with the arms extending to the edge, is a gilt cross, having in the centre a double circle enclosing a punched and nielloed monogram.
*Plate* XXII.

D. 7·3 in.   Weight, 3,960 grains (8¼ oz.).   1886.   The name represented by the monogram is perhaps Menas.

**379.** SIMILAR DISH, with identical design.   On the bottom are the impressions of three stamps, all imperfect, one cruciform twice repeated, one rectangular, and one with an arched end.   The cruciform stamp has in the centre a monogram of the same shape, and at the ends the letters of a name, probably CICINNHC, a variant of CICINNIOC.

*See* figure.

D. 6·2 in.   Weight, 2,880 grains (6 oz.).   Given by Earl Cowley, 1848.
With these stamps cf. those on the lamp-stand (no. 376) and on the silver vessels from Cyprus (nos. 397 and 399).   For similar stamps see also Arneth, *Die antiken Gold- und Silber-Monumente, &c.,* pl. S. vii, and *Archaeologia,* vol. lvii (1900), p. 166; Stephani, in *Compte rendu de la Commission Imp. archéologique,* St. Petersburg, 1867, pp. 50, 52, 211, and 1878–9, pp. 148, 157–8.   For mention of stamps still unpublished, *see Bulletin arch. du Comité des travaux historiques,* Paris, 1893, pp. 88–9; *Compte rendu,* as above, 1897, pp. 28 and 103.

**380.** SPOON, with pear-shaped bowl, engraved on the back with a symmetrical foliated design and having at the end a vertical disc, to the upper edge of which is attached a baluster-moulded handle, hexagonal in section nearest the bowl.   On the top of the hexagon is engraved + MAΘΘEOC, the letters having been once nielloed.   On one side of the disc is engraved a monogram.
*Plate* XXIII (*back view*), and *see* figure.

L. 9·25 in.   Weight, 1,200 grains (2½ oz.).   1886.

**381.** IDENTICAL SPOON, with the name MAPKOC.
*Plate* XXIII.

Given by Earl Cowley, 1848.

**382.** ANOTHER, with the name ΛΟΥΚΑC.

> Given by Earl Cowley, 1848.

**383.** ANOTHER, with the name ΙΑΚѠΒΟC.

> Franks Bequest, 1897.

**384.** ANOTHER, with the name ΠΕΤΡΟC.

> Franks Bequest, 1897.
>
> The names upon inscribed spoons are usually those of the owners (cf. nos. 346–349) but the above four coincide with those of apostles, as in other examples, *see* de Rossi, *Bullettino*, 1878, pp. 117–120, and pl. 8; and Kraus in *Bonner Jahrbücher*, Heft lxxiii (1882), p. 87. On silver spoons of the Early Christian period, *see also Bullettino*, 1868, p. 81 ff.

**385.** SPOON, with similar bowl and identical monogram, but with the lower part of the handle round in section and expanding to the end.

> *Plate* XXIII (*back view*).
>
> L. 9·22 in.   Weight, 1,235 grains (over 2½ oz.).   Given by Earl Cowley, 1848.

**386.** ANOTHER, identical.

> *Plate* XXIII.
>
> L. 9·22 in.   1886.

**387.** SPOON, with pear-shaped bowl terminating in a stout vertical disc connected with the bottom by a keel-like ridge.   The handle is attached to the upper edge of the disc, and near the bowl is square in section, the remainder being round, with a number of turned parallel lines at each end, and terminating in a baluster finial.   On the back of the bowl is a symmetrical foliate design, and round the rim a band of continuous loop-coils.   On one side of the disc is engraved a monogram (*see* figure, no. 390) within a wreath, the whole filled with niello; on the other side is a formal plant (*see* figure).   Along the interior of the bowl and on the upper part of the square section of the handle is engraved the hexameter: ΤΕΡΜΑ Δ ΟΡΑΝ 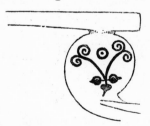 ΒΙΟΤΟΙΟ ϹΟΛѠΝ ΙΕΡΑΙϹ ΕΝ ΑΘΗΝΑΙϹ once filled with niello, and on one side of the same part of the handle: ѠϹ ΔΙ ΧΡΗϹΘΑΙ ΤѠ ΒΙѠ, in the letters of which the niello still remains.

> *Plate* XXIII.
>
> L. 10·3 in.   Weight, 1,133 grains (over 2¼ oz.).   Given by Earl Cowley, 1848.
>
> The saying of Solon is given by Herodotus, Bk. I. c. 32.   *See also* Leutsch, *Corpus Paroemiographorum graecorum*, vol. ii, p. 665.
>
> For the Inscriptions upon this and the following five nos. *see* Dübner, F., *Epigrammatum Anthologia Palatina*, vol. ii, p. 74 (Paris, 1872); Fröhner, W., in *Philologus, Zeitschrift für das klassische Altertum, Supplement-Band V, Kritische Analekten*, p. 56 (Göttingen, 1889).
>
> The four Greek hexameters of nos. 387–390 are found together in an Anonymous Epigram on

the Seven Sages, beginning—Ἑπτὰ σοφῶν ἐρέω κατ' ἔπος πόλιν, οὔνομα, φωνήν. *See Fragmenta Philosophorum Graecorum*, ed. F. G. Mullachius, vol. i, p. 235 (Paris, 1860). The second parts of the inscriptions, upon the sides of the handles, do not appear to be directly connected with the first.

A spoon with Greek inscriptions, probably belonging to the same set, is in the *Salle des Bijoux* in the Museum of the Louvre.

388. IDENTICAL SPOON inscribed: ΧΕΙΛΩΝ Δ ΕΝ ΚΟΙΛΗ ΛΑΚΕΔΑΙΜΟΝΙ | ΓΝΩΘΙ ΣΕΑΥΤΟΝ and Κ ΠΡΟΤΡΕΠΟΥ ΣΥΝΕΧΩΣ (Καὶ προτρέπου συνεχῶς).
*Plate* XXIII.

> L. 10·35 in. 1886.
> The niello is missing in all the letters inside the bowl.
> This saying is that usually attributed to Chilon, though sometimes to Solon or Bias.

389. SPOON, identical with the foregoing, but inscribed ΤΟΥΣ ΠΛΕΟΝΑΣ ΚΑΚΙΟΥΣ ΔΕ ΒΙΑΣ | ΑΠΕΦΗΝΕ ΠΡΙΗΝΕΥΣ on the interior of the bowl and top of handle, and ΤΟΥΣ ΜΙΣΗΔΟΝΟΥΣ on the side of the handle. The inscriptions were once all nielloed, but the niello only remains in the letters upon the handle.
*Plate* XXIII.

> L. 10·4 in. Given by Earl Cowley, 1848.
> The original saying of Bias, as given by Demetrius Phalereus, is: οἱ πλεῖστοι ἄνθρωποι κακοί. The version given by Diogenes Laertius is: Ἔλεγε δεῖν καὶ φιλεῖν ὡς μισήσοντας· τοὺς γὰρ πλείστους εἶναι κακούς (Bk. I, 87). *See* also Leutsch, as above, vol. ii, p. 685.

390. IDENTICAL SPOON, inscribed: ΠΙΤΤΑΚΟΣ ΟΥΔΕΝ ΑΓΑΝ ΟΣ ΕΗΝ ΓΕΝΟΣ | ΕΚ ΜΙΤΥΛΗΝΗΣ and ΦΙΛΙΝ ΔΕ ΛΥΔΟΡΟΥΣ. (φιλεῖν δὲ λοιδόρους.) The niello missing in bowl as before.
*Plate* XXIII.

> L. 10·35 in. Franks Bequest, 1897.
> For the inscription, *see* Leutsch, as above, vol. ii, p. 614.
> Μηδὲν ἄγαν is ascribed by Demetrius to Solon.

391. IDENTICAL SPOON, with bilingual inscriptions: OMNIA VINCIT AMOR ET NOS | CEDAMUS AMORI (Virgil, *Ecl.* x. 69), and on the side of the handle: ΤΡΩΓΕ ΕΡΟΤΟΚΡΟΥΣΤΕ.
*Plate* XXIII.

> L. 10·4 in. 1886.
> Some of the uncial forms here employed are as early as the end of the third century, others become common from the end of the fourth (Hübner, *Exempla Scripturae, Proleg.* p. 67, and pp. 1146–1152). A spoon of very similar character, with bilingual inscriptions (*Balnea Vina Venus faciunt properantia fata*, and ΘΥΩΝ ΤΗΡΙ ΤΗΝ ΚΗΛΗΝ ΣΟΥ), is in the Museum of the Εὐαγγελικὴ Σχολή at Smyrna; *see Mitt. des Deutsch. Arch. Inst.*, 4th year, 1879, p. 121. Τρῶγε is probably the imperative of the word τρώγειν, the sense being 'eat, love-smitten one,' rather than 'O love-smitten Trogus.'

**392.** IDENTICAL SPOON, with bilingual inscriptions ; O FORMOSE PUER NIMIUM NE | CREDE COLORI (Virgil, *Ecl.* ii. 17), ΑΚΕΡΜΙϹ ΟΥΚ ΕΙ ΕΥΜΟΡΦΟϹ. *Plate* XXIII.

L. 5·15 in. Given by Earl Cowley, 1848. Imperfect.

Ἄκερμις perhaps stands for ἀκέρμις, 'penniless,' the sense being that wealth as well as good looks are needed for success in love.

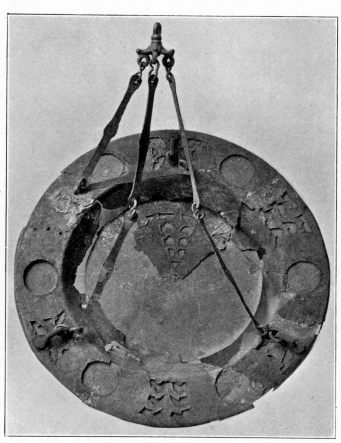

*a*

*b*

**393.** PENDENT LAMP-DISH (*polycandelon*). The flat edge is pierced with six holes one inch in diameter, alternating with either an equal-armed cross or a palmette-like design. The sunk centre has been pierced with six radiating limbs and the interspaces filled with similar palmette-like designs. The dish is suspended by three chains uniting at the top in a star-shaped finial and a ring. *See* figure *a* and figure *b* (*restoration*).

D. 10 in. Given by Earl Cowley, 1848. It is much damaged, and has been mounted on a plate of zinc. Cf. the larger bronze *polycandelon*, no. 529.

**394.** RECTANGULAR BORDER for a table (?) made of thin beaten plates of silver.

L. 30·5 in. B. 21·5 in. Given by Earl Cowley, 1848.

**395.** FRAGMENTS OF A FOLDING STOOL OR STAND, silver with cores of iron. They consist of broken bars of baluster-design, two terminating in bronze human feet in sandals, and one in a silver finial representing a lion's head.

L. of longest fragment, 8 in. Given by Earl Cowley, 1848.

**396.** HANDLE FROM A VESSEL or box, bifurcating at each end, each of the four ends being twisted once upon itself.

L. 7 in. Given by Earl Cowley, 1848.

## V. Cyprus Treasure.

### (Nos. 397 to 424.)

Found within the last few years of the 19th century in a mound near the Monastery of Acheripoetos, six miles west of Kerynia on the north coast of the Island.

*6th century*.

Acquired 1899.

**397.** FLAT CIRCULAR DISH (a paten ?) with low foot-rim and moulded edge. In the centre is a cross with loops at the extremities within a wavy border of conventional ivy leaves. Both designs are filled with niello and enclosed within two gilt circles. On the bottom are the impressions of five stamps, two circular, two originally arched with rectangular bases, and one cruciform (*see* figures *a–e*). Stamp *a* has at the top a nimbed bust of a saint (?) with the legend: ✝ IⲰANNIC, and below, a cruciform monogram which would read ΠⲈTPOY. Stamp *b*, which is imperfect, has a rectangular monogram which might make the same name and the legend : ✝ TPY(Φ)ⲰN. Stamp *c* has a bust with legend, ✝ ⲐⲰM(AC); *d* a monogram with (✝ IⲰ)ANNOY; and *e* (cf. no. 379) a cruciform monogram with the name CICINNIC (Σισίννιος).

*Plate XXIV.*

D. 10·5 in. Weight, 18,460 grains (nearly 3¼ lb.). 1899. Cf. two similar plates in the Stroganoff Coll. found in the government of Perm, S. Russia, *see* Stephani, in *Compte rendu de la Comm. Imp. arch.*, St. Petersburg, 1878–9, pp. 156 and 158.

Figd. *Archaeologia*, vol. lvii (1900), pl. xvi. For similar stamps *see* nos. 376, 379, and 399.

It has been suggested that the names are those of priests or donors, and that the busts are those of saints. But researches, as yet unpublished, by M. Smirnoff of the Imperial Museum of the Hermitage, St. Petersburg, tend to prove that the stamps are 'hall-marks,' and that five was the usual number of impressions. The names and monograms correspond in some cases with those of emperors, but they occur in considerable variety, and would seem to be as a rule those of officials. The ultimate publication of all the examples in the Russian collections will doubtless throw light on points at present obscure. The monogram, fig. *d*, is similar in style to those of Justinian I. The rim is considerably oxydized, and near it two holes have been worn through the metal.

**398.** BOWL on low foot-rim. In a central circular medallion surrounded by a broad band of conventional nielloed ornament (*see* figure) with plain borders turned on the lathe is a half-figure of a nimbed saint in relief, full face. He is youthful and beardless, with curly hair, holding the folds of his garment in his *l.* hand and

a long cross in his *r.*, which is raised. He wears a chlamys fastened on the *r.* shoulder by a fibula, and showing over the breast the rectangular patch of a different colour known as the τάβλιον. On his *r.* shoulder is seen an embroidered rosette, and round his neck a collar of peculiar design. The rim is chased with a double band of conventional leaves.

*Plate* XXIV.

D. 9·45 in. H. 2·85 in. Weight, 15,980 grains (over 2¾ lbs.). 1899.

The saint is clearly St. Sergius or St. Bacchus (Oct. 7th, *see Analecta Bollandiana*, vol. xiv, p. 373). The costume is that of an officer in the Imperial Bodyguard, a distinguishing feature being the peculiar collar, which in some instances at least was set with jewels in the front. For figures of St. Sergius and St. Bacchus illustrating this collar *see* Strzygowski, *Orient oder Rom*, p. 124 (encaustic painting from Sinai, now at Kiev); Millet, *Le Monastère de Daphne*, p. 147, fig. 61, and pl. x, fig. 4 (Paris, 1900); Graeven in *L'Arte*, 1899; *Adamo ed Eva sui cofanetti Bizantini*, fig. 13 A. For other examples of bodyguards wearing the collar *see* Strzygowski and Pokrovsky, *Der Silberschild aus Kertsch*, in *Mat. Russ. Arch.*, no. 8 (1892), (votive shields of Justinian and Theodosius); d'Agincourt, *Sculpt.*, pl. x, fig. 7 (obelisk of Theodosius); Garrucci, *Storia*, pl. 123, fig. 2 (Vienna MS. of Genesis), pl. 264 (mosaic of Justinian at San Vitale); W. Meyer, *Zwei antike Elfenbeintafeln*, &c., pl. iii (Munich, 1879), (ivory carving); Molinier, *Ivoires*, no. 38; *Archaeologia*, vol. lvii, p. 162 (another); Bordier, *Descr. des Peintures et autres ornements contenus dans les MSS. grecs de la Bibliothèque Nationale*, p. 85 (miniature in Homilies of Gregory Nazianzen, 9th century, Bibl. Nat. MS. 510); Schlumberger, *L'Épopée Byzantine*, &c. (Paris, 1896), p. 601 (10th cent. MS.); Uvarov, *Album Byzantin*. pl. v, fig. 8 (Moscow, 1890).

**399.** HEXAGONAL VESSEL, with low circular foot-rim; on the edges are three pierced ears for chains which are now missing. Each face is embossed with a bust within a border of conventional palm-leaves which unite at the angles in small medallions each engraved with a cross; the six busts are arranged symmetrically in two sets of three, of which our Lord and the Virgin are the, central figures. Our Lord is represented full face with long hair and short beard and with the cruciferous nimbus; like

all the other male figures, he holds a book. To his *l.* is St. Peter holding a
long cross over his *l.* shoulder; to his *r.* St. Paul. Both Apostles have the
distinguishing characteristics of Early Christian Art, St. Peter thick hair and
short beard, St. Paul scanty hair and beard of greater length. The Virgin

has her mantle drawn over her head, or wears a veil, with a cross above the
forehead. To her *l.* is St. John the Evangelist, youthful and beardless; to her
*r.* a bearded saint resembling St. Peter, and probably intended for St. James.
To the interior still adhere small fragments of bronze plates showing that the

vessel once had a lining of this metal. On the bottom and within the foot
are impressions of three stamps (*see* figure) similar to those on the plate,
no. 397, one at least, the cruciform example, being identical with fig. *a.* The

stamps have been mutilated by the lathe, which shows that the bottom of the vessel was turned after the application of the stamps.

*See* figures.

D. 4·12 in.   H. 2·66 in.   Weight, 8¼ oz.   1899.
*Archaeologia,* vol. lvii, pl. xvii.

This vessel must have been a censer rather than a lamp, as a bronze lining would hardly be necessary for the latter. It is true that the Byzantine censer, as seen in the illuminations of MSS. *passim* and in extant examples (*see Byz. Zeitschr.* vol. v (1896), p. 567, and vol. vii (1898), p. 29), is usually hemispherical with a high foot. But a hexagonal bronze vessel described as a thurible has been found at Akhmîm (Panopolis), (*see* Forrer, *Frühchristl. Altertümer,* &c., pl. vi, fig. 4), and others of the same shape are still preserved in oriental collections (*see* Strzygowski in *Byz. Zeitschr.* vol. x (1901), p. 731).

The vessel should be compared with a silver reliquary found near Sebastopol, and now in the Hermitage, St. Petersburg (*see Compte rendu de la Commission Imp. arch.* 1897, pp. 28 and 103, figs. 87, 88 = figs. 213, 214); and with a large silver vase found at Emesa in Phoenicia, now in the Museum of the Louvre (*see* Héron de Villefosse in *Bull. des Ant. de France,* 1892, p. 239).

**400.** SPOON, with pear-shaped bowl engraved on the under side with a symmetrical foliate design and ending in a vertical disc, from the upper edge of which issues a straight handle, at first hexagonal and afterwards round in section, expanding slightly to the end. On the top of the  hexagonal part are four engraved and nielloed letters in two pairs divided by a cross (*see* figure, and *Archaeologia,* as above, p. 170, fig. 12 (central spoon)). For the designs engraved on the backs of this and the following spoons *see* cut on p. 35.

**401–403.** THREE IDENTICAL SPOONS.

**404.** SIMILAR SPOON, without inscr. and with knob at end of handle.   Imperfect.

L. 9·3 in.   1889.   Weight of each spoon, 1,198 grains (nearly 2½ oz.).

**405.** SIMILAR SPOON; the part of the handle next the bowl hexagonal in section, the central part a short baluster, the end round in section, terminating in a small knob.  On one side of the hexagonal part is pounced the name ΘΕΟΔΩΡΟΥ.

*See* figure.

L. 8·9 in.   Weight, 1,168 grains (over 2¼ oz.).

**406.** SIMILAR SPOON, uninscribed.

**407.** ANOTHER.

**408.** SPOON, similar; the handle next the bowl hexagonal in section, the rest fluted.

**409-413.** FIVE IDENTICAL SPOONS.

L. 9·5 in.   Weight of each spoon, 1,250 grains (over 2½ oz.).

N

**414.** SPOON, of similar general shape, but with a baluster handle.   In the interior of the bowl a ram to *l.* in relief.

    *Plate* XXV.

      L. 10·15 in.   Weight, 2,098 grains (over 4¼ oz.).   The remaining spoons are uniform with this ; the majority are also figured in *Archaeologia*, vol. lvii (1900), pl. xviii.

**415.** ANOTHER, with a gryphon.   *Plate* XXV.

**416.** ANOTHER, with a panther.   Ditto.

**417.** ANOTHER, with a tiger.   Ditto.

**418.** ANOTHER, with a stag.   *Plate* XXV.

**419.** ANOTHER, with a bear.   Ditto.

**420.** ANOTHER, with a horse.   Ditto.

**421.** ANOTHER, with a boar.   Ditto.

**422.** ANOTHER, with a bull.   Ditto.

**423.** ANOTHER, with a lion.   *See* figure.

**424.** ANOTHER (bowl only), with a hare.   *See* figure.

    *Archaeologia*, vol. lvii (1900), pl. xviii, and figs. 15 and 16, p. 171.

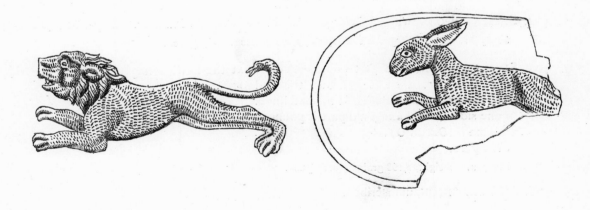

# V. BRONZE.

## A. Exagia and Weights.

Chiefly of the Eastern Empire and dating from the 5th and 6th centuries. The Latin and Greek denominations are both employed, the unit, the equivalent of the older *sextula*, being called *solidus* or νόμισμα. The form of the weights is usually quadrangular or circular, and they are flat, but of varying thickness. The characters are engraved on one or both sides, and frequently inlaid with silver. Several examples are without numbers to indicate weight; but as they closely resemble others which do bear such indications, they have been included in the series, although it is not always certain that they were used for weighing (see de Rossi in *Mitt. K. D. A. I.* vol. i (1886), p. 125, and *C. I. L.* vol. xv, pt. ii, p. 887). A table of weights will be found in Hultsch, *Gr. und Röm. Metrologie,* p. 150.

**425.** QUADRANGULAR, with slightly raised circular medallion engraved IB. (12 *siliquae,* ½ *solidus.*)

> L. ·44 in. Weight, 33 grains. 1882.
> Cf. Kubitschek, in *Archäologisch-epigraphische Mittheilungen aus Oesterreich-Ungarn,* vol. xv (1892), p. 87 note; Papadopoulos Kerameus, Μουσεῖον καὶ βιβλιοθήκη τῆς εὐαγγελικῆς σχολῆς Σμύρνας, vol. iii. 1, p. 86, no. 33 (Smyrna, 1880); Garrucci, in Fiorelli, *Annali di Numismatica,* Rome, 1846, no. 36, p. 206.

**426.** ANOTHER, with bevelled edges; on each side the letter S. (A *solidus.*)

> L. ·56 in. Weight, 66 grains.

**427.** ANOTHER; on one side the letter N. (νόμισμα, or *solidus.*)

> L. ·58 in. Weight, 52 grains. 1868.
> For similar weights in the *Varvakeion,* Athens, *see* Papadopoulos Kerameus in Ἀθηναῖον, vol. vii (1878), nos. 12–20, pp. 263, 264.

**428.** ANOTHER; N.

> L. ·5 in. Weight, 52 grains. 1868.

**429.** ANOTHER; N.

> L. ·6 in. Weight, 60 grains.

**430.** ANOTHER; N

> L. ·6 in. Weight, 64 grains.

**431.** ANOTHER ; N.

L. ·55 in.   Weight, 66 grains.

**432.** ANOTHER ; N.

L. ·52 in.   Weight, 69 grains.   From Benha-el-Aṣṣal, Egypt, 1872.

**433.** QUADRANGULAR ; on one side **TIBERIANI PROC**, on the other **MENA|TIS PREF**, the letters outlined with pounced dots and inlaid with silver.   (A *solidus?*)

L. ·64 in.   Weight, 51·7 grains.   Perhaps from Sardinia.
*See C. I. L.* vol. xv, under no. 7121.   A Menas was *praefectus praetorio,* 528 A. D.   The name of another praetorian prefect (Phocas) occurs on a second example of Justinian's reign (Daremberg and Saglio, *Dict. des antiquités grecques et romaines,* vol. ii, p. 878).

**434.** ANOTHER ; on one face a monogram within a plain border ; on the other the the letters **V. C.** (*vir clarissimus*) ; the whole inlaid with silver. (A *solidus?*)

*See* figure.

L. ·62 in.   Weight, 58 grains.
*See C. I. L.* vol. xv, no. 7124 *g.,* and for a weight with a monogram of similar style cf. Sabatier, *Annuaire de la Soc. de Numismatique et d'Archéologie,* vol. ii (Paris, 1867), p. 278, pl. xviii, fig. 2.

**435.** ANOTHER ; on one face **BITALIS**, on the other **PROCONSVΛ**, the letters outlined with punched dots and inlaid with silver.   Pierced near one corner.   (A *solidus?*)

L. ·66 in.   Weight, 61 grains.
*See C. I. L.* vol. xv, no. 7121.   For other weights signed by proconsuls *see* Daremberg and Saglio, as above, p. 877 ;   Garrucci, as above, p. 204.

**436.** ANOTHER ; on one face **SILB|ANI**, on the other **V̄ L̄** (*viri laudabilis?*).   (A *solidus?*)

L. ·56 in.   Weight, 63 grains.   Blacas Coll. 1867.   From Algeria.
*See C. I. L.* vol. xv, under no. 7124.   A weight in the Museo Kircheriano, mentioned in the same place, has identical inscriptions.   Another has the name of Acacius Silbanus, proconsul. (Garrucci, as above, p. 204.)

**437.** ANOTHER ; on one face two busts rudely engraved and surmounted by a cross, on the other **ΔΙΚЄ**.   (A *solidus?*)

L. ·56 in.   Weight, 64 grains.

**438.** ANOTHER ; on one face the letter **S**.   (*Sicilicus?*)

L. ·66 in.   Weight, 95 grains.
The *sicilicus*=1½ *solidi.*   For weights of this denomination *see* Papadopoulos Kerameus, Μουσεῖον καὶ βιβλιοθήκη, as above, nos. 23–6, pp. 80–81.

**439.** ANOTHER ; on one side **A**, on the other **O** or **Q**.   (A *sicilicus?*)

L. ·54 in.   Weight, 101 grains.   1868.

**440.** ANOTHER ; on one face **S̄OL.** **II** (Two *solidi.*)

L. ·75 in.   Weight, 124 grains.

**441.** ANOTHER, identical inscription.

L. ·54 in.   Weight, 133 grains.

**442.** ANOTHER ; NB (*νομίσματα δύο*, 2 *solidi*) within a wreath.

L. ·68 in.   Weight, 135 grains.

For other weights with NB *see* Renan, *Mission de Phénicie*, p. 490 (Paris, 1864) ; Papado-poulos Kerameus, Ἀθηναῖον, vol. vii (1878), pp. 262, 263.

**443.** OCTAGONAL ; NB within a wreath, the letters inlaid with silver.

L. ·54 in.   Weight, 138 grains.   1867.

**444.** QUADRANGULAR ; on one face D̅ N̅ | THEOD|ERICI, on the other $\overset{\text{SOL}}{\text{III}}$ ; round the edges CATV|LINVS | VC. ET | INL. PꟼV.| (*vir clarissimus et inlustris prae-fectus urbi*), the letters inlaid with silver.   (Three *solidi*.)   *See* figure.

L. ·86 in.   Weight, 184 grains. 1870.

Cf. Daremberg et Saglio, *Dict. des antiquités grecques et ro-maines*, vol. ii, p. 877 (*exagium* in the Louvre) ; J. Friedländer, *Die Münzen der Ostgothen*, p. 29 (figure of an example with the same inscriptions described by Muratori, *Antiquitates Italicae Medii Aevi*, vol. ii, p. 577 and 581 (Milan, 1739) ; *Dissertation* 27, and G. R. Carli, *Delle Monete e delle Zecche d'Italia*, pt. i, p. 89.   A *vir illustris Catulinus* is mentioned by Sidonius Apollinaris (Bk. I, Ep. xi) as living in the time of Majorian, and the twelfth *Carmen* of the same writer is addressed to a *vir clarissimus* of the same name).

**445.** ANOTHER ; on one side N̅Γ (Νομίσματα *τρία*, 3 *solidi*, or ½ ounce) ; above, a rosette with six leaves.

L. 1 in.   Weight, 188 grains.   1872.   From Egypt.

For weights with NΓ cf. Papadopoulos Kerameus, Ἀθηναῖον, as above, p. 262 a, 263, no. 8 ; *id.*, Μουσεῖον &c., as above, p. 83, nos. 11–13.

**446.** CIRCULAR ; N̅Γ within a wreath.

D. ·84 in.   Weight, 198 grains.

Cf. J. Friedländer, in *Zeitschr. für Numismatik*, vol. xi (1884), p. 58 (example at Berlin).

**447.** QUADRANGULAR ; two beardless busts, each with a chlamys, the faces inlaid with silver ; below, the letters IB similarly inlaid. (Half ounce = 3 *solidi*.)   *See* figure.

L. ·8 in.   Franks Coll. 1880.   Cf. nos. 462-3.

IB here stands for ½ ounce, whereas in no. 425 it represented ⅓ *solidus*.

Cf. nos. 462, 463 below, and *see* Kubitschek, as above, p. 86, no. 17, and p. 87, note 4 ; Papadopoulos Kerameus, Μουσεῖον &c. as above, p. 80, no. 20.

**448.** CIRCULAR, rudely engraved on one side with a rude cross between R and M (?), on the other a similar cross between D and C (?).

     D. ·86 in.    Weight, 241 grains.    1868.

**449.** QUADRANGULAR ; N̄ E, surmounted by a star of six rays and within a wreath ; the whole inlaid with silver. (Νομίσματα πέντε, 5 *solidi*, ⅝ oz.)

     L. ·9 in.    Weight, 316 grains.
     Cf. Kubitschek, as above, p. 88, no. 5 ; Papadopoulos Kerameus, ʼΑθηναῖον, as above, p. 263, no. 6.

**450.** ANOTHER ; on one side $\overline{\text{SOL}}$ VI ; on the other, $\overline{\text{X}}$.  (Six *solidi*, one ounce.)

     L. 1·2 in.    Weight, 297 grains.
     Cf. J. Friedländer, *Zeitschr. für Numismatik*, vol. xi (1844), p. 57 (example at Berlin).

**451.** ANOTHER ; above I (for 1 oz.) ; below SOL|Ϛ, the last numeral between two trefoils.  All inlaid with silver.  (Six *solidi*, one ounce.)

     L. ·96 in.    Weight, 395 grains.    1861.

**452** ANOTHER ; the same inscriptions.

     L. ·94 in.    Weight, 402 grains.    1879.

**453.** QUADRANGULAR ; on a slightly raised circular medallion, N̄S surmounted by a monogram which has a trefoil enclosing the letter T above and on each side of it.  (Νομίσματα ἕξ, six *solidi* or one ounce.)
     *See* figure.

     L. ·94 in.    Weight, 359 grains.    Franks Coll. 1866.    Found near Taunton, Somerset.
     For other weights with N̄S see Papadopoulos Kerameus, Μουσεῖον &c., as above, pp. 82, 83, nos. 5–7.

**454.** ANOTHER ; N̄ S, surmounted by a cross.

     L. ·93 in.    Weight, 392 grains.

**455.** ANOTHER ; N̄ S.

     L. ·93 in.    Weight, 408 grains.    1868.

**456.** OCTAGONAL ; N̄ S and a cross.

     D. 1·1 in.    Weight, 413 grains.    1867.

**457.** QUADRANGULAR, the same.

     L. ·96 in.    Weight, 430 grains.    1867.

**458.** ANOTHER ; Γ̄A.  (οὐγκία μία, one ounce, six *solidi*.)

     L. 1·1 in.    Weight, 388 grains.
     For weights with Γ A *see* Papadopoulos Kerameus, ʼΑθηναῖον, as above, p. 259, nos. 5 and 6, and Μουσεῖον &c., nos. 9–17.

**459.** ANOTHER; ᒋA inlaid with silver and surmounted by a rosette of seven dots.

L. ·9 in.   Weight, 391 grains.   Blacas Coll. 1867.

**460.** CIRCULAR; ᒋA surmounted by a cross.

D. 1 in.   Weight, 403 grains.   1880.   From Alexandria.

**461.** QUADRANGULAR; ᖴA surmounted by a cross, the whole inlaid with silver.

L. 1 in.   Weight, 390 grains.   Given by Major·General Meyrick.   1878.

**462.** QUADRANGULAR; two laureated busts wearing the chlamys; below, ᒋA.

L. ·81 in.   Weight, 410 grains.   Blacas Coll. 1867.

Cf. no. 447 above.   The persons are probably two *Augusti*.   Cf. Sabatier in *Revue Numis-matique*, N. S. vol. viii (1863), pl. ii, fig. 2; *Gazette Archéologique*, vol. viii (1883), pl. 50, fig. 6, and p. 300; Papadopoulos Kerameus, Μουσεῖον &c., p. 77 and pl. vi, no. 1.

**463.** ANOTHER; two similar busts, the faces inlaid with silver; below, ᒋA.

L. 1 in.   Weight, 417 grains.

**464.** CIRCULAR; ᒋA.

D. 1 in.   Weight, 410 grains.   1880.

**465.** ANOTHER; ᒋA surmounted by a cross, and within a wreath.   Below the letter A, ᐯN rudely engraved.

D. 1 in.   Weight, 412 grains.

**466.** QUADRANGULAR; ᖴA surmounted by a cross and within a wreath. (One ounce.)

L. 1 in.   Weight, 433 grains.   1879.   From Egypt.

**467.** ANOTHER; H.

L. ·9 in.   Weight, 428 grains.

The numeral suggests that this=8 solidi, or $1\frac{1}{3}$ oz., but the weight seems in this case too little.

For weights with NH *see Revue de l'Art Chrétien*, ivᵐᵉ série, vol. i (1890), p. 226 (Carthage); Papadopoulos Kerameus, 'Αθηναῖον, as above, p. 263, no. 5 (Athens); *id. Μουσεῖον* &c., as above, p. 82, nos. 3 and 4.

**468.** ANOTHER; Ν I, surmounted by a cross and within a wreath. (Νομίσματα δέκα, ten *solidi*, $1\frac{2}{3}$ oz.)

L. 1·16 in.   Weight, 664 grains.   1867.
Cf. Kubitschek, as above, p. 89, fig. 3.

**469.** ANOTHER; above, II (two ounces); below, S̄O̅L̄ XII. (12 *solidi*, 2 oz.)

L. 1 in.   Weight, 793 grains.   Blacas Coll. 1867.
Sabatier, in *Revue Numismatique*, N. S. vol. viii (1863), pl. ii, fig. 1.

**470.** ANOTHER; SOL XII; above, VSLDN (*Vicarius? sacrarum largitionum domini nostri*). (12 *solidi*, 2 oz.)

L. 1·16 in.   Weight, 803 grains.   1850.
The *Comes sacrarum largitionum* was one of the various officials who controlled the standards of weights and measures in the Eastern Empire (*see* Daremberg and Saglio, *Dict. des antiquités grecques et romaines*, vol. ii, pp. 876–7).

**471.** ANOTHER; $\frac{SOL}{XII}$. (12 *solidi* = 2 oz.)

    L. 1·3 in.  Weight, 830 grains.

**472.** ANOTHER; with channeled edges; Γ|Β, on either side of a cross. (Οὐγκίαι δύο, two ounces.)

    L. 1·1 in.  Weight, 711 grains.  1880.
    Cf. Papadopoulos Kerameus, ᾿Αθηναῖον, as above, pp. 2589, and Μουσεῖον &c, as above, p. 78, no. 7.

**473.** ANOTHER; Γ|Β flanking a cross, the whole within a wreath. (Two ounces.)

    L. 1·2 in.  Weight, 806 grains.  1866.

**474.** ANOTHER; Γ|Β flanking a cross. (Two ounces.)

    L. 1·24.  Weight, 831 grains.

**475.** CIRCULAR, N (ΙΒ ?) surmounted by a cross. (Νομίσματα δώδεκα, 12 *solidi* = 2 oz.)

    D. 1·4 in.  Weight, 825 grains.  1880.

**476.** QUADRANGULAR; Ñ Ι Β surmounted by a monogram, the whole beneath an arch.
    *See* figure.

    L. 1·16 in.  Weight, 836 grains.  1880.  From Alexandria.

**477.** ANOTHER, with channeled edges.  On one side two confronted birds perched on a tree; on the other, two confronted birds within a pounced pelta-shaped border. (Three ounces ?)

    L. 1·26 in.  Weight, 1,207 grains.

**478.** CIRCULAR; on one side Γ· Γ (οὐγκίαι τρεῖς, 3 oz.); above, a cross; below, the letter Φ ?, the whole written within a four-lobed border, and inlaid with silver: the other side is the same, but with a trefoil instead of Φ.
    *See* figure.

    D. 1·56 in.  Weight, 1,228 grains.  1877.
    Cf. Kubitschek, as above, p. 89, nos. 2–5 Papadopoulos Kerameus, in ᾿Αθηναῖον, as above, p. 258, no. 2; *id.* Μουσεῖον &c., as above, pp. 70, 71, nos. 2–6.

**479.** QUADRANGULAR, with channeled edges. Upon a slightly raised circular medallion Ϝ|Γ flanking a cross with long lower limb under a rounded arch, the whole formerly inlaid with silver. (Three ounces.)

L. 1·3 in. Weight, 1,254 grains. 1863.

**480.** ANOTHER; under an arcade of two pointed arches and one central rounded arch, the letters Γ S, below which is a cross. Above the arches, a partially effaced inscription ΘЄ/////Ⴗ, perhaps Θεοῦ χάρις (cf. Schlumberger, *Mélanges d'arch. byz.* p. 24). The letters and the cross formerly inlaid with silver (οὐγκίαι ἕξ, six ounces, ½ lb.).

L. 1·7 in. Weight, 2,371 grains. 1880.

Cf. for weights with Γ S, Kubitschek, as above, p. 89, no. 1; Papadopoulos Kerameus, 'Ἀθηναῖον, as above, p. 259, notes α and β.

**481.** ANOTHER; two busts beneath a round arch supported on fluted columns; below, Ϝ S.

L. 1·6 in. Weight, 2,503 grains. 1873.

**482.** SPHEROIDAL, flat at top and bottom; on the top Ⴗ·Γ, on the sides MAPAC and a heart-shaped leaf, all inlaid with silver (οὐγκίαι τρεῖς, three ounces).

D. 1·1 in. Weight, 1,341 grains. 1853.

For weights of this form cf. Kubitschek, as above, pp. 85–7; Papadopoulos Kerameus, Μουσεῖον, &c., as above, p. 78, no. 8, pl. iv, no. 4; de Longpérier in *Bulletin arch. de l'Athenaeum français*, 1855, p. 84 (λίτρα of the time of Justinian); British Museum, *Cat. of Bronzes in the Dept. of Greek and Roman Antiquities*, nos. 3020–30. Μαρᾶς is mentioned by Suidas as a Syrian male name, *see* Pape-Benseler, *Wörterbuch*, *s.v.*, but whether it has that signification here is doubtful.

**483.** QUADRANGULAR; on one side two military saints standing side by side holding spears in their *r.* hands, and in their *l.* imbricated shields. In the lower *r.* hand corner, and threatened by the spear of one of the saints, is a spotted animal resembling a panther (a dragon?). Above its head is a tree without leaves, the branches terminating in round fruits. Below, in the middle, are the letters ΛΑ (λίτρα μία, one pound). The letters, the faces and legs of the saints, and the head of the animal are all inlaid with silver.

*See* figure.

L. 2·46 in. Weight, 4,992 grains. Given by F. W. de Salis, Esq., December 28, 1863.

Sabatier in *Revue Numismatique*, N. S. vol viii (1863), pl. ii, fig. 4; De Linas in *Revue de l'Art Chrétien*, series iii, vol. iii (1885), p. 19; Babelon, in Daremberg and Saglio, *Dict. des antiquités grecques et romaines*, fig.

2851, p. 877 (Paris, 1873).   The saints may be either St. Demetrius or St. George, or St. Theodore Stratelates and St. Theodore Tyron.   On the abbreviation ⋀ (=λίτρα) *see* Garrucci, in Fiorelli, *Annali di Numismatica*, i (1846), p. 207.

**484.** QUADRANGULAR ; engraved IAKѠBOY | ΘE BO| (Θεοτόκε βοήθει) and ⋀Γ (λίτραι τρεῖς) within a circle, the whole inlaid with silver.   In the angles beyond the circle are the letters IAKѠ, similarly inlaid, and beyond these a quadrangular border.

L. 3·12 in.   Weight, 14,612 grains.   1873.
Dumont, in *Rev. Arch.* xxi (1870), pp. 236-248, fig. on p. 237.   Cf. a circular weight of the same denomination from Samos, *Byz. Zeitschr.*, 1900, p. 477.   The name Ἰάκωβος may either be that of an official under whom the weight was verified, or that of the owner of the weight.

**485.** STEELYARD WEIGHT filled with lead, in the form of the bust of a bearded emperor with long hair, wearing a diadem, and a chlamys fastened on the *r.* shoulder by a circular fibula with three pendants. On the tunic covering the upper *r.* arm is a circular ornament marked with a cross.
*See* figure. *Early 7th century.*

H. 7½ in.   Weight, 12 lb. 3 oz. 1867.   From Haifa, Palestine.
The ring at the top of the head is wanting, and the back is imperfect. A comparison with coins of Phocas (602-610) suggests that the weight may represent that emperor.

## B. Stamps.

*4th-6th century.*

**486.** S-SHAPED, with ring at back ; on the front in relief XAꟼAΣOH (possibly χαρὰ ζωή).

L. 3·66 in.   1888.   From Beyrût.

**487.** RECTANGULAR, with ring at back ; on the front is engraved the seven-branched candlestick with a palm branch and bunch of grapes. In the field (reversed) ΛΕΟΝ|ΤΙΟΥ.

> L. 3·1 in. 1888. From Sardis.

**488.** RECTANGULAR ; in relief, ΧΡΙϹΤΕ|ΒΟΗΘΙ.

> L. 4 in. 1875.

**489.** S-SHAPED ; in relief, ΙΧΘΥϹ (reversed) with a heart-shaped leaf between the Θ and Υ.

> L. 2·5 in. 1852.
> *See* C. H. Smith, *Journ. Hellenic Studies*, vol. iv (1883), p. 161, where it is suggested that such stamps may have been used for stamping jars containing fish.

**490.** CRUCIFORM ; in relief, ΔΟΜΙ|ΤΙΑΝΟΥ ; the end of one arm pierced for suspension.

> L. 2·76 in. 1884.

**491.** CRUCIFORM ; with ring at back ; in relief, ΖΟΗ Υ|ΓΙΑ (ζωὴ ὑγίεια), the three last letters at right angles with the first.
> *See* figure.

> L. 3·4 in. 1884.
> The same inscription occurs on two stamps in the Grande Salle of the Cabinet des Médailles, Bibliothèque Nationale, Paris, and on a Cameo Sardonyx in the same collection, with the addition of the word χάρις (Babelon, *Cat. des Camées*, &c., no. 353, pl. 41).

**492.** CRUCIFORM ; in relief, ΕΥΘΥΝ||ΙΑ ; at the back a ring with an oval bezel.

> L. 3·04 in. 1884.

**493.** LOZENGE-SHAPED ; in relief, ΚΗϹΤ, the letters crossing each other at right angles ; at the back a loop. Pierced in four places.

> L. 1·22 in. 1888. From Constantinople.

**494.** CIRCULAR ; in relief, a monogram. At the back a ring with flat oval bezel.

> D. 1·5 in. Franks Coll. 1877.

## C. Lamps and Stands.

Chiefly from the Christian East, especially from Egypt.

*5th to 7th century.*

In the following descriptions the words ' for a stand ' imply that the lamp has an aperture underneath into which the spike of the lamp-stand fitted ; the words ' for suspension ' signify that there are loops for chains on the top. Lamps of both the above descriptions have usually a circular foot, enabling them to be set down upon a flat surface.

**495.** LAMP AND STAND. The stand has a baluster stem with expanding tripod base divided into six concave compartments, and thick disc with grooved edge below the spike. The lamp has a long neck and a low foot pierced with a square hole into which the spike penetrates. The handle consists of two spirals side by side united at the top by an ornamental finial, the ends below terminating in discs ; from the central disc rises a cross pattée. The circular hole for filling is covered by a conical lid with double hinge.

> *Plate* XXVI.

> H. of lamp, 7·9 in.   H. of stand, 12 in.   1850.

**496.** LAMP AND STAND ; of similar style and construction, the tripod stand having at the base three lions with their heads facing inwards. The lamp is similar with double handle of interlacing curves uniting in a cross pattée on which is perched a dove.

> *Plate* XXVI.

> H. of lamp, 6 in.   H. of stand, 11·7 in.   1894.
> Cf. lamp and stand from Akhmîm (Panopolis), Forrer, *Frühchristl. Alterth mer*, pl. vi, fig. 3 (Strasburg, 1893).

**497.** LAMP FOR A STAND, of similar design to no. 496, but without the dove.

> L. 7·22 in.   Franks Coll. 1894.   Probably from Egypt.

**498.** STAND, resembling a pricket-candlestick, with square spike rising from a disc on a baluster-moulded stem with expanding base having three feet in the form of birds' heads.

> H. 11·2 in.   Towneley Coll. 1805.
> Cf. following nos. and no. 376 ; also *Our Work in Palestine (Palestine Exploration Fund)*, 1873, p. 146.

**499.** LAMP WITH TWO SPOUTS, for a stand. The handle is a cross pattée with a loop at the back, and the hinged lid of the hole for filling resembles the half of a bivalve shell.

> L. 8·8 in.   H. 7·4 in.   1875.   From Damanhur, Egypt.   One arm of the cross is broken.

**500.** LAMP FOR A STAND ; the handle is of openwork, lyre-shaped, containing a cross between two palm-branches. The hole for filling has a hinged hemispherical cover with a projection at the top.

> L. 8·3 in.   H. 7 in.   1870.   From Rhodes.

**501.** LAMP FOR SUSPENSION, with hexagonal calix-shaped handle ; the neck and spout are each contained by a collar from which project leaves with upturned ends.   On each side is the monogram ☧ in relief, flanked by the engraved letters A ꞷ.   The lamp stands on a low foot.   The cover is missing.
> *Plate* XXVII.

> L. 10·9 in.   Londesborough Coll. 1879.
> F. W. Fairholt, *Miscellanea Graphica, Reproductions of the Ancient, Mediaeval, and Renaissance remains in the possession of the Earl of Londesborough*, pl. xxxii, fig. 4 (London, 1857).
> Cf. Doublet, *Le Musée d'Alger* (*Musées et Collections archéologiques de l'Algérie*), pl. xiv, fig. 4 (Paris, 1890) ; Garrucci, *Storia*, pl. 470, fig. 2 ; Darcel and Basilewsky, *La Collection Basilewsky*, pl. iii, no. 36.

**502.** LAMP FOR SUSPENSION, the curved handle in the shape of the head and neck of a crested dragon holding an apple (?) in its mouth, and bearing on its head the monogram ☧ surmounted by a dove ; the neck is ornamented by a collar of leaves with projecting ends.   The hole for filling is covered by a dome-shaped lid, and the chain for suspension terminates in a hook.
> *Plate* XXVII.

> L. 8·4 in.   H. 6·2 in.   Given by Miss Sloane Stanley, 1897.
> Cf. similar lamps, de Rossi, *Bullettino*, 1868, pl. opp. p. 77, fig. 1 ; Garrucci, *Storia*, pl. 470, figs. 3 and 8 ; Perret, *Les Catacombes de Rome*, vol. iv, pl. v, fig. 6 ; Darcel and Basilewsky, *La Collection Basilewsky*, pl. iii, no. 32 ; Roller, *Les Catacombes*, pl. xci, fig. 5 ; Bellori, *Le antiche Lucerne*, pt. iii, pl. 25.

**503.** LAMP FOR A STAND, with two spouts.   The curved handle is in the shape of a dragon's head as in the case of the preceding number ; between the ears rises a cross.   On each side and between the spouts is a cross composed of punched circles and dots.
> *Plate* XXVII.

> L. 6·5 in.   H. 4·84 in.

**504.** ANOTHER, with circular body flat at the top, and long neck with crescent-shaped indentations at the sides.   The openwork leaf-shaped handle contains a cross pattée, and the hinged circular cover of the hole for filling has a projecting tongue prolonged almost to the spout.

> L. 5·46 in.   1875.

**505.** ANOTHER, of similar shape, with lyre-shaped openwork handle.

> L. 6·7 in.   1875.

**506.** ANOTHER, similar, the upper part of the handle missing.
> L. 6·2 in.   1875.

**507.** LAMP WITH TWO SPOUTS, one at each end, and hole for filling in the centre with hinged dome-shaped lid in the middle. From the centre of each side projects a ram's head, and from the top, on each side of the hole for filling, rises a cup-shaped projection.
*Plate* XXVII.

L. 8·7 in.  Franks Coll. 1891.

**508.** LAMP, FOR SUSPENSION, in the shape of a bird ; the hole for the wick is at the top of the head, and the hole for filling in the middle of the back.
*Plate* XXVII.

L. 5·9 in.  H. 3·34 in.  1872.  From Medinet el-Fayûm (Crocodilopolis).
For other lamps in the form of birds cf. Garrucci, *Storia*, vol. vi, pl. 472, figs. 3 and 4.

**509.** LAMP FOR A STAND, in the shape of a peacock, with circular foot. The spout is at the end of the tail, and the hole for filling in the back is covered by a hinged leaf-shaped lid.
*Plate* XXVII.

L. 5·7 in.  H. 5·46 in.  1865.  From Egypt.

**510.** LAMP FOR SUSPENSION, of the same shape.

L. 4·5 in.  H. 5·32 i    1873.  From Tel el-Yahûdeh, Egypt.

**511.** ANOTHER, similar.

H. 4·75 in.  L. 6·24 in.  1873.  Tel el-Yahûdeh.

**512.** ANOTHER, in the shape of a duck, with chain of S-shaped links.
*Plate* XXVII.

L. 6 in.  H. 4·1 in.  Given by John Henderson, Esq., 1865.

**513.** ANOTHER, in the form of a bird. The wings and legs are cast, the details of the feathers punched and tooled. The hole for filling is in the centre of the back, and the spout with long neck projects from the tail.

L. 5·5 in.  1875.  The head missing.

**514.** ANOTHER, with a loop-handle faced with a cross pelletée.

L. 4·5 in.  1872.  From Medinet el-Fayûm (Crocodilopolis).
Cf. Roller, *Les Catacombes*, pl. xc, fig. 13.

**515.** ANOTHER, with rounded body and long neck. The loop-handle is surmounted by a horizontal heart-shaped leaf. At each end of the neck, on the upper side, is a pair of small protuberances.

L. 3·62 in.  1875.

**516.** ANOTHER, with concave circular top and flat bottom ; upon the handle a dolphin.

L. 4·3 in.  1875.

**517.** ANOTHER, with circular body and long neck ; large circular hole for filling.

L. 4·2 in. 1875. The handle is broken.

**518.** ANOTHER, shallow, the neck fluted on the upper side. Loop-handle, faced with a cross pattée ornamented with punched circles.

L. 4·86 in. 1875.

**519.** ANOTHER, with circular body, long neck and loop-handle, faced with a heart-shaped leaf.

L. 5·4 in. H. 3·6 in. 1875.

**520.** ANOTHER, shallow, the body circular, with two divergent spouts. The top is open and surrounded by five projecting flowers at equal intervals. Loop-handle, faced with foliated ornament.

L. 6·6 in. 1875.

**521.** ANOTHER, with circular body and long neck. The hole for filling is large and circular, with a border ornamented with concentric circles, and was formerly covered by a hinged lid. Loop-handle, surmounted by a leaf.

L. 5·1 in. 1875.

**522.** ANOTHER, with circular body and angular sides. The neck has at the shoulders two projections in the shape of flowers. Round the hole for filling, which once had a hinged cover, are two concentric bands of hollows divided by zig-zag and straight lines. At the bottom is a low almond-shaped foot-rim. Loop-handle, terminating in a vine leaf pierced with two holes.

L. 6·2 in. 1875.

**523.** ANOTHER, of similar shape.

L. 4·44 in. 1875.

**524.** ANOTHER, with rounded sides, projecting neck, and circular hole for filling, with hinged lid resembling half a bivalve shell. Loop-handle, faced with the remains of a cross.

L. 5·15 in. 1875.

**525.** ANOTHER, WITHOUT FOOT, somewhat in the shape of a shoe, the upturned toe of hexagonal section forming the spout. The hole for filling, which is also hexagonal, is at the ankle. Plain loop-handle.
*Plate* XXVII.

L. 6·7 in. 1875.

**526.** ANOTHER, in the shape of a shoe with cylindrical spout above the toe, and loop-handle. The hole for filling is at the ankle, and the sides are ornamented with triangular compartments chased with a floral design enclosing on each side a cross between four discs.
*Plate* XXVII.

L. 5·32 in. 1875. From Tel el-Yahûdeh, Egypt.

**527.** LAMP-FILLER, hemispherical, with a pierced border chased with scrolls, long straight spout, and flat handle chased with a palm-tree between two confronted birds. *Plate* XXVII.

L. 5·8 in.   1896.   From the ruins at Medinet Habu.

**528.** PIERCED DISC with serrated edges and two loops at opposite points of the circumference.   The design consists of a cross pattée inscribed within the circle ; on each side are punched twelve small concentric circles, five upon the cross and eight round the border.

D. 6·25 in.   1881.   Obtained in Athens.   Probably part of the chain of a lamp or *gabatha*, cf. de Rossi, *Bullettino*, 1871, pp. 66 ff.

**529.** POLYCANDELON, a circular openwork disc, the design consisting of sixteen bars radiating from the centre to as many circles.   Between the bars are an equal number of crosses, resting on and supporting rounded arches.   The whole is suspended by three chains uniting in a hook at the top. *Plate* XXVI.

D. 17·75 in.

Cf. G. Schlumberger, *Mélanges d'Arch. Byzantine*, p. 176, and *Byz. Zeitschrift*, vol. ii (1893), pp. 441 ff. (example in the Louvre).   A somewhat similar *polycandelon* found at Beneventum was sold at the Hôtel Drouot on March 18, present year (Anonymous Collection, no. 290 and the fig.).   On *polycandela* and *coronae* in general *see* S. Beissel in *Zeitschrift für christliche Kunst*, 1896, pp. 339–341, and Kraus, *Real-Encykl.* vol. ii, p. 271.   Cf. also no. 393 above.

## D. Miscellaneous Vessels.

*6th century and later.*

**530.** OVAL BOX for suspension ; it has a flat lid terminating in the head and tail of a bird, probably a duck.   Two holes at each end of the lid correspond with others in the box, and through these passed a chain, a piece of which still remains. *See* figure.

L. 7·4 in.   Given by Signor Alessandro Castellani, 1881.   Found in an ancient Christian tomb in Calabria.

**531.** SPOON, with flat circular bowl and cruciform handle, at the end of which is a rude human head. The handle is engraved with wavy lines, and near the bowl is a loop for suspension.

> L. 2·96 in. 1883.

**532.** CIRCULAR VESSEL with flat bottom, upon the flat projecting rim is engraved ✝ ΥΠΕΡ ΑΝΑΠΑΥCΕΟC ΙΟΥΛΙΑΝΟΥ ΤΟΥ ΑΓΙΟΥ ΖΑΧΑΡΙΑ, the inscription terminating in a palm-branch. A fracture at one point on the rim shows that a handle or cover has been broken off.

> *See* figure.

> D. 3·64 in. 1887.
> The mention of Zachariah suggests that this vessel may have been used for incense, but it does not appear to have been suspended.

**533.** LID OF A VESSEL, circular, with a socket for a hinge, two loops, and a perforation, at four equidistant points of the circumference. It is moulded to represent a human mask, the eyes and mouth being pierced, and the hair and beard conventionally treated. Round the rim is pounced ✝ ΚΥΡΙΕ ΒΟΗΘΙ ΝΙCΙΟΥ ΔΙΑΚΟΥ ΚΕ ΤΥC ΑΛΟΓΥC ΑΥΤΟΥ (Κύριε βοήθει Νισίου διακόνου καὶ τοὺς ἀλόγους αὐτοῦ).

> *See* figure.

> D. 5 in. 1875. From Tartûs, Syria. Ἄλογοι here can hardly mean anything but live stock, though the neuter, τὰ ἄλογα, is usual in this sense.

P

**534.** PATERA, with handle terminating in a grotesque face, surmounted by two equal-armed
crosses of unequal size ; on the
lower part is engraved the figure
✳. The outer edge is formed
by a row of hemispherical bosses,
and opposite to the handle is
a ring fixed in the mouth of a
monstrous head, at the junction
of the handle and bowl are two
indeterminate projections. In
the interior are turned concentric
circles.

*See* figure.

L. 11·75 in. 1859. Said to have
been found in Nubia.

**535.** SHALLOW DISH on high foot pierced with circular holes. Round the rim a
border of hemispherical bosses (cf. no. 534) from which projects a bird's head
with open mouth formerly holding a ring.

H. 3·6 in. 1890. From Akhmîm (Panopolis).

**536.** EWER AND TRIPOD STAND. The ewer is pointed at the bottom and is
ornamented on the sides with engraved horizontal lines in pairs. At the back of
the handle is a curved projection like an animal's tail. The stand is of openwork.

H. of ewer, 4·95 in. 1890. From Akhmîm (Panopolis).

**537.** OCTAGONAL BUCKET with eight low feet and double swing handles with
indented edges, one of which is ornamented with punched circles containing
dots. The sides are ornamented with a triple horizontal moulded band.

D. 3·92 in. 1896. From the ruins of Medinet Habu.

The shape of this vessel may be compared with that of a censer found at Akhmîm, *see*
Forrer, *Frühchristl. Altertümer*, pl. vi, fig. 4.

**538.** AMPHORA AND STAND, with a single remaining handle. The stand is of openwork.

H. 2·82 in. 1872. From Medinet el-Fayûm (Crocodilopolis).

**539.** EWER, with low circular foot, the body facetted vertically and tapering to a slender neck. The handle has at the top a projecting horse's head, and is constricted at the middle, where it takes the form of a square block, below which it describes an acute angle before joining the body.

*See* figure.

H. 6·5 in. 1894. From a Coptic monastery.

**540.** CENSER, with low circular foot and rounded sides, with scenes in relief rudely executed and much worn. The scenes are as follows *The Annunciation* (?); the angel from *l.* approaches the seated Virgin. *The Baptism*; St. John stands to *r.* with his *r.* arm stretched out over the head of a diminutive figure of our Lord; above is the dove, and on either side, an angel. *The Crucifixion*; our Lord is in the centre upon the cross, wearing a long *colobium*; on either side of his head are the sun and moon, and beneath the arms of the cross the Virgin and St. John (?). *The Maries at the Sepulchre*; to *l.* the angel (?) to *r.* the two Maries; in the centre the tomb, a domed building with a rounded doorway in front. On the foot is a seated figure of the Virgin (?) on a chair.

*See* figure.

H. 2·55 in.　D. 3·25 in.　1872.　Obtained at the convent of Mar Muza el Habashi between Damascus and Palmyra.

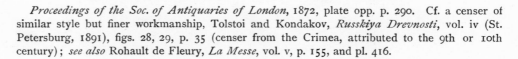

*Proceedings of the Soc. of Antiquaries of London*, 1872, plate opp. p. 290.　Cf. a censer of similar style but finer workmanship, Tolstoi and Kondakov, *Russkiya Drevnosti*, vol. iv (St. Petersburg, 1891), figs. 28, 29, p. 35 (censer from the Crimea, attributed to the 9th or 10th century); *see also* Rohault de Fleury, *La Messe*, vol. v, p. 155, and pl. 416.

**541.** VASE AND BASIN.　The vase, perhaps originally an ewer, stands on a low foot, and has a band of conventional ornament round the upper part.　The basin, which stands on a low foot-rim, has in the centre a boss or *omphalos* with engraved ornament of intersecting lines on the sides. This is surrounded by two bands of herring-bone pattern enclosing the inscription **+ IN NOMINE D(OMI)NI DEOCICI MANEFICIV(M) ADMIRARE.** The rim has on the inner side a similar band of herring-bone, outside which is engraved **+ VICIT LEO DE TRIBVS IV—DA RA——DIS DAVID ALLELVIA.** (Revelation v. 5.)

*See* figures. *Visigothic. 6th–7th century.*

H. of ewer, 6·4 in. D. of basin, 7·2 in. 1900. Obtained in Spain. *Proc. Soc. Ant.* vol. xviii (1900–1901), pp. 363, 364.

These vessels are well made, and have been turned on the lathe; the vase is imperfect at the neck, and has in the sides several holes made by a pick; the handle is wanting. The inscriptions are rudely engraved, and from their character would appear to belong to the 6th or 7th century. The formula *In Nomine Domini* is a common prefix to Christian inscriptions of the period, but the name *Deocicus* does not seem to be found elsewhere. The boss in the centre of the basin, though solid, recalls the *omphalos* in vessels of earlier times, of which it is perhaps a late survival. A basin with the same peculiarity is recorded as having been discovered in the district of Guarda, Province of Beira, Portugal (Hübner, *Inscr. Hispaniae Christianarum Supplementum*, no. 529, p. 135).

**542.** OBJECT RESEMBLING A HANDLE, straight and hollow, the transverse section being semicircular. One end is pointed, and across the top is a sinuous line in relief, at right angles to which is engraved a serpentine figure.

L. 4·9 in. 1900. Obtained in Spain. Found with the preceding number.

### E. Plaques, Medallions, &c.

*6th century and later.*

**543.** RECTANGULAR PLAQUE (*tabella ansata*) with raised border and projection at each end. It is rudely engraved in intaglio with a long-haired beardless figure (an emperor?) riding to *l.* upon an exergual line. He wears a tunic and chlamys,

and high boots. His *r.* hand is raised, and he holds a lance in his *l.* The horse which is richly caparisoned is led by an attendant wearing a tunic and boots, and holding a lance in his *r.* hand. Behind the horse is the word **VΓIA** in a wreath above a vertical palm-branch.  At the top are two confronted snakes and the words ЄIC ΘЄOC ; below is a larger snake to *l.*

*See* figure.   *6th century.*

L. 6·35 in.   1900.   Found near Tyre.

The subject may be derived from a scene representing an emperor entering a town or riding in triumph.   Cf. the gold medallion of Justinian (*Revue Numismatique*, 1899, pl. i) ; the Barberini Diptych now in Paris (Schlumberger, in *Mon. Piot.* vol. vii (1900), pl. x) ; the votive shield of Justinian found at Kertch (Strzygowski and Pokrovsky, *Der Silberschild aus Kertsch*, in *Mat. Russ. Arch.*, 1892, pl. x, and Venturi, *Storia dell' Arte Italiana*, p. 501) ; and the top of a casket in Troyes Cathedral (Molinier, *Ivoires*, p. 92).  In the present case the addition of the serpents and the inscription suggest that the plaque was made to bring health or luck like an amulet.  Serpents and lions are found on objects of this description ; e. g. on a bronze bracelet found near Jerusalem with an inscription beginning εἶς θεός ; on a plaque with a figure of Solomon slaying a demon of disease (*Rev. Arch.* 1892, pt. ii, p. 263) ; and a gem with two serpents, an egg, the rod of Aesculapius, and the word ΥΓIA (*C. I. G.* vol. iv, 1877, no. 7038).  The words εἶς θεός are common in inscriptions in Syria and Palestine ; cf. Clermont-Ganneau, *Archives des missions scientifiques et littéraires*, vol. xi (1885), p. 169.  They are especially frequent on amulets, e. g. an example from Phoenicia, *see Rev. Arch.* 1888, pt. i, p. 385.  The small glass pendants of the class represented by nos. 697 ff. have also occasionally lions with these words.  It may be noted that on copper coins of Constantine the Great, the Labarum stands upon a serpent, though here another explanation may be given (*see* Smith and Cheetham, vol. ii, p. 910, and article *Draconarius*).

**544.** Gɪʟᴛ ᴘʟᴀQᴜᴇ ; St. Theodore in military costume standing full face holding a shield in his *l.* hand and a spear in his *r.* ; on either side Ⓐ ΘЄO|ΔOPOϒ (ὁ Ἅγιος Θεόδωρος) in nielloed letters. At the top is a perforation, at the bottom an irregular projection.

*See* figure.   *About 11th century.*

L. 4·9 in.   1890.

Cf. Schlumberger, *L'Épopée Byzantine à la fin du X^{me} siècle*, pt. i, p. 173 (Paris, 1896), and pt. ii, p. 493 (Paris, 1900).

**545.** RECTANGULAR PLAQUE. The Virgin in relief seated with the Child upon her knees, her head inclined to *l.*; both figures are nimbed. In the top *r.* hand corner ΘY above a rosette (part of the inscription Θ̄Ȳ M̄P̄). Wavy border.

    L. 2·34 in. 1888.

**546.** ANOTHER; half-length figure of the Virgin holding the Child in her *l.* arm; both are nimbed. In the field M̄P̄ Θ̄Ȳ and Ī̄C̄ X̄C̄.

    L. 1·6 in. Franks Coll. 1880.

**547.** ANOTHER; bust of St. Paul in relief holding a book in his *l.* hand, and with his *r.* hand over his breast. He is nimbed, and wears tunic and pallium. On either side Ⓐ ΠAY|ΛOC.

    L. 1·6 in. 1880.

**548.** OVAL MEDALLION. *Obv.* The Virgin with arms extended holding in her *r.* a distaff (?) and in her *l.* a skein of wool (?). On either side M̄P̄ Θ̄Ȳ. *Rev.* St. Theodore riding to *r.* and transfixing the prostrate dragon with his spear. To *r.* and *l.* O ΘEω|ΔOPOC.

    L. 1·14 in. 1889.

**549.** CIRCULAR MEDALLION. St. George riding to *r.* and transfixing the prostrate dragon with a lance with cruciform butt.

    D. 2·26 in. 1888. From Egypt.

**550.** ANOTHER. Bust of our Lord with cruciferous nimbus holding the book of the gospel in his *l.* hand. On either side Ī̄C̄ X̄C̄.

    D. 1·4 in. Franks Coll. 1880.

**551.** ANOTHER. *Obv.* A cross with bifurcating ends dividing the inscription Ī̄C̄|X̄C̄ NI|KA. *Rev.* An inscription in three lines A(ΓI)OC | ΓEOPΓIOC, within a twisted border.

    D. 1 in. 1884.

**552.** ANOTHER. *Obv.* A cross crosslet. *Rev.* inscription in three lines ΠAN|-AΓIA|A✝O.

    D. ·84 in. 1880. From Cyprus.

**553.** PLAQUE FROM THE COVER OF A BOOK, Γ-shaped. On the vertical limb in relief St. Matthew, nimbed and holding a book in both hands; to *l.* of his head are the letters MT one above the other, and to *r.* Θ (MATΘAIOC). On the horizontal limb is an angel holding a book. Between the two figures is a branch.

    L. 3·1 in. 1853.

**554.** EMBOSSED FRAGMENT. Below is a circular medallion with a beardless bust of St. Luke, full face, holding a gospel with jewelled cover; to *r.* of his head ΛOYKAC. Above are two flying angels supporting a second imperfect medallion on the border of which is the inscription ✝ ANENOΘ̄C̄EN ΛΛΛΛΛ////.

    L. 6·2 in. 1889. From Smyrna.

**555.** FLAT OVAL PENDANT, with loop at the top. *Obv.* An engraved nimbed figure
in a mantle, standing to *l.* and holding a whip over a nude figure crouching before
him. On either side of his head are the sun and moon, and above is an inscription
in four lines continued round the field, ЄΙС ΘЄΟС | Ο ΝΙΚѠΝ ΤΑ ΚΑΚΑ | ΙΑѠ
CΑΒΑѠ | ΟΝ CΟΛΟΜѠΝ | ΜΙΧΑΗΛ ΓΑΒΡΙΗΛ ΟΥΡΙΗΛ ΦΥΛΑΞΟΝ ΚΑΙ ΙΔΙΑ (?)
*Rev.* ΑΝ ΜΗ ЄΑΝ Η | ΜЄΤΑΥΡΟΥ ΙΤΙ| ѠC ΛЄΛЄΟΝ ΜЄΝ| ΗΤΙ ѠC ΤΑΥΡΟC|
ΜΥΚΑC ЄΤΙ ѠC ΔΡΑΚѠΝ ЄΙΛΙЄC ΜΑΝ| ΗΜΟC ЄΔΗCЄΝ ΑΓΓ|ЄΛΟC ЄΛΥCЄΝ
ΚΥΡΙ|ΟC ΜΑΤΗΡΑΑΠΟΥ| ΓΙCЄΝ CΦΟC ΑΚΟ|ΥCΑC ЄΦΥΓЄΝ| ΦΥΛΑΞΟΝ
ΒΑΒΙ|ΝΑΝ ΗΝ ЄΤΗΚЄΝ ΘЄΔѠCΙΑ.

> H. 6·3 in. 1887. From the neighbourhood of Akka, Palestine.
> This object is an amulet invoking divine assistance, and the aid of the Archangels and
> Solomon against any disease which may menace one Babina, daughter of Theodosia. The first
> part of the inscription on the reverse referring to the disease as bellowing like a bull, roaring
> like a lion, and coiling like a snake, is of comparatively frequent occurrence, but the conclusion
> is usually an appeal to it to lie down like a lamb. On the whole subject of such amulets *see*
> G. Schlumberger, *Mélanges d'Archéologie Byzantine*, pp. 116 ff., where the principal existing
> examples are quoted. The superstitious ideas illustrated by this and similar objects probably
> originated in Alexandria before the time of Constantine, but continued in use down to a late
> period.

**556.** RELIEF, with a peg at the back for fixing to a flat surface. It is in the shape of
a mounted saint (St. George ?) nimbed and beardless holding in his *r.* hand a long
cross or lance with cruciform butt, and extending his *l.* arm over the horse's head
which is turned backwards towards him. On the horse's shoulder is engraved
a cross.

> H. 6·3 in. 1887. From the neighbourhood of Akka, Palestine.

**557.** MOULD, flat and roughly rectangular, for casting a figure of St. George and the
dragon. The saint stands on foot holding a shield in his *l.* hand and piercing
a serpent-like dragon with a spear. In the field ΓЄѠΡΓΙΙΟC. Pearled border.

> L. 1·96 in. Given by Charles Dawson, Esq., 1895.

## F. Crosses.

### *6th century and later.*

**558.** CROSS FOR A RELIC, imperfect ; the edges are flanged behind, and at top
and bottom project parts of the hinge and fastening by which the back was
attached ; at the corners of the transverse arms are loop-shaped projections. On
the front is rudely incised the figure of a nimbed saint in the attitude of an *orans*.
*About the* 12*th century.*

> L. 3·32 in. 1887. From Beyrût.
> Cf. de Rossi, *Bullettino*, 1888-9, pl. xi, and pp. 161 ff.

**559** ANOTHER; on the front a standing figure of St. Stephen in the attitude of an *orans*. He is nimbed and wears a dalmatic; in his *r*. hand he carries a censer (?). In the field Ⓐ ϹΤΕΦΑΝΟϹ. *See* figure.

> L. 3·84 in. 1880. From Smyrna.

**560.** ANOTHER; on the front St. Stephen in the same attitude; under each arm, a rosette. In the field above the head ΑΓΗΕ ϹΤΕΦΑΝΕ.

> L. 3 in. 1884.

**561** ANOTHER; on the front St. George standing in the same attitude; above his head Ο ΑΓΗΟ (Γ)ΗΟΡΓΙ. In the centre of the cross is a small circular cavity perhaps intended to contain a glass paste.

> L. 2·96 in. Castellani Coll. 1872.

**562.** ANOTHER; on the front a saint in the same attitude.

> L. 3·1 in. 1887. From Antioch. The left arm broken.

**563.** CROSS, flat, with a double incised band across the end of each lateral arm.

> L. 1·9 in. 1879. Qûft, Egypt.

**564.** ANOTHER, with equal arms each surmounted by a cap, making it resemble a cross potent.

> L. ·5 in. 1875.

**565.** ANOTHER, made of two thin plates fastened by a stud in the centre. Both ends pierced.

> L. 3·3 in. 1868.

**566.** ANOTHER, with pellets at the extremities of the upper limbs. On the lower limb is a pounced inscription ΙѠΑΝ|ΝΗϹ ΥΕΙΟϹ | ΕΝΓΟ|ΛΙΟΥ | ΕΥΖΑ|ΜΕΝΟϹ | ΤΗΝ ΕΥ|ΧΗΝ Α|ΠΕΔѠ|ΚΑ.

> L. 9·7 in. Franks Coll. 1896. From Seleucia.

**567.** ANOTHER, thin and flat, the ends of the upper limbs bifurcating.

> L. 5·75 in. Given by Henry Wallis, Esq., 1894. From Erment.

Q

**568.** ANOTHER, pattée, with loop for suspension and cross-hatching on the ends of the arms.

  L. ·86 in.

**569.** ANOTHER, thin and flat, the lower limb longest.

  L. 3·3 in.  1896.  Probably from Medinet Habu, Thebes, Egypt.

**570.** ANOTHER, pattée, with loop for suspension.

  L. ·72 in.  1875.

**571.** ANOTHER, with loop for suspension, the front ornamented with punched circles containing dots.

  L. 1·16 in.  1876.  From Qûft, Egypt.

**572.** ANOTHER, with similar ornament.

  L. 1·22 in.  1876.  From Qûft.

**573.** ANOTHER, imperfect, ornamented with groups of similar circles.

  L. 4·32 in.  1880.  From Smyrna.

**574.** ANOTHER, part of the upper limb, with a small disc at each extremity, ornamented with an engraved cross between dots.  It is engraved with the head and shoulders of a saint, above which is inscribed O ΔΓHOC X|PVCOXON.

  L. 1·9 in.  1883.  From Hierapolis.  The saint is perhaps St. Chrysogonus, martyr under Diocletian.

**575.** ANOTHER, surmounted by a dove.

  L. 2·04 in.  1876.  From Egypt.  Perhaps an ornament from the handle of a lamp.

**576.** CROSS, WITHIN A QUATREFOIL, on a long circular shaft.

  L. 9·38 in.  1867.  From Egypt.

**577.** CROSS WITH ROUNDED LIMBS, expanding at the ends and loop for suspension.

  L. 1·53 in.  1880.  From Smyrna.

**578.** ANOTHER, flat ; the arms are rounded at the ends, each of which has a pair of lateral projections.  On each surface is an obliterated inscription.

  L. 2·4 in.  1883.  From Hierapolis.

**579.** ANOTHER, with loop-like projections at the extremities of the limbs.  At the top is part of a hinge and an attachment like the tongue of a buckle.  In the centre is a raised circular medallion, and at the back are two loops.  The surface is pitted with small circular hollows.

  L. 3·1 in.  Franks Coll. 1877.

**580.** ANOTHER, with loop for suspension ; on the front our Lord as crucified wearing a long garment. Above the head, an oval medallion with the letters I͞C X͞C.

L. 2·56 in. 1880. From Smyrna.


## G. Miscellaneous.

### *6th century and later.*

**581.** BROOCH, in the form of an animal with a cross above the head, and ornamented with punched circles each with a dot in the centre ; at the back, spring and catch for a pin.

L. 1·66 in. 1883. From Egypt.
Cf. similar brooch from Akhmîm (Panopolis), Forrer, *Frühchristl. Altertümer*, pl. x, fig. 11.

**582.** ANOTHER, in form of a dove, with similar ornament ; the pin missing.

L. 1·62 in. 1883. From Egypt.

**583.** ANOTHER, in the form of a bird. Imperfect.

L. 2·1 in. 1879. From Qûft, Egypt.

**584.** BUCKLE, the plate chased to resemble a disc supported on two leaves ; on the disc the monogram

*6th–7th century.*

L. 1·62 in. 1872. Medinet el-Fayûm. With this and the following two nos. cf. a buckle found on the Hill of St. Louis, Carthage. *See Bulletin arch. du Comité des Travaux Hist. et Scientifiques*, Paris, 1893, p. 98.

**585.** ANOTHER, of identical design but with the monogram

L. 1·7 in. 1880. From Athens.

**586.** PLATE OF A BUCKLE, in openwork, ornamented with engraved scrolls and wavy lines. At the narrower end is engraved the monogram at the broader end and at the back are two pierced projections.

L. 2·66 in. 1881. From Athens.

**587.** ANOTHER, part of ; on one surface in relief a bird standing opposite a vase : a corresponding bird has been broken off the other side.

L. 1·2 in. 1880. From Athens.

**588.** BUCKLE, the plate in the form of a cross with bifurcating ends. It is ornamented on the front with punched circles containing dots, and has two loops on the back.

L. 2·4 in. 1881. From Athens.

**589.** ANOTHER, oval, ornamented with two horizontal pearled bands ; on the upper part of the tongue, a cross with bifurcating ends.

>  L. 1·7 in.   1876.

**590.** PLATE OF A BUCKLE (?), rectangular and pierced, with traces of gilding.   It is engraved with eight busts in circular medallions superposed in pairs.

>  L. 1·5 in.   1889.   From Smyrna.

**591.** PART OF A BUCKLE, in openwork ; a cross pattée enclosed in a rectangle.

>  L. 1·3 in.   1877.

**592.** PART OF A BUCKLE, engraved with a cross pattée within a pearled circle ; at the back three loops.

>  L. 1·9 in.   1880.

**593.** PART OF A CHAIN (?) formed by a small circular capsule and two oval medallions connected by hinges.   On the capsule is engraved a cruciform monogram, and on each of the medallions is a quadruped in relief.

>  L. 2·52 in.   1875.

**594.** PEDESTAL, with quadrangular base on four feet, the upper part a hollow cylinder.

>  H. 4·22 in.   1872.   From Medinet el-Fayûm (Crocodilopolis).

**595.** ROD, with moulded stem and screw at the lower end.   At the top a bird.

>  H. 2·6 in.   1881.   From Egypt.

**596.** FIGURE OF A GOOSE, concavo convex.

>  L. 4·1 in.   Egypt.   Probably from Medinet Habu.

**597.** ANOTHER, in the round.

>  L. 1·9 in.   Egypt.   Probably from Medinet Habu.

# VI. GLASS.

## A. Gilded Glasses (Fondi D'Oro).

### *3rd–5th century.*

CHIEFLY the bottoms of bowls made as wedding and family gifts; the majority found in the Roman Catacombs and in graves at Cologne. The numbers given immediately after the name Vopel refer to the list of gilded glasses at the end of Dr. H. Vopel's work, *Die altchristlichen Goldgläser*. (Vol. v of J. Ficker's *Archäologische Studien zum christlichen Altertum und Mittelalter*. Freiburg, 1899.)

**598.** FRAGMENT ; ZH CAIC ; below, five lozenge-shaped dots.

L. 1·7 in. Slade Bequest, 1868. Vopel, no. 3. The protecting layer of glass has almost entirely disappeared.

**599.** FOUR FRAGMENTS ; an inscription in five lines, alternating with rows of lozenges, `////// EDONI FR(//////) | ////// CARIS COIV|GE TVA // IE ZESES | OMNIBV// //ENET |////// IS ///// A.` (*Edoni Frater cum caris coniuge tua pie zeses. Omnibus Venetianis vita.*) At the end of each line is a terminal ornament—dots, and leaves or flowers. The protecting glass is missing.

L. of larger fragment, 4·8 in. D. of the whole, c. 6 in.

Garrucci, *Vetri*, pl. xxxviii, fig. 6. *See also ibid.*, p. 216; Vopel, no. 6, and p. 81, note; *C. I. L.* vol. xv, 7044. The inscription is a congratulatory expression of good wishes to Edonius, or perhaps Macedonius, a member of the Blue Faction in the Circus (Venetiani). *Carisia* has been suggested as an alternative reading for *Caris*.

**600.** FRAGMENT OF A CUP, very thick, with a small part of the sides remaining. Inscription (A)NNI BONI, in two lines, executed in gold wire with a border of the same ; above, a wavy line in the same material ; below, a horizontal rod of blue glass

L. 1·9 in.

Vopel, p. 85, fig. 9. Cf. Fröhner, *La Collection Tyszkiewicz, Choix de Monuments Antiques,* pl. viii, fig. 2 (Munich, 1892); *C. I. L.* vol. xv, 7055, and *Collection Auguste Dutuit*, no. 138, p. 68 (Paris, 1879). The cup may have been a gift at the *Strenae*.

**601.** DIMINUTIVE MEDALLION, imperfect. Inscription $\overset{VIT}{A}$. The protecting glass at the back is green.

*Plate* XXXI.

D. ·56 in. Franks Coll. 1886.
Vopel, no. 28 and p. 82.

**602.** ANOTHER. To *r.* a recumbent bull; to *l.* a nude beardless figure with his back to the animal and his *r.* arm extended. The protecting glass at the back is blue.

*Plate* XXXI.

L. ·66 in.   Garrucci, *Vetri*, pl. xxxv, fig. 10.   *See* also Vopel, no. 45 and p. 97.

‘Medallions’ of this kind are really fragments broken from the bottoms of bowls like no. 629. The designs were executed on the transparent bottom of the bowl, and rough discs or backings of coloured glass laid upon them, a flux being placed between the two. The bowl was then heated in the furnace until the fusion took place. It is possible that the glass employed, which must have been made with a wood furnace, may have been sometimes sufficiently soft to coalesce of itself, but in most examples the presence of a flux is undoubted.

**603**. BOTTOM OF A DRINKING VESSEL, with parts of the thin transparent sides still remaining. On the circular bottom, which has a blue background, is a gladiator (*retiarius*) advancing to *l.*, holding a sword in his *r.* hand and a trident in his *l.* His loincloth is of silver foil with indented edges, and his belt is outlined and ornamented in red. The upper part of his body is nude, but the *l.* arm is protected by being covered with padding tightly bound with leather thongs, and to the upper part of it is fastened the *galerus*, a piece of defensive armour peculiar to gladiators. Across his body is a baldric, perhaps part of the attachment of the *galerus*, and his ankles are protected in much the same way as his *l.* arm. Behind, to *r.*, is a *cippus* on which rests a windbag (*corycus*, or *follis pugilatorius*) used in practising boxing. On the front of the *cippus* are two crossed swords. Round the field is the inscription STRATONICAE BENE VICISTI VADE IN AVRELIA (*Stratonice, bene vicisti, vade in Aureliam*).

*Plate* XXVIII.

L. 3·44 in.   Tyszkiewicz Coll. 1898.

*Catalogue de la Coll. Alessandro Castellani*, Rome, 1884, no. 428, fig. on p. 62 ; Lanciani, *Bullettino della Commissione Arch. Comunale*, 1884, p. 55 ; Fröhner, W., *La Collection Tyszkiewicz, Choix de Monuments*, pl. viii, fig. 3 ; *Arch. Journ.* vol. lviii (1901), p. 234, pl. ii. See Vopel, no. 56, and for the inscr. *C. I. L.* vol. xv, 7041. For the equipment of gladiators *see* P. Meier, *De gladiatura Romana quaestiones selectae*, Bonn, 1881, and for the *galerus*, Overbeck, *Pompeii und seine Gebäude*, &c., p. 458 (Leipzig, 1884). For good examples of the *retiarius* in a similar equipment on Roman pottery *see Bonner Jahrbücher*, lxxiv (1882), pp. 150, 151, and C. Roach Smith, *Collectanea Antiqua*, vol. iv, pl. xxi, fig. 1, and p. 80. The Aurelia referred to in the inscription must be the province of that name in Cisalpine Gaul.

**604**. FRAGMENT, much defaced. A beardless man wearing a *toga contabulata* and holding in his *r.* hand a short staff curved like a *lituus* or a *pedum*. In the field to *r.* of the head s a wreath. Round the figure and within a rectangular border is the inscription /// ACHI DVLCIS VIVAS C//////.

L. 2·5 in.

Buonarruoti, *Osservazioni sopra alcuni frammenti di vasi*, &c., pl. xix, fig. 1 ; Garrucci, *Vetri*, pl. xxxii, fig. 4, and *Storia*, pl. 200, fig. 4 ; Smith and Cheetham, vol. ii, p. 1568 ; Vopel, no. 72.

The glass has suffered considerably since the time of its publication. The protecting glass is gone and the design has been much worn. The inscription originally ran *Amachi dulcis vivas cum caris tuis*.

**605**. MEDALLION, with ground edges. Half-length portrait of a beardless man full-face, the hair cut straight across the forehead. He wears a long-sleeved tunic with pattern represented by cross-hatching, and a chlamys fastened on the *r.*

shoulder by a fibula. In his *l.* hand he holds a *volumen* the top of which he almost touches with the extended fingers of his *r.* In the field to *l.* of the head is a case containing three styli. Within a plain linear border is the inscription EVΓ////TA VIVE VIVAS PIE ZESES.

*Plate* XXVIII.

D. 2·1 in. Given by the Executors of Felix Slade, Esq., 1870.

Vopel, no. 77, p. 44, fig. 1. The person represented was perhaps an official or scribe. The reduplication in *vive vivas* is curious. Perhaps the first word should have been BIBE as e. g. *Bonner Jahrbücher*, Hefte v–vi, p. 379, though here again there would be a repetition.

**606.** DIMINUTIVE MEDALLION. A youthful beardless bust wearing a mantle (*lacerna*) fastened over the breast with a circular fibula. Octagonal linear border.

*Plate* XXXI.

D. ·96 in.

Garrucci, *Vetri*, pl. xx, fig. 5 ; *Storia*, pl. 189, fig. 5 ; Vopel, no. 91.

**607.** BOTTOM OF A DRINKING VESSEL, with low foot-rim ; a female bust in tunic and mantle, holding a *volumen* in her hand. In a circular border the inscription BI//AS PA////N//IB/////IVIS V /// O TVO (*Vivas parentibus tuis viro tuo*).

D. 3·1 in.

Garrucci, *Storia*, pl. 200, fig. 5 ; Vopel, no. 100.

The upper layer of glass is imperfect and both surfaces are highly iridescent. There are three layers, so that the design must have been already protected when the bottom was fused to the bowl.

**608.** ANOTHER, with similar foot-rim. In the circular field are the half-figures of a husband and wife between whose heads is a small figure of Hercules standing on a disc about the level of their shoulders. The husband is beardless ; he wears a tunic with a red stripe on the *r.* shoulder and over this the *toga contabulata.* The wife has her hair dressed in a succession of curls round the forehead, and wears a *diadema* with a green gem (?) in each of the lower corners near the ears. She is clothed in a mantle, and has round her neck a broad collar ornamented with a row of rectangular green gems between two rows of smaller red stones and having a fringe of pear-shaped green pendants. The figure of Hercules stands to *l.* and wears the lion's skin over his *l.* shoulder pressing it against his body with his *l.* arm. In his *l.* hand he holds three globular objects coloured green ; his club rests on his *r.* shoulder. The group is inclosed in a circular inscription ORFITUS ET COSTANTIA IN NOMINE HERCVLIS, which is continued in smaller letters in the upper part of the field about the heads of the figures, ACERENTINO FELICES BIBATIS·

*Plate* XXIX.

D. 4·25 in. Matarozzi Coll. 1863.

Garrucci, *Vetri*, pl. xxxv, fig. 1 ; Passeri, *Lucernae Fictiles*, vol. iii, pl. xcii ; Parker, *The Archaeology of Rome*, pt. xii, *The Catacombs*, pl. viii (Oxford, 1877) ; Deville, *Hist. de l'Art de la Verrerie*, pl. xlviii (Paris, 1873) ; *Arch. Journ.* vol. lviii (1901) ; O. Pelka, *Altchristliche Ehedenkmäler*, p. 104. *See* also *C. I. L.* vol. xv, 7036 ; Vopel, no. 113, p. 230, pl. i.

The inscription has been variously read. 'Orfitus and Constantia may ye live happily in the name of Hercules Acheruntinus!' ACERENTINO being thus an error for ACHERUNTINI, an epithet given to Hercules in honour of his descent into Hades; or 'drink in happiness of Cerentinian wine,' the wine-bearing district alluded to being either Cerinto in Boeotia, or Ceretano in Italy, *see* Garrucci, *Vetri*, pp. 69, 70; Vopel, p. 29. Cavedoni, *Osservazioni sopra alcuni frammenti di vasi di vetro*, in *Bullettino dell' Instituto*, 1859, p 62, would read *Acerentini* as an adjective from *Aceruntia* or *Acerentia* (Acerenza), a town in Apulia. Sanclementi, *Musei Sanclementiani Numismata Selecta*, vol. iii, p. 202 (Rome, 1809), suggests *Ferentino*. Hercules is invoked in favour of a fruitful union.

**609.** ANOTHER, imperfect. A family group, husband and wife (Pompeianus and Theodora), and their two children standing between two trees. The husband, who is beardless, stands on the *r.* wearing the *toga contabulata* and sandals. His *l.* hand rests on the shoulder of the little girl standing before him, his *r.* on the *l.* shoulder of his wife, who stands by his side; she in her turn rests her *l.* hand on the shoulder of her little son who stands in the foreground by his sister's side. The headdress of Theodora is the same as that of Constantia in no. 608, but she wears a narrow necklace and is wrapped in a richly embroidered mantle. The boy wears a long tunic (*dalmatica*) with circular embroidered ornaments (*orbiculi*) on the *l.* shoulder and in front of each knee, and boots; in his *l.* hand he holds a partly opened roll, and his *r.* is extended as if speaking. The girl, who also carries a roll, wears a *paenula* or *planeta* with embroidered vertical stripes down the front, and embroidered shoes. In the field between the heads of the two principal figures is the inscription POMPEIANE TEODORA VIBATIS, and lower down between the heads of the children is the sacred monogram ☧. The group is enclosed in a border of conventional floral scrolls.

    *Plate* XXIX.

    D. 4·3 in. Matarozzi Coll. 1863.

    Garrucci, *Vetri*, pl. xxix, fig. 4, and *Storia*, pl. 198, fig. 4; Sanclementi, *Numism. Selecta*, vol. iii, p. 192; Kraus, and *Geschichte*, vol. i, p. 167; O. Pelka, as above, p. 155; Vopel, no. 116. *Real-Encykl.* vol. i, p. 385. The lower surface is much cracked, and only part of the foot-rim remains.

**610.** ANOTHER; a family group, half-length portraits of a husband and wife, and their little daughter. The costume of both resembles that of Orfitus and Constantia in no. 608, the daughter is dressed like her mother, but appears to have her hair drawn up in a knot on the top of her head. Between the heads of the principal figures is the sacred monogram ☧ between two dots, and surmounted by a wreath or diadem. The group is enclosed in a double toothed border. Round the upper part of the field is the inscription SEBERE COSMAS LEA ZESES.

    *Plate* XXVIII.

    D. 3·3 in. Matarozzi Coll. 1863.

    Garrucci, *Vetri*, pl. xxix, fig. 5, and *Storia*, pl. 198, fig. 5; Sanclementi, *Numism. Selecta*, vol. iii, pl. xliv, fig. 4; d'Agincourt, *Peintures*, xii. 26; O. Pelka, as above, p. 154; Vopel, no. 119.

    The name Lea suggests a Jewish origin for this family (Vopel, p. 83, note). The name of the mother is probably intended for *Severa*, but Garrucci, *Storia*, Descr. of plate, 198, fig. 5, reads it as the vocative of *Severus*, taking Cosmas as a female name.

**611.** SEVEN FRAGMENTS from the bottom of a drinking vessel of unusual size. Within a double border, consisting of an inner serrated band and an outer band of detached inverted triangles, is a family group consisting of a husband (*r.*), wife (*l.*), and little boy in the middle. The *l.* half of the man's body alone remains. He wears a short tunic and apparently a chlamys with two purple stripes, while with both hands he holds a small tunic (?) edged with purple stripes. Within the border behind him is the inscription //// JUGE TVA ET FORTUNIO FILIO TVO. The figure of the husband covers three fragments. On three others are the head and *l.* shoulder of the mother and the lower part of her body and that of the boy Fortunius. She wears an embroidered mantle and the boy a short tunic.

Original Diameter, c. 6 in.

Garrucci, *Vetri*, pl. xxxi, fig. 3, and *Storia*, pl. 201, fig. 3 ; O. Pelka, as above, p. 159. The scene perhaps represents the assumption by the boy of the distinctive garments of manhood. The Christian origin of the glass is not certain.

The protecting layer of glass is missing, and the designs have suffered much from exposure. The surface is in parts highly iridescent.

**612.** BOTTOM OF A DRINKING VESSEL, imperfect, with low foot-rim. Busts of a bride and bridegroom. Between them hovers Cupid with his hands resting on their heads and his legs crossed. Round the upper part of the field is the inscription ////// INE TZVCINVS BIBITE with interpunctuations of heart-shaped leaves. Tzucinus is beardless with curly hair. He wears a tunic and the *toga contabulata*, and holds a roll with both hands. His wife wears an embroidered mantle and a *diadema* above which her hair is tied up in a net (*reticulum*). She also holds a roll in both hands. In the field beyond the heads are two trefoils.

*Plate* XXVIII.

D. 3·8 in. Matarozzi Coll. 1863.

Garrucci, *Vetri*, pl. xxviii, fig. 6, and *Storia*, pl. 197, fig. 6; Sanclementi, *Numism. Selecta*, vol. iii, pl. xlii, fig. 6 ; O. Pelka, as above, p. 104 ; Vopel, no. 125.

**613.** ANOTHER ; busts of a bride and bridegroom, the former in a richly embroidered mantle and collar, the latter in the *toga contabulata*. Above them stands a small figure of our Lord in tunic and pallium, with arms extended, holding a wreath over each of their heads. Inscription DVLCIS ANIMA VIVAS.

*Plate* XXVIII.

D. 2·22 in. Tyszkiewicz Coll. 1898.

Vopel, p. 47, and no. 137 ; O. Pelka, as above, p. 103. The back of this glass has been photographed to obtain a clearer result ; the inscription is therefore reversed.

**614.** FRAGMENT from the bottom of a drinking vessel, with foot-rim. Lower part of the busts of a man and woman, the latter wearing an embroidered mantle. Border as in no. 611.

L. 3 in. Bunsen Coll. 1854.

Garrucci, *Vetri*, pl. xxxii, fig. 5 ; Vopel, no. 145.

**615.** LOWER HALF of the bottom of a drinking vessel, with foot-rim. The seven-branched candlestick with foliated ends to the branches. In the field below are,

R

to the *l.*, an amphora, a circular cake perhaps of unleavened bread, and a ram's horn (*shofar*) ; to the *r.*, a citron (*ethrog*), and a bundle of palm, willow, and myrtle branches (*lulab*).    Round the edge, /// **LV · PIE · ZESES.**
*Plate* XXVIII.

D. 3·04 in.   Matarozzi Coll. 1863.
Garrucci, *Vetri*, pl. v, fig. 4, and *Storia*, pl. 490, fig. 4 ; Sanclementi, *Numism. Selecta*, vol. iii, pl. xlii, fig. 10 ; Vopel, no. 164.
The objects here represented are connected with the Jewish Cult, and are frequently found on other Jewish monuments such as sarcophagi, mosaics, and frescoes.   For mosaic *see Rev. Arch.* 1883, p. 157 f., and 1884, pl. ix and x (Hammam Lif, Tunis).   For paintings *see Rev. Arch.* 1889, pt. i, pp. 178 ff. (Gamart, near Carthage).   The *lulab* and *ethrog* are still used at the feast of tabernacles.   The horn was blown at various festivals.

**616.** DIMINUTIVE MEDALLION, with protecting layer of blue glass.   A nude male figure (Adam) standing to *r.* extending his *r.* hand and covering his nakedness with his *l.*   In the field four leaves ; octagonal linear border.
*Plate* XXXI.

L. ·98 in.
Garrucci, *Vetri*, pl. ii, fig. 3, and *Storia*, pl. 172, fig. 3 ; Vopel, no. 171.

**617.** BOTTOM OF A DRINKING VESSEL, with foot-rim.   Within a rectangular field, Moses, a beardless figure in tunic and pallium, holding out a rod in his *r.* hand towards a rock from which issues a stream of water.   Below the rock to *l.* is a beardless youth in a tunic kneeling on his *r.* knee and extending his *r.* hand towards the water.    Between the two figures is a tree, and in the *r.* hand top corner above Moses a *volumen* or roll.    Round the border is the inscription **HILARIS CVM TVIS PIE ZESES IN DEO.**

D. 3 in.   Matarozzi Coll. 1863.
Garrucci, *Vetri*, pl. ii, fig. 10, and *Storia*, pl. 172, fig. 9 ; Sanclementi, *Numism. Selecta*, vol. iii, pl. xlii, fig. 5 ; Vopel, no. 188.   The design is much clouded by a milky substance, perhaps the flux used to unite the two layers of glass.

**618.** DIMINUTIVE MEDALLION, with protecting layer of blue glass.   Within an octagonal linear border a nude beardless figure (Daniel), full-face, his body inclined towards the *l.* and his arms extended in the attitude of an *orans*.   In the field four leaves and a circular dot.
*Plate* XXXI.

L. ·92 in.   Matarozzi Coll. 1863.
Garrucci, *Vetri*, pl. iii, fig. 12, and *Storia*, pl. 173, fig. 12 ; Vopel, no. 201.

**619.** BOTTOM OF A DRINKING VESSEL, with foot-rim.   Daniel killing the dragon of Bel with a poisoned cake (*see History of Bel and the Dragon*, v. 27).   To *r.* the dragon, with long sinuous neck and crested head, issues from a rocky hole and bites at the cake held towards it by Daniel with both hands.   The prophet, who is beardless, wears a tunic and chlamys, and turns his head backwards towards our Lord, who stands behind him. The Saviour is also beardless, has a plain nimbus and is clothed in tunic and pallium. His *r.* hand is extended towards Daniel, and in the *l.* is the rod of power. The group is enclosed in a rectangular ornamental border with a pyramidal projection in the centre of each side.

*Plate* XXIX.

D. 3.56 in. Matarozzi Coll. 1863.
Garrucci, *Vetri*, pl. iii, fig. 13, and *Storia*, pl. 173, fig. 14; *Arch. Journ.* vol. lviii (1901), p. 238, pl. iii; Vopel, no. 206 and p. 67.

**620.** DIMINUTIVE MEDALLION, with blue protecting glass. Within a plain oval border a youthful figure in a tunic walking to *l.* and carrying a spherical object in both hands. In the field three leaves. Possibly Daniel carrying the poisoned cake.

*Plate* XXXI.

D. .92 in. Bunsen Coll. 1854.
Garrucci, *Vetri*, pl. iv, fig. 11, and *Storia*, pl. 174, fig. 5; Vopel, no. 212.

**621.** ANOTHER, with amber-coloured protecting glass. Within a horizontal oval border a beardless male figure, one of the Three Children of Babylon, standing full-face in the attitude of an *orans*. He wears a double oriental tunic and cap with pendant strings. Round his feet rise conventional flames. In the field two dots and two leaves.

*Plate* XXXI.

L. 1.06 in. Bunsen Coll. 1854.
Garrucci, *Vetri*, pl. iii, fig. 10, and *Storia*, pl. 173, fig. 19; Vopel, no. 220.

**622.** ANOTHER, with green protecting glass. A monster with contorted body and widely opened mouth. The monster which swallowed Jonah.

*Plate* XXXI.

L. 1.2 in. Bunsen Coll. 1854.
Garrucci, *Vetri*, pl. iv, fig. 2, and *Storia*, pl. 174, fig. 11; Vopel, no. 228.

**623.** ANOTHER, with blue protecting glass. Jonah lying upon his back beneath the gourd with his *r.* arm behind his head.

*Plate* XXXI.

D. .86 in.
Garrucci, *Vetri*, pl. iv, fig. 4, and *Storia*, pl. 174, fig. 15; Vopel, no. 231.

**624.** ANOTHER, with blue protecting glass. In an oval border Lazarus standing swathed like a mummy beneath the portico of a tomb with gabled roof and walls of masonry.

*Plate* XXXI.

D. 1 in. Bunsen Coll. 1854.
Garrucci, *Vetri*, pl. ix, fig. 5, and *Storia*, pl. 178, fig. 5; Vopel, no. 265.

**625**. ANOTHER, with green protecting glass. A female figure kneeling to *r*. with both hands extended. She wears a mantle and a veil which is blown out behind her by the wind. Probably Mary or Martha at the tomb of Lazarus.

*Plate* XXXI.

L. ·94 in.    Matarozzi Coll. 1863.
Garrucci, *Vetri*, pl. ix, fig. 2, and *Storia*, pl. 178, fig. 2 ; Vopel, no. 269.

**626**. ANOTHER, with blue protecting glass. Within an octagonal border a beardless male figure (our Lord) in tunic and pallium moving to *l*. In his *r*. hand he holds out the rod of power, in his *l*. he grasps the folds of his mantle. In the field three leaves and three dots.

*Plate* XXXI.

D. ·94 in.    Matarozzi Coll. 1863.
Garrucci, *Vetri*, pl. vii, fig. 6, and *Storia*, pl. 176, fig. 8 ; d'Agincourt, *Peinture*, pl. xii, fig. 25 ; Vopel, no. 271.

**627**. ANOTHER, with blue protecting glass. Within an octagonal border a beardless figure (our Lord) standing full-face in tunic and pallium and holding out the rod of power in his *r*. hand. In the field a leaf and a dot.

*Plate* XXXI.

D. ·88 in.    Matarozzi Coll. 1863.
Garrucci, *Vetri*, pl. vii, fig. 8, and *Storia*, pl. 176, fig. 10 ; Vopel, no. 273.

**628**. LARGE DISC or plate with ground edges and without protecting glass. The designs, which are in gold and silver foil coloured in places with red and green, are upon a blue ground and are disposed in eight compartments divided by columns, radiating from a central circular medallion. Of this central medallion, which was surrounded by a serrated border, only a few fragments now remain ; on one is visible part of the body of a lamb (?), on two others are the letters EC DVLCI (*Ecce dulcis*?) ; the scene perhaps represented the Good Shepherd. Of the surrounding compartments two, which adjoin each other, represent the story of Jonah. In one is seen the ship moving to *l*. with large square sail etched with checkers, and with the yard and the planks of the hull painted red. There appears to be a second sail near the bows, though this may possibly belong to another ship in the background. In the ship are two nude figures, one in the bows the other near the stern ; they are facing each other and holding the nude body of Jonah which has half disappeared in the jaws of the monster. The water is coloured blue, and in the *r*. hand top corner is a standing dove, probably with a symbolic meaning. In the next compartment to the *l*. the monster is vomiting forth Jonah upon the shore, while in the background the prophet is again represented lying beneath the gourd. The water in the foreground is represented by horizontal streaks of blue. The next compartment to the *l*. shows Daniel standing in the attitude of an *orans* between four lions. He is youthful and beardless, wearing a girded tunic of silver or pale gold with red *clavi* and red stripes at the wrists. In the background are four trees with leaves painted green above the gold. The next compartment, again to the *l*., contains the Three Children of Babylon standing in a broad furnace of masonry represented in pale gold or silver from which issue red flames. The central figure stands full-face in the attitude of an *orans*, the two others are seen in profile with their arms stretched out before them. Continuing again to the *l.* we find a scene which has been variously interpreted as the sacrifice of Isaac, the restoration to sanity of Nebuchadnezzar, the abduction of Habakkuk by the angel, and the healing of the blind man by our Lord. On the *r.*, near a tower or wall of masonry, stands a beardless figure in a tunic with red *clavi* and a pallium, turned slightly to the *r.* and laying his *r.* hand upon the head of a smaller figure before him ; in the background is a tree with double top and leaves painted green above the gold. If the scene is interpreted as the healing of the blind man, the walls would probably represent those of Jericho (Luke xviii. 35). The next compartment has again given rise to controversy, the several interpretations being The Nativity, Daniel on the walls of Babylon with Nebuchadnezzar in the form of an ox beneath, and Susanna : the last interpretation is perhaps the least improbable. Above a wall of masonry stands a figure in the attitude of an *orans* wearing a long girded tunic with red *clavi*. On either side is a tree the leaves of which are coloured green above the gold. In front of the wall to *l.* is a recumbent ox, while on the *r.* are traces of a second ox or other animal. Upon the top of the wall is an indeterminate object consisting of a long horizontal bar supported on a number of vertical bars all slightly curved. It has a general resemblance to a swathed corpse but its length makes it impossible to describe it as the infant Saviour (as Nesbitt). On the other hand the curvature of the lines is rather against the interpretation as a railing. If the scene represents Susanna praying to God on the wall of the garden, the oxen may have been merely added to give local colour, or they may be symbolical of the elders. In the adjoining compartment is the healed paralytic in a tunic with red *clavi*, standing and holding across his shoulders with extended arms a bed with rectangular framework, the top of which is filled in with cross-hatching probably to represent straps or bands : in the background are trees. The subject of the last compartment has also provided matter of dispute. A youthful figure in pallium and tunic with red *clavi* stands to *l.* holding with his *r.* hand a wand or staff over a surface coloured bluish-green and bordered on both sides by a broad wavy band of gold like a twisted column. Upon the coloured surface may be seen scattered a head, two arms, and two legs. One suggestion is that the scene represents Moses striking the rock, the scattered limbs representing in a very unusual fashion the Israelites crowding to drink at the miraculous stream ; another is that it is intended for Ezekiel quickening the valley of dry bones. Whichever conclusion is adopted the treatment is very remarkable.

D. 7 in. Slade Bequest, 1868. Formerly in the Herstatt Collection. Found in 1866 with other fragments of glass and objects of jet in a cist containing the burned bones of a woman in the Ursulagartenstrasse, Cologne.

*Bonner Jahrbücher*, xlii (1867), pl. v ; Garrucci, *Storia*, pl. 169, fig. 1 ; Nesbitt, *Catalogue of the Collection of Glass formed by Felix Slade, Esq.*, p. 50 (London, 1871) ; Kraus, *Real-Encyklopädie*,

i. 619, and *Geschichte der christlichen Kunst*, vol. i, p. 481 (Freiburg, 1896). *See* also *Bonner Jahrb.*, as above, p. 168 (Prof. Düntzer), and xli, p. 132; de Rossi, *Bullettino*, 1856 (Prof. Heuser); *Kölnisches Pastoralblatt*, 1867, pp. 42-56 (Heuser); Nesbitt, as above, pp. 50-52. Vopel, no. 291 and pp. 2, 16, 66, 69, 73, 76, 83.

The condition of this remarkable object is far less perfect than the published reproductions would lead one to suppose. The fractures are numerous, almost the whole of the central medallion being lost, while the absence of any protecting glass has resulted in the loss by attrition of many details in the design. It would be almost useless to photograph it in its present condition, and as the drawings already published are sufficiently good for all practical purposes, it has not been thought worth while to reproduce it again by the same means. The purpose for which it was made is not certain. Some have supposed that it was a paten on which the host was placed and buried with the corpse, others that it was simply a medallion of an ornamental character of a kind manufactured by Christians for presentation to each other (*see* Düntzer, *Bonner Jahrb.* xlii, p. 176; Aus'm Weerth, *ibid.* xliii (1867), pp. 219, 220). The curious fact that it was found in the tomb of a pagan Roman lady is then explained on the supposition that it was placed with the body by a Christian friend. It does not appear that there was ever anything in the shape of a protecting glass, and this would militate against the use of the medallion for any purpose which would necessitate frequent handling or rubbing. It may have been used as a paten, but there is no positive evidence of this. The originality of the treatment of so many of the subjects points to a strong individuality in the artist, and it may well be that it is a local product made on the Rhine, where the usual iconographic uniformity may have been less rigidly maintained than in Italy. The excellence of the work points to a comparatively early date of manufacture, not later in any case than the middle of the 4th century, and quite possibly considerably earlier. The fact that the body with which it was found was incinerated would favour the 3rd century rather than a later period.

**629**. TWO PORTIONS OF A BOWL of transparent glass, each composed of three fragments. They are ornamented with twenty-one medallions, protected at the back with green and blue glass; these are of two classes, the larger kind which are about 1 in. long, having figure subjects, the smaller, which only average half that length, stars or eight-petalled flowers. They are arranged in concentric circles, the smaller kind being placed in the spaces between the larger. Of the four medallions remaining from the outermost circle one (green) represents our Lord or Moses with the rod of power (cf. nos. 626–7), a second (blue) Adam and Eve standing on either side of the tree round which the serpent is coiled, a third the sacrifice of Isaac, the fourth Susannah (?) wearing a long girded tunic with *clavi* and standing in the attitude of an *orans* between two trees. In the scene of the sacrifice of Isaac, the boy lies nude upon the ground to *l.* with his hands bound behind him, Abraham stands in the centre, bearded and wearing a striped tunic. With his *l.* hand he grasps Isaac by the hair, with his *r.* he brandishes a knife: his head is inclined backwards towards the arm of the Almighty which issues from heaven behind him. In the *r.* hand corner stands the ram to *r.* also with its head turned backwards; in the upper part of the field between Abraham's head and the knife is the altar of sacrifice. The eight remaining figured medallions illustrate three subjects, the stories of Jonah, Daniel, and the Three Children of Babylon. To the first subject are devoted four contiguous medallions. In the first (green) is the ship occupied by four men; above them is a large dolphin. Beneath this on the *r.* (green) is the monster swallowing the prophet, whose legs project from its jaws. To the *l.* of this (blue) the monster vomits forth Jonah on the shore. To the *l.* again (blue) Jonah is seen lying beneath the gourd. Beyond the cycle of Jonah begins that of Daniel, only two medallions of which remain. On the lower (blue) is a seated lion; on the higher (green) Daniel, a nude youthful figure, stands in the attitude of an *orans*. The two medallions with the story of the Three Children are both on the smaller portion of the bowl. They are very similar, each representing a youthful figure in oriental costume standing in the attitude of an *orans* in the midst of conventional flames. (Cf. no. 621.) The protecting glass is in one case blue, in the other green.

*Plate* XXX.

L. 6·5 in. Formerly in the Disch Collection, 1881. Found in a cemetery in the quarter of St. Severinus' Church, Cologne.

Disch, *Römisches Glas*, pl. i, figs. 1 and 2; de Rossi, *Bullettino*, 1864, plate opp. p. 81; Garrucci, *Storia*, pl. 170, fig. 1; *Bonner Jahrbücher*, 1864, xxxvi, pl. iii, fig. 3; Kraus, *Real-Encyklopädie*, i, p. 618 (1880); *id.*, *Geschichte der christlichen Kunst*, vol. i, p. 482, fig. 358. The bowl had a rounded bottom and curved sides, and was engraved round the top with two pairs of parallel lines, a section of which is preserved on one of the fragments. Prof. Kraus (*Geschichte*, p. 481) is inclined to suppose that it served a liturgical purpose, and that it may have been one of the glass patens sanctioned by Zephyrinus.

**630.** BOTTOM OF A DRINKING VESSEL; within a lozenge itself contained in a square, a bust of our Lord, beardless and youthful with hair cut across the forehead and falling in flowing curls upon the shoulders. He wears a tunic and a mantle fastened over the breast with a circular brooch. In the field on either side of the head is the inscription CRIS|TVS, with five dots. Within each of the angles of the outer square is a beardless bust clothed in a similar manner and flanked by two dots. Beyond each side of the square is a triangle with the apex outwards.

*Plate* XXVIII.

L. 3·6 in. Matarozzi Coll. 1863.

Garrucci, *Vetri*, pl. xviii, fig. 1, and *Storia*, pl. 187, fig. 1; Sanclementi, *Numism. Selecta*, vol. iii, pl. xlii, fig. 9; C. Torr, *On Portraits of Christ in the British Museum*, fig. 2, p. 5 (London, 1898); Vopel, no. 297. The glass of this example is of exceptional thickness.

**631.** ANOTHER, imperfect; a central circular medallion surrounded by six radiating compartments divided by columns. In the centre a bust of our Lord closely resembling the last no., and with the same inscription. In each of the surrounding compartments, none of which are perfect, was a standing figure in tunic and pallium.

*Plate* XXVIII.

L. 3·4 in. Matarozzi Coll. 1863.

Garrucci, *Vetri*, pl. xviii, fig. 2, and *Storia*, pl. 187, fig. 2; Sanclementi, *Numism. Selecta*, vol. iii, pl. xlii, fig. 7; Torr, *On Portraits of Christ in the British Museum*, fig. 1, p. 5 (1898); Vopel, no. 300. This example has three layers of glass. The columns dividing the standing figures were probably surmounted by labels bearing their names. Cf. Garrucci, *Vetri*, xix, 6 and 7.

**632.** ANOTHER; with foot-rim. The circular field is divided into two halves by a horizontal line. In the upper half stand four beardless figures in tunic and pallium holding rolls in their hands and separated by spirally fluted columns with foliated capitals connected by a festoon-like curtain.   Above is the inscription PIƎ ZESES.   On either side of the three figures to the *r*. are their names PAVLVS, SVSTVS (*Xystus*), and LAVRENTEVS.   The lower half contains three bearded half-figures in tunics and mantle, their heads bald above the forehead, with their names IPPOLITVS, CRISTVS, TIMoTEVS, in the field to *l*. of their heads.   The lateral figures look towards the central person who is full-face and holds a roll in his hand.   The space behind the head of St. Timothy is occupied by a roll.

> *Plate* XXIX.

> D. 3·86 in.   Matarozzi Coll. 1863.
> Garrucci, *Vetri*, pl. xvii, fig. 2, and *Storia*, pl. 186, fig. 2 ; Sanclementi, *Numism. Selecta*, vol. iii, pl. xli, fig. 1 ; Roller, *Les Catacombes de Rome*, vol. ii, pl. lxxvii, fig. 2 ; Vopel, no. 305.
> It is difficult to suppose that the central figure in the lower division of this glass can be intended for any other person than our Lord (though *see* Garrucci, *Vetri*, expl. of pl. xviii, fig. 2).   But the type is very exceptional, being that usually adopted for apostles, especially for St. Paul.   It has been suggested that *Cristus* is a mistake for *Calistus*.

**633.** FRAGMENT ; bust of St. Peter full-face, bearded and wearing tunic and pallium.   In the field to *l*. of the head the inscription PE|TRV|S PRO|TEG|A (T).

> L. 1·46 in.
> Garrucci, *Vetri*, pl. x, fig. 1, and *Storia*, pl. 179, fig. 1 ; Vopel, no. 316.   This specimen has three layers of glass.

**634.** FRAGMENT, with foot-rim.   To *l*. St. Peter, bearded and wearing a tunic, is seated on a folding stool : he holds a roll with both hands.   In the field behind him are the letters PET, with a trefoil and a dot.   Before him stands a female figure of which the lower part only remains.   She wears a long tunic and mantle above which is visible the border of a veil.

> D. 3·42 in.   Bunsen Coll. 1854.
> Garrucci, *Vetri*, pl. xvi, fig. 2, and *Storia*, pl. 185, fig. 2 ; Vopel, no. 318.
> The female figure has been conjectured to represent St. Petronilla, St. Pudenziana, St. Praxed, or the Church.

**635.** DIMINUTIVE MEDALLION with dark blue protecting glass.   Bust of St. Paul, youthful and beardless, in tunic and pallium.   In the field PAV|LVS.

> *Plate* XXXI.

> D. ·94 in.   Hamilton Palace Coll. 1856.
> Garrucci, *Vetri*, pl. xiv, fig. 5, and *Storia*, pl. 183, fig. 5 ; Perret, *Les Catacombes de Rome*, vol. iv, pl. xxi, fig. 2 ; Vopel, no. 320.   Set in a modern gold ring.

**636.** BOTTOM OF A DRINKING VESSEL, with foot-rim.   Busts of St. Peter and St. Paul side by side, their faces turned towards each other.   Above and between them stands a small figure of our Lord, beardless and with long straight hair parted in the middle ; he wears the tunic and pallium, and extends both his arms, each hand holding a wreath over the head of an apostle.   St. Peter and St. Paul are both of the same type, bearded and with their heads bald over the forehead.   They wear mantles (*lacernae* ?) fastened over the breast with circular brooches.

Their names **PETRVS** and **PAVLVS** are in the field behind their heads. Round the border the inscription **BICVLIVS DIGN(ITAS AM)ICORVM VIVAS PIE ZESES**.

*Plate* XXIX.

D. 4 in. Matarozzi Coll. 1863.

Garrucci, *Vetri*, pl. xii, fig. 4, and *Storia*, pl. 181, fig. 4; Vopel, no. 333. The name Biculius is strange, and perhaps stands for Buculeus or Bucolus or even Vigilius (Vopel, p. 82, note 5). Dignitas Amicorum is probably a complimentary term, 'the pride of thy friends.' The broken edges of this example, which project a little further than is usually the case, show by their curvature that the vessel must have been a shallow bowl.

**637.** ANOTHER, of a larger size, with foot-rim. Within a double circular border, consisting of an engrailed band and an outer line of half-ovals, St. Peter and St. Paul seated in discourse upon folding-stools. The apostles are both beardless and clothed in the tunic and pallium, St. Peter to *l.*, St. Paul to *r.*; their names **PETRVS** and **PAVLVS** are in the field behind their heads. St. Peter extends his *r.* hand as if speaking, St. Paul holds a roll over his breast. Between their heads is a wreath of oak-leaves with ribbons and a detached leaf in the centre.

*Plate* XXIX.

D. 4.9 in. Matarozzi Coll. 1863.

Garrucci, *Vetri*, pl. xiv, fig. 4, and *Storia*, pl. 183, fig. 4; Sanclementi, *Numism. Selecta*, vol. iii, pl. xli, fig. 3; Vopel, no. 344. The design is largely obscured by a milky substance, possibly caused by the melting of the flux in process of manufacture.

**638.** FRAGMENT; bust of St. Peter, bearded, and in tunic and pallium; to his *r.* is the head of a similar figure, and between the two a branch or flower. In the field to *l.* //**ETRVS**.

L. 2.04 in. Bunsen Coll. 1854.

Garrucci, *Vetri*, pl. xi, fig. 4, and *Storia*, pl. 180, fig. 4; Vopel, no. 360.

**639.** ANOTHER; part of bust of St. Peter to *r.*; in the field **PETRS**.

L. 1.42 in. Given by Major-General Meyrick, 1878.

Vopel, no. 368.

**640.** ANOTHER; a beardless head of St. Paul to *l.*; in the field **PAVL|S**; border similar to that of no. 637.

*Plate* XXIX.

L. .74 in. Franks Coll. 1893.

Vopel, no. 369.

**641.** BOTTOM OF A DRINKING VESSEL, with foot-rim. Within a plain circular border two beardless male busts in tunics and mantles folded over the breast. In the field **SVSTVS TIMOTEVS**. Between the heads a quatrefoil.

*Plate* XXVIII.

D. 2.72 in. Matarozzi Coll. 1863.

Garrucci, *Vetri*, pl. xxix, fig. 1, and *Storia*, pl. 193, fig. 1; Sanclementi, *Numism. Selecta*, vol. iii, pl. xlii, fig. 8; Vopel, no. 412. The form *Sustus* is equivalent to *Xystus* or *Sixtus*.

**642.** FRAGMENT; with foot-rim.  It contains three imperfect compartments out of six which formerly radiated from a centre as in no. 631, pl. xxviii.  In the two to the *l.* are two beardless busts with the names (SIM)ON and DAMAS.  The third is very incomplete, containing only the letter S.

> L. 3·8 in.
> Garrucci, *Vetri*, pl. xxv, fig. 8, and *Storia*, pl. 194, fig. 8; Vopel, no. 426.  The name in the third compartment was perhaps *Sustus*.

**643.** ANOTHER; part of a draped figure seated on a folding-stool with a border like that of no. 637, pl. **xxix.**

> L. 1·6 in.  Franks Coll. 1886.  Formerly in the Nesbitt Collection.  The figure was probably St. Peter or St. Paul.

**644.** ANOTHER; with foot-rim.  Part of a circular temple or sanctuary supported on round columns with foliated capitals and architraves ornamented with scrolls, the whole standing on a draped basement.  From the front architrave is suspended a vase or lamp with a foot, and below this the space between the columns is crossed by a rail (*cancellus*) indicated by cross-hatching.  In the field to *r.* are the words IN DEO.

> L. 3·5 in.  Bunsen Coll. 1854.
> Garrucci, *Vetri*, pl. xxxix, fig. 10, and *Storia*, pl. 203, fig. 7; Vopel, no. 459.

**645.** ANOTHER; with a roll and the letters IES.

> L. 1·8 in.
> Garrucci, *Vetri*, pl. xxxii, fig. 8, and *Storia*, pl. 200, fig. 8; Vopel, no. 464.

**646.** ANOTHER; the letters CI.

> L. 1 in.  Franks Coll. 1886.
> Vopel, no. 472.  Perhaps the inscription was *Dulcis Anima*.

**647.** ANOTHER; the letters RV.

> L. ·7 in.  Bunsen Coll. 1854.
> Vopel, no. 473.  Perhaps part of the name *Petrus*.

**648.** ANOTHER; with foot-rim.

> L. 1 in.

**649.** ANOTHER; without protecting glass.

> L. ·82 in.

**650.** ANOTHER; with part of a border similar to that of no. 637.

> L. 1·1 in.  Slade Bequest.  Slade Cat. no. 121.

**651.** ANOTHER; without protecting glass.

> L. 1·46 in.

## B. Other Vessels.

### *4th and 5th centuries.*

**652.** GOBLET, expanding from the base to the rim. The sides are rudely engraved with three biblical scenes, Adam and Eve, Moses striking the rock, and the Raising of Lazarus. In the first scene Adam and Eve are standing on either side of the tree round which the Serpent is coiled. Adam stands to *r.*, and turns his head towards a figure standing behind him in tunic and pallium and holding up the *r.* hand as if in discourse (our Lord?). In the second scene Moses in tunic and pallium stands to *l.*, holding the rod in his *r.* hand; before him is the rock conventionally treated. In the third, our Lord, similarly attired and in the same attitude, stands before the erect and swathed figure of Lazarus.

*4th or 5th century.*

H. 5.1 in. Given by the Executors of Felix Slade, Esq., 1872. Found at Cologne.

*See Bonner Jahrbücher*, Heft lxiv (1878), p. 127, note 4. For similar glasses, cf. de Rossi, *Bullettino*, 1867, p. 48, and 1868, p. 35; A. Kisa, *Die antiken Gläser der Frau Maria vom Rath zu Köln*, p. 73 and pl. xix and xx (Bonn, 1899); *Rev. Arch.* xliv (1882), p. 280 f.; Kraus, *Real-Encykl.* vol. i. p. 621.

**653.** GLOBULAR VESSEL of **crystalline** glass, with short narrow cylindrical neck. The body is divided by a raised band of herring-bone pattern into two zones, on the upper of which is cut in relief ΠΙΕ ΖΗϹΑΙϹ ΑΕΙ, on the lower ΕΝ ΑΓΑΘΟΙϹ, a leaf preceding the inscription in each case. The horizontal lines in the Α and Θ are omitted. At the bottom are engraved radiating lines within a circle surrounded by a milled band. Round the shoulders is a band of sunk ovals.

*See* figure.

H. 3.9 in. D. 3.7 in. Disch Coll. 1881.

*Bonner Jahrbücher*, Heft lxxi. pl. vi, no. 1360, mentioned *ibid.* p. 124, and Heft lxiv (1878), pp. 127-8. A glass bearing the same inscription is alluded to in *Bonn. Jhrb.* Heft xvi, p. 75, and others with very similar Greek inscriptions, *ibid.* Heft lix (1876), p. 67. De Rossi, *Bullettino*, New Series, iv. p. 23, mentions others. An inscription similarly cut in relief is described by Héron de Villefosse, *Rev. Arch.* vol. xxvii (1874), pp. 388-9.

**654.** FISH of transparent blown glass, the eyes and fins applied.

> L. 8·25 in.  1875.  Found at Cologne.  Imperfect.  Perhaps intended for a flask.

**655.** FRAGMENT from the side of a cup of thin transparent glass, with a fish of opaque white glass in relief.

> L. 1·62 in.
> For a complete cup, found in the cemetery of Calixtus, *see* de Rossi, *Bullettino*, 2nd Series, 1873, pl. ix and p. 142.

**656.** DRINKING CUP in the shape of a tumbler, of plain transparent glass imbedded in a mass of mortar.

> D. 2·6 in.  Sloane Coll. 1753.  Said to have been found in the Catacombs, Rome.

**657.** FLASK of transparent blown glass, with two handles.  On each side is a Latin cross with a St. Andrew's cross under each arm, all applied in dark blue glass.

> L. 3·06 in.  Sloane Coll. 1753.  Said to have been found in the Catacombs, Rome.  The attribution is however doubtful.

**658.** VASE, of blue glass, with two handles.  It has an expanding lip, globular fluted body, and expanding fluted foot.
> *See* figure.  *5th century.*

> H. 6·4 in.  D. at mouth, 5·55 in. Total breadth, 9·35 in.  D. of foot, 6·4 in.  From the Pourtalès Collection. Found near Amiens (*Samarobriva*).
> Nesbitt, *Cat. of the Collection of Glass formed by Felix Slade, Esq.*, p. 55, fig. 72 (1871); *Bonner Jahrbücher*, Heft lxiv (1878), pl. x.  The vase, which may be a chalice, resembles the vessels of Cantharus form so frequently seen on Christian sarcophagi and reliefs.  A vase of this type, standing on the altar and therefore certainly a chalice, is seen in the mosaics of San Vitale at Ravenna (*see* V. Schultze, *Archäologie der altchristlichen Kunst*, p. 118, Munich, 1895).  On early glass and other chalices, *see Bonner Jahrbücher*, as above, pp. 120 ff.  This form of vase was made by the Franks in metal, but it does not seem necessary to ascribe the present example to them, as it may with equal probability be regarded as a product of Roman provincial art.

**659.** SIMILAR VASE of the same colour, but without the handles.

> D. of top, 5·2 in., of foot, 4·4 in.  H. 6·25 in.  Slade Bequest, 1868.
> Nesbitt, *Cat. of the Coll. of Glass*, &c., no. 318.

## C. Money Weights.

*Mostly of the 6th century.*

Small discs stamped on one face only. The design usually consists of a bust or monogram, surrounded by the name of an Eparch or Prefect. There is another series of these weights in the Department of Coins and Medals.

**660.** DARK BLUE; three imperial (?) busts one above the other; between the two lower a monogram.

> D. ·8 in. Weight, 32 grains. Franks Coll. 1893.
> Schlumberger, *Revue des Études Grecques*, vol. viii (1895), p. 76, no. 42 (the article reprinted in *Mélanges d'Arch. Byz.* pp. 319–335); Mordtmann in *Byz. Zeitschr.* 1898, p. 603 f. The name may be Theodotus or Theodosius.

**661.** DARK BLUE; bust of an emperor (?) between two crosses; below, a monogram.

> D. 1 in. Weight, 62 grains. 1884.
> Schlumberger, p. 75, no. 40.

**662.** PALE GREEN, considerably worn. Bust surrounded by a partly effaced inscription ////// NN४ ///APX४ (ἐπὶ Ἰωάννου ἐπάρχου). To *l.* and *r.* ⒷᎾ and ᙏᵫ ('Ρώμης).

> D. ·7 in. Weight, 22 grains 1884.
> Schlumberger, p. 64, no. 5. *See* also E. Cuq., in *Rev. Arch.* 1897, pt. ii, pp. 109 f.; cf. a bronze weight in *Gazette Archéologique*, 1883, pp. 298 f.

**663.** PALE GREEN; a bust surrounded by the inscription ✠ ЄΠΙ ΙѠΑΝΝ४ ЄΠΑΡΧ४.

> D. 1 in. Weight, 69 grains. Franks Coll. 1892.
> Schlumberger, p. 64, no. 5. Cf. Mordtmann, p. 605, no. 4.

**664.** PALE GREEN; a monogram surrounded by the inscription ЄΠΙ ΙѠΑΝΝΟ४ ЄΠΑΡΧ४.
> *See* figure.

> D. 1 in. Weight, 67 grains. Franks Coll. 1893. From Egypt.
> Another example in the Department of Coins and Medals. Schlumberger, p. 67, no. 13.

**665.** PALE GREEN; a bust with the *r.* hand held up and containing an object resembling a *mappa*. Inscription ✠ ЄΠΙΦΛΣΓЄΡΟΝΤΙS (ἐπὶ Φλα(βίου) Γεροντίου).

> D. 1 in. Weight, 66 grains. Franks Coll. 1892.
> Schlumberger, p. 67, no. 11; Mordtmann, p. 605, no. 5. Flavius Gerontius was *Praefectus Urbi*, 559–60.

**666.** PALE GREEN, with identical bust and inscription.

> D. ·86 in. Weight, 34 grains. Franks Coll. 1892.

**667.** PALE GREEN ; a bust with *r.* hand held up as before.  ✛ ЄΠΙ ΘЄΟΔΟΤΥ ЄΠΑΡΧΥ.   In the field to *r.* a cross.

> D. ·76 in.   Weight, 18 grains.   1891.   Another example in the Department of Coins and Medals.
> Cf. Schlumberger, p. 66, no. 10; *Archäologischer Anzeiger*, 1860, pp. 103-4.

**668.** PALE GREEN ; a bust as before.  ✛ ЄΠΙ ΚΟϹΜΑ ЄΠΑΡΧΥ.

> D. 1 in.   Weight, 69 grains.   Slade Coll. no. 322.
> Schlumberger, p. 64, no. 4.   Found on the site of Porphyrion near Sidon by M. Charles Schefer and presented by him to the Emperor Napoleon III.

**669.** PALE GREEN ; a bust holding up a staff (?) in his *r.* hand and an object shaped Δ in his *l.*  ✛ ЄΠΙ ΡΟ////Υ ЄΠΑΡΧΥ (ἐπὶ Ῥογάτου ἐπάρχου, or Ῥομάνου ἐπάρχου).

> D. ·8 in.   Weight, 28 grains.   1879.   From Egypt.
> Schlumberger, p. 65, no. 7 ; cf. Mordtmann, pp. 605-6.   Rogatus (?) may possibly be the father-in-law of Heraclius, *see* Theophanes (ed. de Boor), vol. i, p. 298, 21.

**670.** PALE BLUE ; bust with inscription ΔΟΜΙΑΝΥ ✛ ΤΟΥ ЄΝΔΟΞϹ (Δομιτιάνου τοῦ ἐνδοξοτάτου ἐπάρχου).

> D. ·96 in.   Weight, 68 grains.   1882.
> Cf. Schlumberger, p. 62, no. 1.

**671.** DARK BLUE ; a bust with inscription ΔΑΜЄΙΑΝΥ within a scalloped border.

> D. ·92 in.   Weight, 63 grains.   1884.
> Schlumberger, p. 62, no. 1, 2nd example.

**672.** BLUE ; a monogram with inscription ✛ ЄΥΠΡΑΞΙΟΥ.

> D. ·94 in.   Weight, 65 grains.   Franks Coll. 1893.   From Egypt.
> Schlumberger, p. 67, no. 12, 3rd example.

**673.** PALE GREENISH BLUE ; a bust between two crosses.

> D. ·74 in.   Weight, 32 grains.   Given by the Executors of Felix Slade, Esq.   1872.   From Beyrût.

**674.** PALE GREEN ; a bust.

> D. ·8 in.   Weight, 30 grains.   Franks Coll. 1874.

**675.** PALE GREEN ; transparent, a monogram.
> *See* figure.

> D. ·8 in.   Weight, 35 grains.   Franks Coll. 1893.
> Schlumberger, p. 73, no. 34.   The monogram might be Κωνσταντίνου, cf. Mordtmann, p. 607, no. 11.

**676.** PALE GREEN ; a monogram.
> *See* figure.

> D. ·76 in.   Weight, 32 grains.   Franks Coll. 1892.
> Cf. Schlumberger, p. 74, no. 35.

**677.** PURPLE ; the same monogram.

>  D. ·66 in.   Weight, 18 grains.   Franks Coll. 1892.
>  Cf. Schlumberger, p. 74, no. 35.

**678.** PALE TRANSLUCENT ; the same monogram.

>  D. ·72 in.   Weight, 20 grains.   Franks Coll. 1892.

**679.** GREENISH BLUE ; a monogram.
>  *See* figure.

>  D. ·94 in.   Weight, 71 grains.   Franks Coll. 1893.   From Egypt.
>  Another example in the Department of Coins and Medals.   Cf. Schlum-
>  berger, p. 74, fig. 36.

**680.** GREEN, translucent ; a monogram.
>  *See* figure.

>  D. ·84 in.   Weight, 33 grains.   1865.

**681.** PALE GREEN, translucent ; a monogram.

>  D. 1 in.   Weight, 69 grains.   1891.   Another example in the Department of Coins
>  and Medals.
>  Schlumberger, p. 68, no. 16.

**682.** PALE GREEN ; a monogram.

>  D. 1·12 in.   Weight, 70 grains.   Given by the Executors of Felix Slade, Esq., 1872.
>  Schlumberger, p. 71, no. 25.   The monogram may read Κύρου, Mordtmann, p. 604.

**683.** BLUE ; a monogram.

>  D. ·74 in.   Weight, 19 grains.   Franks Coll. 1892.
>  Schlumberger, p. 71, no. 24.

**684.** GREEN ; a monogram.

>  D. ·82 in.   Weight, 23 grains.
>  Schlumberger, p. 71, no. 26.

**685.** GREEN ; a monogram.

>  D. ·96 in.   Weight, 68 grains.   Franks Coll. 1896.

## D. Miscellaneous.

### PASTES, PENDANTS, CROSSES, &c.

Nos. 686–696 represent a class of cameo pastes usually opaque red, brown, or blue, which appear to date from about the 11th to the 13th century. They have been obtained in various places (Athens, Smyrna, Akhmîm (Panopolis), and Rome), and they bear inscriptions in both Latin and Greek. Among the examples omitted from the catalogue on account of their presumably Western and Mediaeval origin are pastes with the following subjects: The Nativity; The Crucifixion; St. John Baptist, with inscription S. IOҺ⊓S ҺATI; St. Christopher, with inscription S. CRISTOFORI; and St. James (of Compostella?) adored by two kneeling pilgrims with flat hats and staves, with inscription S̄· IACOB. For other pastes of the same class, *see* Von Stosch, *Gemmae Ant. Caelatae*, &c., pp. 16–18.

686. CIRCULAR, dark blue; bust of our Lord full-face. He has the cruciferous nimbus, and with the *r.* hand makes the gesture of benediction. On either side I̅C̅ X̅C̅.

    *See* figure.

    D. 1·3 in. Slade Bequest, 1868.

687. HEXAGONAL, dull brown streaked with red; our Lord with cruciferous nimbus seated on a throne with footstool, his *r.* hand raised in the gesture of benediction. To *l.* stands a nimbed female figure (the Virgin?), to *r.* a male(?) figure (imperfect). On either side of the head of our Lord I̅C̅ (X̅C̅).

    L. 1·8 in. 1880. Obtained with a collection from Egypt and Asia Minor.

688. ANOTHER, oval, clear; a half-figure of the Virgin to *l.*, holding the Child in her *r.* arm. Inscription M̅P̅ Θ̅Y̅.

    L. 1·24 in. 1883. Obtained with objects from Egypt and Asia Minor.

689. ANOTHER, green translucent; the same subject.

    L. 1 in. 1874.

690. ANOTHER, opaque red; the same subject.

    L. 1·2 in. 1889. Obtained in Athens.

691. ANOTHER, opaque red; the Virgin standing in the attitude of an *orans* between two palms. Inscription M̅P̅ Θ̅Y̅.

    L. ·92 in. 1884.

**692.** ANOTHER, opaque red; St. Theodore riding to *r.* and transfixing the dragon with his lance. In the field Ⓐ ΘΕⲰ|ΔΟΡΟC.

L. 1·22 in. 1889. From Athens.

**693.** ANOTHER, opaque brown; St. Theodore as before. Ⓐ ΘΕⲰ|ΔΟΡΟC.
*See* figure.
L. 1·24 in. 1874.

**694.** ANOTHER, blue; half-length figure of St. Demetrius, full-face. The saint is beardless, and carries a spear in his *r.*, and a circular shield over his *l.* arm. In the field on either side of the head Ⓐ ///ΗΜΗ|ΤΡΙΟC.

L. 1·2 in. Given by Major-General Meyrick, 1878.

**695.** ANOTHER, red; the same subject and inscription.

L. 1·16 in. Given by the Executors of Felix Slade, Esq., 1872.

**696.** ANOTHER, red; half-figure of St. Nicholas, full-face, in episcopal vestments with a book in his *l.* hand, and his *r.* in the gesture of benediction. On either side of the head Ⓐ ΝΙΚΟ|ΛΑΟC.

L. 1 in. Franks Coll. 1893.

**697.** PENDANT, of amber-coloured glass, with the Good Shepherd in relief.
*See* figure.

L. ·8 in. 1900. The loop broken. Probably from a necklace.
Cf. two similar pendants from Syria with different subjects, Garrucci, *Storia*, pl. 479, figs. 20, 21; *see also* Chabouillet, *Camées et pierres gravées de la Bibl. Impériale*, nos. 3474–5. This example and nos. 698–706 appear to date from the 3rd to the 5th or 6th century. The subjects of these pendants are not always Christian, some having, e. g. figures of the god Bes upon them.

**698.** ANOTHER, yellow; the same subject.

L. 1 in. Given by the Executors of Felix Slade, Esq., 1871. From Cyprus.

**699.** ANOTHER, amber-coloured; the same subject.

D. ·8 in. 1881. From Alexandria.

**700.** ANOTHER; the same colour and subject.

D. ·76 in. 1883. From Egypt.

**701.** ANOTHER, blue; Daniel wearing a tunic, and standing in the attitude of an *orans* between two lions.

D. ·82 in. Given by the Executors of Felix Slade, Esq., 1871. From Cyprus, Cesnola Coll.

T

**702.** ANOTHER ; same colour and subject.

> L. ·74 in.    Given by the Executors of Felix Slade, Esq., 1871.    From Cyprus, Cesnola Coll.

**703.** ANOTHER, amber-coloured.    The seven-branched candlestick between a horn (?) and a branch (?).

> L. ·9 in.    Franks Coll. 1889.    From Tyre.

**704.** ANOTHER, pale green ; the same subject.

> L. ·94 in.    1882.

**705.** ANOTHER, of blue glass, with loop for suspension.    On one side a cross pattée in relief between four dots inscribed in a circle.

> L. 1·22 in.    1891.

**706.** ANOTHER, pale green ; on one side ✳.

> D. ·66 in.    1875.

**707.** CROSS of translucent green glass, pierced for suspension.

> L. 1·4 in.    1882.

**708.** ANOTHER, imperfect.

> L. 1·4 in.    1876.

**709.** ANOTHER.

> L. 1·2 in.    1880.

**710.** SEAL FROM A BOTTLE of greyish-green glass, with ☦ in relief within a pearled border.

> D. 1·72 in.    1881.    From Alexandria.

**711.** DISC of opaque green glass, with a cross pattée in relief within a cable border. Pierced for suspension.

> D. ·7 in.    1888.    From Akhmîm (Panopolis).

**712.** ANOTHER, with a cross in relief within a circle of raised dots.

> D. 1 in.    1878.    Formerly in the Garthe Coll., Cologne.

# VII. POTTERY.

## A. Lamps.

*4th to 7th century.*

### i. From Carthage, Sicily, Italy, &c.

Where no description of the shape of the lamp is given, it is understood that the type resembles no. 714, pl. xxxii. The majority of the specimens are of a rather bright red ware, but they vary considerably in fineness of execution.

**713.** FRAGMENT ; half of a lamp with loop-handle ; a rosette bordered by a raised inscription /// VIVAS IN ⚹ ; on the bottom, the letters NIVI, impressed.
*4th century.*

    L. 4 in. Sloane Coll. no. 1073. 1753.
    In the MS. Catalogue of the Sloane Coll. the inscription is given as HERENNIA POR VIVAS IN ⚹, so that at the time the entry was made the lamp must have been complete. It belongs to an earlier type than those which follow. Cf. de Rossi, *Bullettino*, 1875, p. 152.

**714.** MALE BUST, wearing a chlamys and Phrygian cap, and holding in the *l.* hand a staff resembling a standard. Border of concentric circles, flowers and chevrons. On the bottom two concentric circles.
*Plate* XXXII.

    L. 5·3 in. Towneley Coll. 1805.
    Cf. Garrucci, *Storia*, vol. vi, pl. 476, fig. 2 ; Delattre in *Rev. de l'Art Chrétien*, 1892, p. 139, no. 740, and 1893, p. 38, no. 906. The mark on the bottom is common on Carthaginian lamps.

**715.** AN IMPERIAL (?) BUST to *l.* ; border of chevrons, quatrefoils and concentric circles.

    L. 5·44 in. Towneley Coll. 1805.
    Cf. Garrucci, *Storia*, vol. vi, pl. 476, fig. 1 (lamp in Museo Kircheriano).

**716.** BEARDLESS BUST to *l.*, within a wreath. Border of palmettes, cinquefoils and heart-shaped leaves, having at one end a rectangle containing the sacred monogram ⚹.

    L. 4·42 in.
    Cf. Delattre in *Rev. de l'Art Chrétien*, 1892, no. 702, p. 137 (in Musée de St. Louis, Carthage).

**717.** SIMILAR BUST. Border of concentric circles, squares inscribed with circles, and palmettes.

    L. 4·38 in. Given by Lord Stratford de Redcliffe, 1856. Obtained at Calymnus.

**718.** JONAH lying under the gourd, before him the monster with open mouth. Border of dolphins alternating with heart-shaped leaves.
*Plate* XXXII.

> L. 5·36 in. Sloane Coll. no. 620. 1753.
> Cf. Garrucci, *Storia*, vol. vi, pl. 475, fig. 5; Delattre, *Rev. de l'Art Chrét.* 1892, p. 134, no. 675; Kraus, *Real-Encykl.* vol. ii, p. 271, fig. 112.

**719.** MALE FIGURE, holding a shield in his *r.* and in his *l.* a spear, with which he menaces a lion. Border of concentric circles terminating at each end in a chevron.

> L. 6·2 in. Sloane Coll. no. 621. 1753.
> For a similar scene from the amphitheatre upon a lamp cf. Stuhlfauth in *Mittheilungen des kaiserlich deutschen Archäologischen Instituts* (Rome, 1898), p. 286.

**720.** DANIEL standing between two lions in the attitude of an *orans,* and wearing a girded tunic. To *l.* is an angel, to *r.* Habakkuk holding out a cake. Border of alternating squares and concentric circles.

> L. 5·42 in. 1860. From Carthage.
> Cf. Stuhlfauth, as above, pl. x, fig. 6; Delattre, as above, 1892, p. 135, nos. 676 ff.; Le Blant in *Rev. de l'Art Chrétien,* 1875, p. 91; Kraus, *Real-Encykl.* vol. ii, p. 273, fig. 118.

**721.** OUR LORD holding a long cross and standing upon a dragon. Border of concentric circles and quatrefoils.

> L. 5·25 in. 1860. From Carthage.
> Cf. Stuhlfauth, as above, pl. ix, fig. 8; Delattre, as above, 1892, p. 136; Forrer, *Frühchristl. Altertümer,* pl. iv, fig. 2 (example from Cologne); de Rossi, *Bullettino,* 1867, pp. 9–16, 1874, pp. 129 ff., 1887, p. 164, 1890, p. 13; Garrucci, *Storia,* vol. vi, pl. 466, fig. 2; *Rev. Arch.* xiii (1889), pl. viii, fig. 33; La Blanchère et Gauckler, *Cat. du Musée Alaoui,* p. 195, nos. 499-501.

**722.** YOUTHFUL FIGURE in a striped tunic standing and holding a hare on his breast. Border of doves and ornamental squares. On the bottom a mark in the form of a reversed S.

> L. 4·34 in. 1857. From Carthage.
> Cf. Stuhlfauth, as above, p. 287, pl. v, fig. 19; La Blanchère et Gauckler, *Cat. du Musée Alaoui,* no. 521, p. 196; Delattre, as above, 1892, p. 133, nos. 662, 663. For the mark cf. Delattre, *ibid.* 1890, no. 22, p. 134, &c.

**723.** THREE FIGURES in short tunics standing in a line. Border of sixfoils and leaves.

> L. 4·1 in. 1857. From Carthage. Perhaps the Three Children of Babylon after their rescue.
> Cf. Stuhlfauth, as above, p. 286, pl. x, fig. 14; Delattre, as above, 1892, p. 133.

**724.** THREE SIMILAR FIGURES. Border of sixfoils and leaves.

> L. 4·5 in. 1857. From Carthage.

**725.** STANDING FIGURE in a tunic, drawing a sword (?). Border of concentric circles alternating with heart-shaped leaves.

> L. 5·62 in. Sloane Coll. no 1101. 1753.
> Cf. Delattre, as above, 1892, nos. 735, 736, and 742, p. 139.

**726.** A HUNTER (?), carrying in one hand an animal; in the other, fruit (?). Border of squares alternating with butterflies.

    L. 4·5 in. 1857. From Carthage.
    Cf. Stuhlfauth, as above, pl. x, fig. 21 ; Delattre, as above, 1892, nos. 726 and 727.

**727.** THE TWO SPIES, carrying the grapes of Eshcol on a pole across their shoulders. Beneath their feet is stamped another conventional bunch of grapes. Border of alternating doves and heart-shaped leaves. On the bottom two concentric circles.

    L. 5·26 in. 1860. From Carthage.
    Cf. Delattre, as above, 1892, pp. 133, 134 ; Stuhlfauth, as above, pl. x, fig. 16 ; de Rossi, *Bull.* 1887, p. 49 ; *Rev. Arch.* 1883, p. 50 ; Garrucci, *Storia*, vol. vi, pl. 475, fig. 3, and pl. 476, fig. 4 ; La Blanchère et Gauckler, *Cat. du Musée Alaoui*, no. 512, pl. xxxvi ; *R. Q. S.* 1887, pl. x, figs. 3 and 4, and 1899, p. 142.

**728.** A LION, seated. Border of quatrefoils with a dolphin in the centre of one side. On the bottom, concentric circles.

    L. 5 in. 1860. From Carthage.
    Cf. Delattre, as above, 1890, pp. 136–138, and 1893, p. 34 ; La Blanchère et Gauckler, as above, nos. 559–564 ; *Bulletin des Musées*, 1890, p. 291.

**729.** A LION, recumbent. Border of palmettes, rosettes and circles inscribed in squares.

    L. 4·6 in. Towneley Coll. 1805.

**730.** A LION, standing. Twisted border.

    L. 4 in. 1859. From Cnidus.

**731.** ANOTHER, walking. Arched border.

    L. 6·8 in. Sloane Coll. no. 622. 1753.

**732.** ANOTHER, running.

    L. 4·2 in. 1857. From Carthage.
    Cf. *Notizie degli Scavi*, 1885, p. 295, fig. 25.

**733.** ANOTHER, running. Border formed by two palm-branches.

    L. ·4 in. Sloane Coll. no. 603. 1753. Very rough work.
    Cf. lamps found at Syracuse, Orsi, *Di alcuni ipogei Cristiani*, &c., in *R. Q. S.* 1897, pl. ii, fig. 16, and pl. iii, fig. 16.

**734.** A STAG (?). Border of palm-branches.

    L. 4·46 in.
    For the stag cf. La Blanchère et Gauckler, as above, nos. 536, 537, p. 198.

**735.** A HOUND, running. Border of lozenges alternating with squares enclosing circles. On the bottom a circle.

    L. 3·75 in. 1857. From Carthage.
    Cf. Delattre, as above, 1891, nos. 162, 168, 171, p. 42. The mark is common on Carthaginian lamps.

**736**. A FOX.   Border of cinquefoils, pellets, and arches.

> L. 4·8 in.   Sloane Coll. no. 591.   1753.
> Cf. La Blanchère et Gauckler, as above, nos. 578, 579, pp. 200, 201.

**737**. A LAMB.   Border of concentric circles and other figures, much worn.

> L. 5·2 in.   1860.   From Carthage.
> Cf. Stuhlfauth, as above, pl. ix, fig. 13 ; *Bulletin des Musées*, 1890, p. 291 ; Delattre, as above, 1890, pp. 40-42 ; La Blanchère et Gauckler, as above, nos. 527-533, p. 197.

**738**. FRAGMENT, PART OF A LAMB.   Border of rosettes and squares.

> L. 3·5 in.   1857.   From Carthage.

**739**. AN IBEX, running.   Border of quatrefoils, branches, and concentric circles, with a palmette at one end.

> L. 4·5 in.   1860.   From Carthage.

**740**. FRAGMENT, A HARE (?).   Border of triangular leaves.

> L. 3·5 in.   1880.
> Cf. Delattre, as above, 1891, p. 40 ; Forrer, *Frühchristl. Altertümer*, pl. iv, fig. 4 (example from Cologne).

**741**. A DOVE.   Border of quatrefoils, concentric circles, interlaced designs, &c.

> L. 5·42 in.   1857.   From Carthage.
> Cf. Delattre, as above, 1891, pp. 44–46, and 1893, p. 35 ; La Blanchère et Gauckler, as above, nos. 544-552, p. 198 ; Venturi, *Storia dell' Arte Italiana*, vol. i, p. 473.

**742**. ANOTHER ; border of concentric circles and heart-shaped leaves.

> L. 5·6 in.   1860.   From Carthage.

**743**. ANOTHER ; border indistinct.

> L. 5·4 in.   1857.   From Carthage.

**744**. ANOTHER ; border of circles, quatrefoils and leaves.

> L. 4·1 in.   1857.   From Carthage.

**745**. TWO BIRDS, upon a vase with two handles.   Border of heart-shaped leaves and chevrons.

> L. 4·9 in.   1882.   Obtained in Naples.
> Cf. Delattre, as above, 1891, no. 259, p. 46 ; Forrer, *Frühchristl. Altertümer*, pl. v, fig. 1.

**746**. TWO BIRDS, beak to beak.   Border of concentric circles.

> L. 4·68 in.   1881.

**747**. TWO BIRDS, peacocks (?).   Border of squares, heart-shaped leaves and lozenges, with a dove at each end.   On the bottom a stamp B.

> L. 5·52 in.   1860.   From Carthage.
> For the stamp *see* Delattre, as above, 1890, no. 9, p. 134, no. 40, p. 136, and 1891, no. 151, p. 41, no. 190, p. 43, no. 595, p. 305, &c.

**748**. A COCK. Border of lozenges and quatrefoils.

 L. 4·62 in. Sloane Coll. no. 601. 1753.
 Cf. Delattre, as above, 1890, pp. 46, 47 ; Stuhlfauth, as above, 1898, pl. ix, fig. 15 ; La Blanchère et Gauckler, as above, p. 198, nos. 541–543 ; Orsi, *Di alcuni ipogei Cristiani a Siracusa*, in *R. Q. S.* 1897, pl. ii, fig. 5 ; Cherbonneau, *Album du Musée de Constantine*, pl. vi, no. 666.

**749**. ANOTHER ; border of concentric circles alternating with squares inscribed with circles.

 L. 4·4 in. 1867. From Ephesus.

**750**. A BIRD with long beak within a wreath. On the bottom a stamp in the form of a branch within a pear-shaped loop.

 L. 4·64 in. 1860. From Carthage.

**751**. A FISH. Border of concentric circles, squares inscribed with circles, and heart-shaped leaves.

 L. 5·32 in. 1857. From Carthage.
 Cf. Delattre, as above, 1890, p. 134 ; Forrer, *Frühchristl. Altertümer*, pl. ii, figs. 1–4 ; La Blanchère et Gauckler, as above, p. 200, nos. 571–574 ; Roller, *Les Catacombes de Rome*, pl. xc, fig. 5 ; *Notizie degli Scavi*, 1885, p. 295.

**752**. ANOTHER ; border of squares and heart-shaped leaves.

 L. 5·4 in. 1860. From Carthage.

**753**. A DOLPHIN (?). Border of circles, heart-shaped leaves, quatrefoils, &c. The whole worn and indistinct.

 L. 4·6 in. 1857. From Carthage.
 For the dolphin on terra cotta lamps cf. Delattre, as above, 1890, pp. 134 f. ; La Blanchère et Gauckler, as above, nos. 553–555, p. 199 ; *Bulletin des Musées*, 1890, p. 291.

**754**. A PALM-TREE. Border of quatrefoils and concentric circles.

 L. 4·24 in. 1889. Obtained at Pozzuoli.
 For N. African lamps with the palm-tree *see* Delattre, as above, 1891, p. 50 ; La Blanchère et Gauckler, as above, p. 205, nos. 621–633.

**755**. A VASE, from which issues a vine (?).

 L. 4·4 in. Given by Lord Stratford de Redcliffe, 1856. Obtained at Calymnus.

**756**. THE SEVEN-BRANCHED CANDLESTICK. Border of a double row of raised dots.

 L. 4·6 in. 1857. From Carthage.
 For the seven-branched candlestick on fictile lamps *see* Delattre, as above, 1891, p. 298 ; La Blanchère et Gauckler, as above, p. 201, nos. 589–591 ; de Voguë in *Rev. Arch.* 1889, pt. i, pp. 183, 184, and pl. viii ; d'Agincourt, *Recueil de fragments de sculpture antique en terre cuite*, pl. xxiv, fig. 3 (Paris, 1814). For lamps with similar border *see* Forrer, *Frühchristl. Altertümer*, pl. ii, fig. 6 ; Delattre, as above, 1889, p. 153.

**757**. ANOTHER, represented with nine branches. Border of two palm-branches. On the bottom are stamped three circles.

 L. 3 in. 1860. From Carthage.
 For the mark cf. Delattre, as above, 1890, p. 137.

**758.** THE SACRED MONOGRAM ⳩ jewelled.   Border of chevrons.

> L. 4·7 in.   Given by H. Martin Gibbs, Esq., 1900.
> Cf. Delattre, as above, 1891, pp. 299, 300 ; 1893, p. 36.

**759.** ANOTHER ; border of heart-shaped leaves.   On the bottom a stamped mark **V**.

> L. 4·94 in.   1857.   From Carthage.
> The mark is common on lamps from this locality, *see* Delattre, as above, 1890, p. 135, no. 26, &c.

**760.** ANOTHER, within a wreath.   Border of two palm-branches.

> L. 4·1.   1876.

**761.** ANOTHER ; border of two palm-branches.

> L. 3·92 in.   1860.   From Carthage.

**762.** ANOTHER ; similar border.

> L. 4·10 in.   Towneley Coll. 1805.

**763.** ANOTHER ; on the bottom is stamped a palm-branch.

> L. 3·9 in.
> For the mark cf. Delattre, as above, 1891, p. 39, no. 111, &c.

**764.** ANOTHER ; border of concentric circles alternating with quatrefoils.

> L. 4 in.   1857.   From Carthage.

**765.** THE SACRED MONOGRAM reversed, ⳩, within a wreath.   Border of chevrons alternating with concentric circles.

> L. 5·3 in.   Given by H. Martin Gibbs, Esq., 1900.
> For the reversed monogram *see* Delattre, as above, 1891, pp. 300, 301.

**766.** ANOTHER ; border of concentric circles, lozenges and flowers.

> L. 4·6 in.   Towneley Coll. 1805.

**767.** ANOTHER ; border of two palm-branches.

> L. 4·54 in.   Towneley Coll. 1805.

**768.** ANOTHER ; border of concentric semicircles.   On the bottom is stamped a palm-branch.

> L. 4·6 in.   Given by H. Martin Gibbs, Esq., 1900.

**769.** ANOTHER, having beneath it a two-handled vase.   Border of chevrons alternating with scrolls.

> L. 4 in.   1877.   Imperfect.

**770.** ANOTHER, lower part only.   Border of concentric circles, a palmette, a leaf, and a quatrefoil.

> L. 3·5 in.   1857.   From Carthage.   Imperfect.

**771.** THE SACRED MONOGRAM, *crux monogrammatica,* ☧, jewelled. Border of quatrefoils and leaves.

L. 5·15 in. 1860. From Carthage.

For this form of monogram on Carthaginian lamps *see* Delattre, as above, 1891, p. 300, and 1893, p. 37; La Blanchère et Gauckler, as above, nos. 619 ff., p. 204.

**772.** ANOTHER, jewelled. Border of squares alternating with circles enclosing the monogram ☧.

L. 5·6 in. 1847. Found at El-Jem in Tunis.

**773.** ANOTHER; border of leaves, &c., much worn.

L. 4·94 in. 1876. From Syracuse.

**774.** ANOTHER; border of quatrefoils.

L. 4·42 in. 1857. From Carthage.

**775.** ANOTHER; border of concentric circles, rosettes, &c.

L. 4·2 in. 1856. From Sardinia.

**776.** ANOTHER; border of alternating sixfoils and leaves.

L. 5 in. Towneley Coll. 1805. From Syracuse.

**777.** ANOTHER; border of heart-shaped leaves.

L. 4·7 in. 1857. From Carthage.

**778.** THE SAME MONOGRAM REVERSED, ☧, and jewelled. Border of heart-shaped leaves, having on each side of the handle a vase (?), and at each lower end concentric circles.

L. 4·35 in. Given by Lord Stratford de Redcliffe, 1856. Obtained at Calymnus.
For the *crux monogrammatica* reversed *see* Delattre, as above, 1891, pp. 303, 304; 1893, p. 37.

**779.** ANOTHER; border of heart-shaped leaves with a cross at one end.

L. 5·26 in. Sloane Coll. no. 623. 1753.

**780.** ANOTHER; border of conventional ornament much worn.

L. 5·32 in. 1857. From Carthage.

**781.** ANOTHER; border of quatrefoils with dolphins? in three places.

L. 5·2 in. 1857. From Carthage.

**782.** A CROSS JEWELLED; border of sixfoils alternating with heart-shaped leaves.

L. 4·5 in. 1860. From Carthage.
For N. African lamps with cross *see* Delattre, as above, 1891, pp. 304–7, and 1893, p. 37; La Blanchère et Gauckler, as above, nos. 594 ff., p. 203; Stuhlfauth, as above, xiii (1898), pl. ix, figs. 9 and 12.

**783.** ANOTHER; border of quatrefoils, &c., much worn.

L. 3·32 in. Temple Bequest, 1856. Obtained in Pozzuoli.

U

**784.** ANOTHER; border of squares inscribed with circles alternating with concentric circles.

> L. 5·44 in. 1857. From Carthage.

**785.** A CROSS PATTÉE ; border of quatrefoils and circular flowers.

> L. 4·9 in. 1857. From Carthage.

**786.** ANOTHER, jewelled ; border of heart-shaped leaves.

> L. 4·6 in. 1857. From Carthage.
> Cf. Forrer, *Frühchristl. Altertümer*, pl. iii, fig. 12 (Akhmîm).

**787.** ANOTHER ; identical border.

> L. 5·15 in. 1860. From Carthage.

**788.** ANOTHER ; identical border.

> L. 4·7 in. 1857. From Carthage.

**789.** ANOTHER; border of quatrefoils, &c.

> L. 4·96 in. 1857. From Carthage.

**790.** ANOTHER ; border of heart-shaped leaves.

> L. 4 in. Given by Major-General Meyrick, 1878.

**791.** ANOTHER ; border of bearded heads, originally twelve in number and representing the Apostles.

> L. 3·94 in. 1881. Upper part only.
> For lamps with a similar border of Apostles' heads *see* Perret, *Les Catacombes de Rome*, vol. iv, pl. xiii, fig. 2 ; Roller, *Les Catacombes*, pl. xci, fig. 4 ; de Rossi, *Bullettino*, 1867, pp. 25 and 27, and 1883, p. 98 ; Garrucci, *Storia*, vol. vi, pl. 473, figs. 1, 2, and 5 ; Tourret in *Rev. Arch.* 1883, p. 49.

**792.** A CROSS WITHIN A SQUARE PANEL ; border of leaves, much worn.

> L. 4·5 in. 1857. From Carthage.

**793.** A CROSS ; border of leaves and flowers. The handle pierced.

> L. 3·24 in. Given by Major-General Meyrick, 1878.

**794.** A SCALLOP SHELL ; ribbed border. On the bottom is stamped a mark.

> L. 6·3 in. Sloane Coll. no. 619. 1753.
> With the shell cf. Delattre, as above, 1891, p. 296, and La Blanchère et Gauckler, as above, nos. 592, 593, p. 202. With the mark cf. Delattre, 1890, p. 135, nos. 26 ff.

**795.** GEOMETRICAL DESIGN ; a square ornamented with lozenges and triangles forming a St. Andrew's cross. Border of concentric circles, scrolls, quatrefoils, &c.

> L. 6 in. Given by Lord Stratford de Redcliffe, 1856. Obtained at Calymnus.
> For lamps with geometrical ornament *see* Delattre, as above, 1891, p. 308 ; La Blanchère et Gauckler, as above, p. 201, nos. 584–588, and pl. xxxvi.

**796**. THE LETTER I, jewelled ; border of concentric circles alternating with squares.

L. 4·2 in. Given by Lord Stratford de Redcliffe, 1856. Obtained at Calymnus. It has been suggested that the character represents the first letter of the name Jesus.

**797**. A LOZENGE, jewelled with a triangular projection on each side. Border of heart-shaped leaves alternating with sixfoils.

L. 4·42 in. 1857. From Carthage.

**798**. A SQUARE ; border of concentric semicircles alternating with S-scrolls.

L. 4 in. Given by Lord Stratford de Redcliffe, 1856. Obtained at Calymnus.

**799**. A ROSETTE ; border of two palm-branches.

L. 3 in. 1857. From Carthage.
Cf. Delattre, as above, 1891, pp. 296, 297, and La Blanchère et Gauckler, as above, pp. 205, 206, nos. 634–642.

**800**. TWO TRIANGLES interlaced, with concentric circles within the angles ; border of chevrons alternating with quatrefoils.

L. 3·75 in. 1877.

**801**. AN ARCH (?).

L. 5 in. 1860. From Carthage.

**802**. INDISTINGUISHABLE DESIGN ; the surface much worn.

L. 5·3 in. 1860. From Carthage.

**803**. ANOTHER.

L. 4 4 in.

**804**. MOULD, for the upper part of a lamp. In the centre an ibex (?), on the neck a figure in the attitude of an *orans* ; geometrical border.

L. 5·8 in. 1881.
For other lamp-moulds *see* La Blanchère et Gauckler, as above, nos. 396, 397, p. 253 ; Doublet et Gauckler, *Cat. du Musée de Constantine*, p. 60 ; Clermont-Ganneau in *Archives des Missions scientifiques et littéraires*, vol. xi (1885), p. 183.

## ii. From Egypt, Syria, and Asia Minor.

The lamps from these countries are more varied in form, but most of them approximate to the outline types A—E on p. 148. The larger number have only a single hole for pouring in the oil, and are commonly made of a paler ware than the lamps found at Carthage.

**805**. OVATE, of red pottery. The top is convex, with a flat central disk on which is a monogram ✕ interpunctuated with circles. Above the spout is a cross between two beardless busts to *r*. Round the inscription : ЄΥΜΟΡΦΟΙ ΚΑΛ// (εὐμόρφῳ καλῷ).
*Plate* XXXII.

L. 3·54 in.  Given by H. Martyn Kennard, Esq., 1894.  From the ruins of the town of Coptos.
Inscribed lamps mostly come from Egypt.  *See* V. Schultze, *Arch. der altchristl. Kunst*, p. 299;
de Rossi, *Bullettino*, 1866, p. 72, 1877, p. 70, 1879, p. 32, and pl. iii, fig. 2, 1880, p. 73, 1882,
p. 109, 1884, p. 33; d'Agincourt, *Recueil de fragments de sculpture antique en terre cuite*,
pl. xxii, fig. 14; Forrer, *Frühchristl. Altertümer*, pl. i, fig. 11, and p. 12, pl. v, fig. 4.  Other
inscribed examples are in the Department of Egyptian and Assyrian Antiquities.

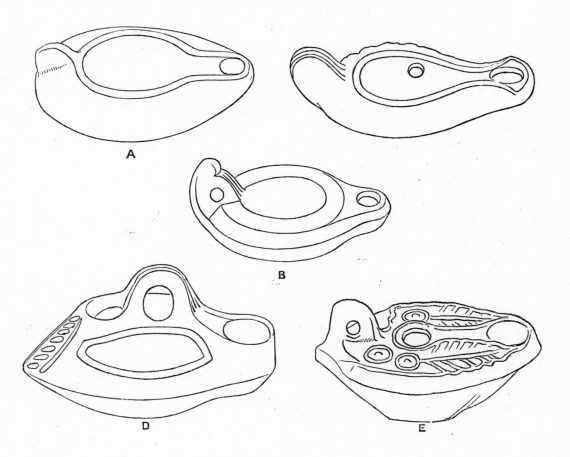

**806.** UPPER PART of a lamp, pear-shaped, of buff ware.  At the top a foliate design
  with a number of small circles; round the sides the inscription: ΤΟΥ ΑΓΙΟΥ
  (A)BBA ΔΙΟΥ with a leaf at each end.

L. 3·2 in.  1876.  From Egypt.

The inscription probably refers to a saint whose name began with ΔΙ, perhaps Dionysius.
The word *Abba* at the beginning of the name is a prefix used as a mark of honour, and occurs on a
lamp, *C.I.G.* vol. iv (1877), 8981.  Cf. *Le Musée Archéologique*, 1876, p. 125; and G. Schlumberger
in *Byz. Zeitschr.* vol. ii (1893), p. 178.  It is also found on silver dishes in the Gizeh Museum,
which will be included in the forthcoming volume on Coptic Monuments forming part of the
*Catalogue Général.*

**807.** FLAT ALMOND-SHAPED ; on the top a small cross potent above a vertical band of nine disks, the whole enclosed within a border of three raised bands.

L. 4·4 in. 1879. From Luxor.

**808.** LAMP OF TYPE A (*see* p. 148) ; a cross pattée with a pellet enclosed in each limb. Broad border of small bosses.

L. 3·72 in. Given by T. W. U. Robinson, Esq., 1886.

**809.** ANOTHER ; a cross pattée with three pellets in each limb.

L. 5 in. 1877.

**810.** ANOTHER, circular, with prominent spout and no handle ; large central opening with conventional border. On the neck is impressed a palm-branch, and on the bottom three palm-branches united at their bases.

L. 3 in. 1881.

**811.** ANOTHER, OF TYPE A, with single hole for oil ; border of small circles.

L. 3·8 in. 1871. From Alexandria.

**812.** ANOTHER, resembling in form no. 835 ; it has a single large opening, between which and the spout is impressed a palm-branch. Round the sides a debased Cufic inscription in relief.

L. 3·66 in. Given by E. J. Rogers Bey. 1883. Found in the ruins of Fostât.
On lamps with Cufic and Arabic inscriptions cf. Clermont-Ganneau, *Archaeological Researches in Palestine during the years* 1873 *and* 1874, vol. i, p. 69 (London, 1899) ; the same author in *Recueil d'Arch. Orientale*, vol. ii, pp. 19 and 67 ; in *Archives des Missions scientifiques et littéraires*, vol. xi (1885), no. 81, p. 190, and in *Rev. Arch.* 1898, pt. ii, pp. 296, 297. The earliest of these lamps probably date from a period soon after the Arab invasions of Egypt and Syria, the latest may go down to the middle ages. There is in the Department a small almond-shaped lamp, approximating to the Christian forms, bearing in Arabic characters the inscription, 'perpetual honour to the owner,' such as is found on pottery of the Mameluke period.

**813.** ANOTHER, with prominent spout, above which is a cross pattée ; on each side a diagonal band of geometrical ornament, and at the back a St. Andrew's cross.

L. 3·9 in. 1880. From Alexandria.

**814.** ANOTHER, OF TYPE A (*see* p. 148), but with a loop-handle ; a rudely executed human figure standing between two palms ; twisted border.

L. 3·38 in. 1882. From Alexandria.
Cf. a border of a Syracusan lamp, Orsi, *Di alcuni ipogei Cristiani a Siracusa*, in *R. Q. S.* 1897, pl. ii, fig. 2.

**815.** ANOTHER, of the same type, and with the same design. On the bottom is a cross with bifurcating ends between dots in four groups of three, and within a border of dots in larger groups, concentric circles and S-shaped lines.

L. 3 in. 1882.

**816.** ANOTHER, same type, but with loop-handle; a cross pattée between four palm-branches. Dark red pottery.

L. 4.3 in. 1876. From Egypt.

**817.** ANOTHER, same type the seven-branched candlestick.

L. 3.46 in. Given by T. W. U. Robinson, Esq., 1886. From Alexandria.
Cf. Forrer, *Frühchristl. Altertümer*, pl. ii, fig. 5.

**818.** ANOTHER, same type; the same subject.

L. 3.56 in. 1877.

**819.** LAMP IN THE FORM OF A FROG, of grey pottery. On the bottom is impressed a cross formed of palm-branches.
*Plate* XXXII.

L. 3.12 in. Given by the Rev. G. J. Chester, 1878. From Egypt.
Cf. de Rossi, *Bullettino*, 1879, p. 32, and pl. iii, fig. 2; d'Agincourt, *Recueil de fragments de sculpture antique en terre cuite*, pl. xxviii, fig. 4; Forrer, *Frühchristl. Altertümer*, pl. iii, fig. 17. The frog is supposed to have been the mark of a heretic, *see* E. Le Blant, *Notes sur quelques lampes égyptiennes en forme de grenouille*, in *Mémoires de la Société Nationale des Antiquaires de France*, vol. xxxix (1878), pp. 99 ff.; and the same author in *Rev. Arch.* xxxvii (1879), pp. 87 and 243. Cf. also no. 360 above.

**820.** LOWER HALF OF A LAMP, ovate. In the centre of the bottom a cross potent; at the broader end a similar but smaller cross; at the narrower end a palm-branch.

L. 4 in. 1879. From Egypt.

**821.** LAMP WITH PROJECTING SPOUT, of red pottery. The flat body is rounded at the back and angular in front. In the centre is a square enclosing a central cross pattée surrounded by four similar smaller crosses. Border of conventional flowers and small circles.
*See* figure.

L. 4.3 in. 1879. From Abydos, Egypt.
Cf. a Syracusan lamp, Orsi in *R. Q. S.* 1897, pl. ii, fig. 12.

**822.** ALMOND-SHAPED, elongated and with loop-handle. Near the handle is a rosette, in the centre of which is the opening ; below this is a cross pattée. The border is a band of zigzag with small circles in the angles.

*Plate* XXXII.

L. 5·76 in. 1876.

**823.** LAMP OF TYPE C ; on the top a cross. Border of vine-leaves and grapes.

L. 4·1 in. 1884.

**824.** LAMP OF TYPE A ; a cross within a wreath, with three circles between each of the arms.

L. 3·3 in. 1881.
Cf. a lamp from Akhmîm, Forrer, *Frühchristl. Altertümer*, pl. iii, fig. 3.

**825.** ANOTHER, similar ; a cross.

L. 3·5 in. 1878.

**826.** ANOTHER, of similar type ; the *crux monogrammatica* ⳨ ; on the bottom are stamped concentric circles.

L. 3·3 in. 1881.
Cf. lamp from Akhmîm, Forrer, *Frühchristl. Altertümer*, pl. iii, fig. 2 ; and another from Athens, V. Schultze in *Christliches Kunstblatt*, 1893, p. 18, fig. 2ᵃ.

**827.** ANOTHER, similar ; a cross with the limbs formed of short transverse bars. The border is a broken guilloche enclosing pyramidal bosses.

L. 3·5 in. 1882.

**828.** LAMP RESEMBLING TYPE C, with prominent spout and handle in the form of a cross. Border of scrolls.

L. 4·92 in. Franks Coll. 1892.

**829.** ANOTHER, with similar handle. Border of radiating lines.

L. 2·8 in. 1881.

**830.** LAMP OF TYPE A, but broad and shallow and with loop-handle. A seated figure holding a cross and cornucopiae.

L. 4·2 in. 1883.

**831.** LAMP OF TYPE D. The top and sides are ornamented with rude impressed geometrical designs, the bottom with concentric circles.

L. 5 in. Towneley Coll. 1805.
Cf. Forrer, *Frühchristl. Altertümer*, pl. ii, fig. 7 (Akhmîm) ; Perret, *Les Catacombes de Rome*, vol. iv, pl. xix, fig. 6 ; d'Agincourt, *Recueil de fragments de sculpture antique en terre cuite*, pl. xxvii, fig. 12.

**832.** ANOTHER ; on the top two lenticular panels and an impressed palm-branch.

L. 4·2 in.

**833.** LAMP OF TYPE B ; a peacock displayed.

    L. 3·56 in.   1878.

**834.** LAMP OF TYPE A, but convex at the top ; it is of exceptionally large size, and dark red in colour ; large central opening surrounded by a conventional border ; near the spout a cross with bifurcating ends.

    L. 5·36 in.   1878.

**835.** ALMOND-SHAPED ; on the top a concave circle with hole in the centre, and a cross ; on the sides two pairs of peacocks confronted eating berries.

    *See* figure.

    L. 4 in.  Given by the Rev. G. J. Chester, 1884. From Beyrût.

    Cf. a lamp from Sarfend, Clermont-Ganneau in *Archives des Missions scientifiques et littéraires,* vol. xi (1885), no. 105, p. 196.

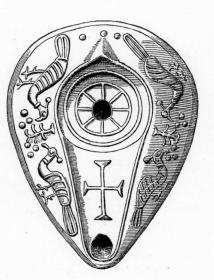

**836.** ANOTHER, similar ; the top ornamented with lozenges and pellets.   Border of vine-scrolls.

    L. 3·9 in.   1883.   From Beyrût.

**837.** ANOTHER, similar ; on the top a cross between dots in groups of three.   Border of scrolls.

    L. 4·1 in.   Franks Coll. 1894.   From Tyre.

**838.** LAMP IN THE SHAPE OF A SWATHED HUMAN FIGURE, the head rising to form a handle, the face on the inner side.

    L. 3·74 in.   Franks Coll. 1894.   From Tyre.

**839.** ANOTHER, of similar shape, but the face replaced by a cross.

    L. 3·5 in.   Franks Coll. 1894.   From Tyre.

**840.** LAMP OF TYPE B ; a cross with bifurcating ends ornamented with impressed concentric circles between four holes ; border of raised bosses.   The bottom is ornamented with small impressed circles and the under sides with radiating lines.

    L. 4·2 in.   1867.

    Cf. Forrer, *Frühchristl. Altertümer*, pl. iii, fig. 3.

**841.** ANOTHER ; border of radiating lines ; near the spout a cross.

    L. 3 in.   1867.   From Ephesus.

**842.** LAMP OF TYPE A, but convex at the top ; border of palm-branches (?) ; on the bottom and under sides small raised rings.

L. 3·73 in.  1853.  Very rude work.

Cf. lamp from Niané, Clermont-Ganneau, *Archives des Missions scientifiques et littéraires*, vol. xi (1885), p. 184.

**843.** ANOTHER, similar.

L. 3·82 in.  1853.  From Tarsus.

**844.** FLAT CIRCULAR LAMP, with large central opening surrounded by a border of geometrical ornament.  On the bottom is impressed a quadruped surmounted by a palm-branch, the whole within a circle.

L. 3·2 in.  1887.

This shape has been found at Syracuse, *see* Orsi, in *R. Q. S.* 1897, pl. i, fig. 5.

**845.** LAMP OF TYPE C, with two holes ; on the top a cross ; plaited border and fluted neck.

L. 3·7 in.  Given by Lord Stratford de Redcliffe, 1856.  Obtained at Calymnus.

**846.** ANOTHER, similar ; a cross, with a second smaller cross on the neck.  Border of small bosses.

L. 4·2 in.  Given by Lord Stratford de Redcliffe.  1856.

**847.** ANOTHER, similar ; a cross.  Border of circles containing dots.

L. 4 in.  Given by Lord Stratford de Redcliffe, 1856.  Obtained at Calymnus.

**848.** ANOTHER, similar ; an animal seizing a man by the leg.  Border of circles.

L. 3·8 in.  1884.

**849.** LAMP OF TYPE B ; a cross.  Border of small bosses.

L. 4 in.  Given by Lord Stratford de Redcliffe, 1856.

**850.** LAMP OF TYPE C ; the *crux monogrammatica* ⳨.

L. 4 in.  Given by Lord Stratford de Redcliffe, 1856.  Obtained at Calymnus.

**851.** ANOTHER, similar ; a palm-tree, below which is a cross.  Border of concentric circles.

L. 4 in.  1884.

**852.** ALMOND-SHAPED LAMP, resembling no. 835 above.  Single hole near the handle, between which and the spout is the figure ✖.  On each side a pair of peacocks confronted.

L. 3·52 in.  1883.  Obtained in Athens.

**853.** ANOTHER, elongated ; a cross pattée.

L. 4·5 in.  1883.  From Malta.  Very rough work.

**854.** ANOTHER, similar ; a cross pattée with border of two palm-branches.

> L. 4·54 in.   Towneley Coll. 1805.

**855.** LAMP OF TYPE E ; on each side of the handle a conical boss ; border formed of two palm-branches.

> L. 3·6 in.
> Cf. Perret, *Les Catacombes de Rome*, vol. iv, pl. xiii, fig. 3.

**856.** ANOTHER, similar, with a group of bosses near the handle.

> L. 3·8 in.

**857.** ANOTHER, similar, but with circles containing dots instead of bosses.

> L. 3·7 in.

**858.** ANOTHER, similar, but with ornament identical with no. 856.

> L. 3·7 in.   Sloane Coll. no. 1061.  1753.

**859.** ANOTHER, similar, with the same design.

> L. 3·7 in.   Sloane Coll. no. 1065.  1753.

## B. Pilgrims' Flasks.

Made at the shrines of various saints. They were filled with oil from the lamps burning at the tombs and carried away by pilgrims. The majority come from the shrine of St. Menas, near Alexandria, and are *ampullae*, with flat circular sides with designs in relief. The handles are in most cases imperfect.

> *4th to 6th century.*

**860.** AMPULLA ; St. Menas in tunic and chlamys, between two camels, and legend O ΑΓΙC (M H N)AC, the whole within a wreath ; *rev.* the same design within a border containing the retrograde inscription : TOY (AΓ) ΙOY MHNA ΕΥΟΛΟΓΙΑ ΛΑΒΟΜΕΝ. (Τοῦ Ἁγίου Μῆνα εὐλογίαν λάβομεν, We receive the blessing of St. Menas.)

> *Plate* XXXII.

> H. 5·5 in.  1875.
> Cf. E. Le Blant in *Rev. Arch.*, vol. xxxv (1878), pp. 299 ff. ; É. Michon, *La Collection d'Ampoules à Eulogie du Musée du Louvre*, in *Mélanges G.-B. de Rossi, Supplément aux Mélanges d'Archéologie et d'Histoire* (*École française de Rome*), 1892, pp. 183 ff. ; V. Schultze, *Arch. der altchristl. Kunst*, pp. 300 ff., and *Arch. Studien*, p. 282.

**861.** ANOTHER, identical on both sides ; St. Menas between two camels. On either side of the head : O ΑΓΙΟC | MHNA.

> H. 4·5 in.  1878.  Imperfect.

**862.** ANOTHER ; the same designs within wreaths. The inscriptions partially obliterated.

> H. 4·5 in.  1880.  From Alexandria.

**863.** ANOTHER ; the same designs.

H. 3·7 in.  1882.

**864.** ANOTHER ; the same designs ; a cross on each side of the saint's head ; border of bosses.

H. 3·75 in.  Franks Coll. 1876.

**865.** ANOTHER ; the same designs.

H. 3 in.  Given by Major-General Meyrick, 1878.

**866.** ANOTHER ; the same designs ; double pearled border.

H. 4 in.  Given by the Rev. G. J. Chester, 1886.

**867.** ANOTHER ; on one side the saint standing between two camels as before, with legend : ΕΥΛΟΓΙΑ ΚΥΡΙΟΥ ΕΠΙ ; on the other a cross with : ΤΟΥ ΑΓΙΟΥ ΜΗΝΑ.

H. 3·5 in.  1882.

**868.** ANOTHER ; on one side the saint as before ; on the other a cross surrounded by the legend, ΤΟΥ ΑΓΙΟΥ ΜΗΝΑ within a wreath.

H. 2·85 in.  1883.  Very rough work.

**869.** ANOTHER ; the same designs.

H. 2·5 in.  1877.  From Alexandria.

**870.** ANOTHER ; on one side the saint as before within a wreath ; on the other a cross without inscription within a border of bosses.

H. 3·75 in.  Franks Coll. 1880.

**871.** ANOTHER ; the same designs on a smaller scale.

H. 3·25 in.  1877.

**872.** ANOTHER ; the same designs ; a cross on each side of the saint's head.

H. 2·8 in.  1876.

**873.** ANOTHER ; on one side the saint as before ; on the other two crosses, one placed over the other, forming a star with eight rays within a dentated border.

H. 3·13 in.  1881.  From Alexandria.

**874.** ANOTHER ; on one side the saint as before within a pearled border ; on the other a circle enclosing a cross surrounded by six smaller circles containing dots.

H. 3·75 in.  1883.

**875.** ANOTHER ; on one side the saint as before ; on the other a rosette within a pearled border.

H. 2·75 in.  1876.

**876.** ANOTHER ; on one side the saint as before ; on the other the legend : ΕΥΛΟΓΙΑ ΤΟΥ ΑΓΙΟΥ ΜΗΝΑ within a wreath.

H. 4 in.  1876.

X 2

**877.** ANOTHER ; the same, with a slight variation in the inscription : ΑΓΙΟ(Υ) ΜΗΝΑ (Є)ΥΛΟΓ(ΙΑ).

H. 3·63 in. 1883.

**878.** ANOTHER ; the same.

H. 3·25 in. Given by Lord Stratford de Redcliffe, 1856. Obtained at Calymnus. One-half wanting.

**879.** ANOTHER ; the same ; the inscription obliterated.

H. 3·5 in. 1875. From Alexandria.

**880.** ANOTHER ; similar, but with inscription, ΕΥΛΟΓΙΑ ΤΟΥ ΑΓΙΟΥ, beneath which is a palm-branch.

H. 2·5 in. 1875. From Alexandria.

**881.** ANOTHER ; on one side the saint as before ; on the other $\frac{ЄΥΛ}{ΟΓΙΑ}$.

H. 3·5 in. 1875. Very rough work.

**882.** ANOTHER ; on one side the saint as before within a wreath ; on the other a female figure between two bulls and two dogs (?).
*Plate* XXXII.

H. 5·5 in. 1876. The surfaces considerably worn.

**883.** ANOTHER ; on one side the saint as before ; on the other a ship.
*Plate* XXXII.

H. 3·6 in. 1882.
Cf. *Archaeologia*, vol. xliv, p. 330 ; É. Michon, as above, p. 190, note 1.

**884.** ANOTHER ; on one side the saint as before ; on the other a bird (?).

H. 3·15 in. 1883. The surfaces much worn.

**885.** ANOTHER ; on one side the saint as before ; on the other an architectural design between a cross and an amphora (?).

H. 3·5 in. 1878. Imperfect.

**886.** ANOTHER ; on one side the saint as before ; on the other a female bust, full face.

H. 3·62 in. 1882. It has been suggested that the female head may represent St. Catherine. *See R. Q. S.*, 196, pp. 244 ff.

**887.** ANOTHER ; on one side the saint as before ; on the other a youthful head of negroid appearance to *r.* within a wreath.

H. 4·1 in. Given by Lord Stratford de Redcliffe, 1856.
On this negroid type, possibly representing a Libyan as representative of the peoples among whom St. Menas is said to have lived, *see* É. Michon, as above, pp. 188, 189 ; but *see also R. Q. S.*, as above, p. 246, where it is suggested that the negroid head may represent St. Peter of Alexandria or St. Anthony.

**888.** ANOTHER; on one side the same negroid head to *r.* within a double pearled border; on the other ЄУΛ|ОГІА ТО|УАГІОУ |МНΝА in four lines within a pearled circle.

H. 3·5 in. Franks Coll. 1876. Found in Egypt.

**889.** ANOTHER; the same head and inscription.

H. 3·75 in. Given by the Rev. G. J. Chester, 1883.

**890.** ANOTHER; identical.

H. 5·25 in. 1877.

**891.** ANOTHER; on one side the same head; on the other a cross, each within a wreath.

H. 3 in. Franks Coll. 1880.

**892.** ANOTHER; the same head on both sides.

H. 2·9 in. 1882.

**893.** ANOTHER; on one side $\frac{\text{ЄУΛ}}{\text{ОГІА}}$ ; on the other a cross within a wreath.

H. 4 in. Franks Coll. 1876. Found in Egypt.

**894.** ANOTHER; on one side ТОУ АГІОУ МНΝ, in two lines; on the other a cross within a wreath

H. 3 in. 1881.

**895.** ANOTHER; on one side ТОУ АГІОУ МНΝА; on the other a palm-tree.

H. 3·85 in. 1882.
Cf. É. Michon, as above, p. 190.

**896.** ANOTHER; on one side ✝ ЄУΛОГІА ХАРІС; on the other ТОУ АГІОУ МНΝА.

H. 3·25 in. 1882.

**897.** ANOTHER; on one side a cross between four pellets within a circle of geometrical patterns; on the other a larger cross.

H. 3 in. 1876. From Egypt.

**898.** ANOTHER; on each face a rosette within a pearled circle.

H. 3·5 in. 1883.

**899.** ANOTHER; on both sides concentric pearled circles within wreaths.

H. 3 in. 1881. From Egypt.

**900.** ANOTHER; concentric circles on one side.

H. 3·25 in. 1881.

**901.** ANOTHER; on each side an eagle (?) impressed.

H. 3·5 in. 1875. From Alexandria. Very rude work.

**902.** ANOTHER ; on each side a bird.

H. 2·65 in.   1877.   From Egypt.

**903.** LARGE AMPULLA, of red ware.   To *l.* the Virgin holding the Child (?), to *r.* a bearded figure standing to *l.* and holding a book in both hands, each figure under a rounded arch. Behind the man is a cock perched on a column. In the spandril between the arches is a cock, while below are three goats.   On the other side the same design, with the exception that below are a goat and two cocks.

*See* figure.

H. 7·65 in.   1882.

**904.** ANOTHER, of pale ware ; on one side a horseman (? St. George) to *r.* piercing a dragon (?) with a lance; on the other two pairs of animals fighting, with a single animal behind.

H. 5·65 in.   1882.

**905.** OVAL FLASK of red ware, pierced at the shoulders.   On each side a cross within a wreath.

H. 3·75 in.   Given by Lord Stratford de Redcliffe, 1856.

**906.** ANOTHER ; a cross on each side.

H. 2·65 in.   1883.   From Ephesus.

**907.** ANOTHER ; on each side a cross with bifurcating ends.

H. 2·85 in.   1876.

**908.** ANOTHER ; on each side a cross within a wreath.

H. 2·5 in.   Franks Coll. 1891.   From Smyrna.

**909.** ANOTHER; on one side K̄Ȳ ƐΛƐΗΟΝ; on the other TH CIONKET///, the inscription in each case having above it three arches surmounted by a cross between two palm-branches, and below it a bird.

> H. 3·8 in. Franks Coll. 1876. Found in Egypt.

**910.** ANOTHER; on one side a long-bearded evangelist (?) holding over his breast an open book, on which are the letters AΓ///, and having in his *l.* hand a cross; on the other a standing beardless figure in a mantle, holding a book over his breast with both hands.

> H. 2·75 in. 1887.
> Cf. É. Michon, as above, pp. 194 ff.

**911.** ANOTHER; the same subjects.

> H. 2·55 in. 1877.

**912.** ANOTHER; on one side a saint with long hair and beard standing between two palms, and holding a book over his breast with both hands; on the other a bearded figure (an evangelist?) seated to *r.* at a desk and writing in a book.

> H. 2·65 in. 1883. From Ephesus.
> Cf. a flask in the Louvre, É. Michon, as above, pp. 195, 196.

**913.** ANOTHER; on each side a half-length bearded figure holding a book over the breast.

> H. 2·65 in. Franks Coll. 1892.

**914.** ANOTHER; on each side a beardless figure (St. George or St. Theodore), full-face, standing upon a serpent or dragon. He wears a short tunic and holds a lance with cruciform end in his *l.* hand.

> H. 2·8 in. Given by Lord Stratford de Redcliffe, 1856. Obtained at Calymnus.

**915.** ANOTHER; on one side three beardless figures in a boat, the central person larger than the others; on the other a single figure standing beneath a pointed arch, holding a book over his breast with his *l.* hand and touching a cup (?) with his *r.*

> H. 5·65 in. 1882.

## C. Other objects of Pottery.

**916.** BOWL of buff ware covered with a vitreous glaze. In the interior is a subject incised in the paste; on the outside a chequer pattern, the squares of which are alternately blue and white.

*Interior.* The bottom is occupied by a three-quarter figure of our Lord seated, with his *r.* hand extended and open; the position of the *l.* hand is uncertain, as the bowl is imperfect at this point, but it very probably held a book. The head, which is surrounded by a cruciferous nimbus, is bearded and almost enclosed by long flowing hair ; on each check is a small circle. The costume consists of a richly embroidered tunic, and a mantle hanging down over the *l.* shoulder, but only drawn slightly forward over the *r.* Across the middle of the bowl, and visible on each side of the figure, are three parallel lines. Above these, and near the shoulders, are two circular medallions, that above the *r.* shoulder with a profile head evidently intended for Constantine the Great, the other with a similar profile of the Empress Fausta. Round the edge is a band formed of two groups of three lines, having between them the inscription

/// VAL · COSTANTINVS · PIVS · FELIX · AVGVSTVS · CVM · FLAV · MAX · FAVST//// which when perfect probably commenced : ✝ FLAV. and terminated // A AVGVSTA.

*Exterior.* The chequer pattern has its outlines in relief, and the hollows filled alternately with white slip and light blue glaze. The foot-rim encloses radiating lines in relief glazed a canary yellow. The chequer design may be compared with the Roman enamelled Rudge cup at Alnwick (Horsley, *Britannia Romana*, p. 192, no. 74, London, 1732).

*Plate* XXXIII, and *see* figure.

D. 5·06 in. H. 2 in. Given by The Friends of The British Museum, 1901.

H. Wallis, *Typical Examples of Egyptian Ceramic Art*, &c., pl. xii (London, 1900). *See also* Strzygowski, *Orient oder Rom*, pp. 61 ff. (Leipzig, 1901).

This interesting bowl is remarkable for its style, date, and technical peculiarities. The incised lines of the subject and of the inscription, as well as the white squares of the exterior, have been filled up with a fine white slip; while the whole has been covered somewhat unequally with a vitreous glaze, which has in the thicker parts a pale greenish tinge, and is full of bubbles of varying sizes. The chemical changes which have followed upon long burial in the soil have altered the relative qualities of glaze and body, so that the incised subject is no longer as clearly visible as without doubt it was originally intended to be; but upon immersing the whole bowl in water, the saturation of the body darkens its tint, and thus allows the white colour which fills the incised lines to be clearly seen. The bowl was bought by the late Count Tyszkiewicz from a dealer in Rome, who professed to be unaware of the existence of the subject in the interior, and to have only discovered the fact by accident in the process of washing. For the reasons stated below it was probably found in Egypt, but may have remained for some time in Rome, as pieces of pottery of quite a different class but with the same incised design have been counterfeited in imitation of it.

The bowl is probably to be attributed to Egypt not only on account of the method of its manufacture but also from the treatment of the figure of our Lord. Thus the manner in which the mantle is worn is characteristic of other Egyptian monuments (Strzygowski, as above, pp. 63, 64). The busts in medallions on either side of our Lord's head may be paralleled by other examples, while the cruciform nimbus does not imply a late date, for, contrary to the former belief, its use as early as the 4th century has already been proved. The whole figure of Christ is indeed of the greatest importance to the study of Byzantine iconography (Strzygowski, as above, pp. 63 ff.).

The circumstances connected with the death of the Empress Fausta make it certain that any object on which she is represented with her husband could only have been made during her lifetime, i. e. before 329. The inscription is correct in form, but the omission of the first N in the name of Constantine caused the genuineness of the bowl to be called in question by Professor Strzygowski, who has recently, however, changed his opinion (as above, p. 64, and *Byz. Zeitschr.* vol. x (1901), p. 734). The omission is certainly very unusual, but would appear to be not unexampled (cf. *C. I. L.* vol. viii, no. 10,035; and Mommsen, *Ephemeris Epigraphica*, vol. v, no. 10,999). In Greek the omission of the *n* is more frequent, and it is not unnatural to suppose that if the bowl was made in a place where Greek was commonly spoken, the Latin spelling of the name may have been influenced by the vulgar pronunciation. The whole appearance of the bowl is such as to make it difficult to believe that it could have been produced in modern times; and it may therefore be claimed as a unique example of the ceramic industry of the late Empire. From a technical point of view it is admirable, showing that perfection of the potter's art which might be expected in a town like Alexandria, where the craftsmen of Egypt practised their inherited skill for the benefit of the wealthy citizens of the Empire.

**917.** CIRCULAR STAMP, with pierced conical handle engraved with a cross with double traverse, having on either side o the shaft in two lines $\overline{\text{IC}}$ $\overline{\text{X}}$ | θ |Є ('Ιησοῦς Χριστὸς Θεοῦ υἱός ?).

> D. 1·9 in. 1856.

**918.** ANOTHER; with a cross pattée.
> *About the 6th century.*

> D. 3·6 in. 1892.
> Cf. stamps found at Akhmîm (Panopolis), Forrer, *Frühchristl. Altertümer*, pl. i and ix.

**919.** ANOTHER; a horseman (St. George ?) transfixing a dragon. Above, letters of mutilated inscription.

> L. 2·2 in. 1874. Found on the site of the temple of Diana at Ephesus.

**920.** ANOTHER, with cylindrical handle; the *crux monogrammatica* ☧, with a small cross within the loop.

*5th century.*

H. 1·4 in. 1882.

**921.** ANOTHER; a nimbed figure standing in the attitude of an *orans*. To *l.* a bird with long neck, to *r.* an indeterminate object.

*About the 6th century.*

D. 2·6 in. Given by E. J. Rogers Bey, 1883. Probably found near Cairo.

**922.** ANOTHER, with conical handle; a cross within a quatrefoil border.

*About the 6th century.*

D. 4 in. 1881.

**923.** FRAGMENT OF A PLATE, of fine red pottery impressed with a jewelled cross within a circle.

*5th or 6th century.*

L. 3·36 in. 1882.

Cf. Delattre, in *Revue de l'Art Chrétien*, 1893, p. 39; Doublet et Gauckler, *Le Musée de Constantine*, p. 62 (Paris, 1892); La Blanchère et Gauckler, *Catalogue du Musée Alaoui*, pp. 246, 247, nos. 343–355 (Paris, 1897); Stuhlfauth in *Mitt. K. D. A. I.* vol. xiii (1898), pp. 287, 288.

**924.** ANOTHER; part of a cross within a circle.

L. 2·4 in. 1882.

**925.** ANOTHER; two doves.

L. 3 in. Given by H. Martyn Kennard, Esq., 1894.

Cf. Garrucci, *Storia*, vol. vi, pl. 465, fig. 3; Delattre, as above, no. 61, p. 39; Stuhlfauth, as above, pp. 287, 288.

**926.** ANOTHER; a jewelled cross flanked by two lambs to *r.* Above the back of each lamb are two palm-branches.

*See* figure.

L. 6·9 in. 1891. From Minyeh, Egypt.

**927.** ANOTHER ; the *crux monogrammatica*, ⚹, jewelled, twice impressed.   The border formed of a series of doves.

L. 6·1 in.   Given by H. Martyn Kennard, Esq., 1894.   From Coptos, Egypt.

**928.** FRAGMENT OF A TILE impressed with a circular stamp containing the *crux monogrammatica* reversed ⚹ surrounded by the legend : ✝ VIR EX-CELLENTISSIMVS NARSIS FECIT.

*See* figure.   *5th century.*

D. 3·7 in.   Temple Bequest, 1856.   Found in ruins of a house near Catania, Sicily.
*C. I. L.* vol. x, pt. ii, no. 8045 (14).

**929.** ANOTHER ; with the same stamp.

L. 4·9 in.   Temple Bequest, 1856.

**930.** FRAGMENT from the side of a vessel of red pottery having five impressions of a circular stamp, with a standing figure of the Archangel Michael, a monogram, and the name MHXAHΛ.

*See* figure.   *6th century.*

L. 5 in.   1874.

# VIII. STONE.

## Sepulchral Monuments, Architectural Fragments, &c.

(Nos. 931–942, Tombstones of the 4th—6th century.)

**931.** SEPULCHRAL SLAB; inscription: LEVBORICVS HIC REQIESCIT IN PACE VIXIT ANNVS VIII. Below, three crosses.

    H. 13 in. W. 13·25 in. Given by John Evans, Esq., 1890. From St. Louis, Amiens.

**932.** ANOTHER, of red earthenware, engraved with the sacred monogram A ☧ ω within a wreath; above and below the inscription: VRSICINVS IACET|CVM PACE.

    L. 10 in. Given by John Evans, Esq., 1889. From St. Acheul, Amiens.
    Le Blant, *Inscriptions Chrétiennes de la Gaule*, vol. ii, pl. xci, no. 544, and p. 568. For the name Ursicinus cf. Le Blant, *Nouveau Recueil des Inscr. Chrét. de la Gaule*, no. 289, p. 314; Kraus, *Die christlichen Inschriften der Rheinlande*, vol. i, no. 122, pl. ix, no. 26.

**933.** ANOTHER; inscribed: ✝ GVNDEBEBIUS | FAMVLVS DEI VIXIT ANNOS///.

    H. 6·25 in. W. 9·25 in. From Santiponce (Italica), near Seville, Spain.
    Hübner, *Inscr. Hispaniae Christianae*, no. 64.

**934.** ANOTHER, of grey earthenware, with the monogram ☧ in relief under a rounded arch between two columns. To *l.* two imperfect letters of an inscription, continued to *r.*: VIVAS C(VM) TVIS.

    H. 12·75 in. 1889. Obtained in Spain.

**935.** ANOTHER; inscribed: CDLONICVS FID|ELIS IN PACE VI|XIT MS III. (*menses tres.*)

    H. 13·25 in. W. 14·5 in. 1860. From Carthage.
    With the name *Colonicus* cf. *Colonica* at Cherchel, *see Rev. Arch.* 1891, pt. i, p. 29. On the formula *fidelis in pace* as characteristic of N. Africa *see* Le Blant in *Rev. Arch.* vol. xlii (1881), p. 240.

**936.** FRAGMENT OF A SEPULCHRAL SLAB, engraved with a cross with a small R on the upper limb (a Latinized form of the *crux monogrammatica* ✝) and the inscription IN PACE /// Q. ATT ////.

    L. 8·5. 1860. From Carthage. The name was probably Attilius.

**937.** ANOTHER, marble.   Inscription : **ANNOS VII| MENSES IIII.**

> H. 8 n.   W. 8·75 in.   1860.   From Carthage.

**938.** ANOTHER ; inscription : **FIDELIS IN | ////PRIMVS**(*Fidelis in primis*).

> H. 7 in.   W. 9 in.   1860.
> From Carthage.

**939.** ANOTHER ; inscription :
**//// ωТω | /////Є/// | ///
ОУΛОС //// ΧΑΡΙΝ.**

> H. 6·5 in.   W. 3·5 in.   1860.
> From Carthage.

**940.** ANOTHER ; inscription :
**///ЄΙΡΗΝΗС | МЄТΑ ТΗ |
ΛΚΡΟΠС///.**

> B. 12 in.   H. 8·7 in.   1873.
> From Ephesus.

**941.** MARBLE   FRAGMENT ;
two right hands holding
a tablet on which is en-
graved the sacred mono-
gram ☧.

> L. 5 in.   1865.

**942.** SEPULCHRAL SLAB of
limestone carved in relief
with two subjects sepa-
rated by an inscription
and surrounded by a
double border of vine-
scrolls and guilloche. The
upper panel contains a
cross pattée with a loop on
the upper limb, between
two twisted columns with
foliated capitals ; in the
lower is a dove stand-
ing above a branch with
its wings raised above its
head so as to enclose a
medallion containing a
cross.   Round its neck
is tied a pendant disk,
and beneath its beak a small cross.   The inscription is in four lines : **ЄΙС ΘЄОС**

OBOHΘѠ|NCѠФPONHETEΛE | VTHCEN ПAXѠN ITH|CIA//INΔIK/////, showing that the stone is in memory of *Sophrone*, who died on the tenth day of the month *Pachôn*, in the eleventh year of an indiction which the effacement of the last part of the inscription leaves uncertain.

   *See* figure.   *Coptic.*   *7th or 8th century.*

   H. 32 in.   W. 15.5 in.

   Cf. Gayet, *Les Monuments Coptes du Musée de Boulaq* (*Mémoires publiés par les membres de la Mission Archéologique française au Caire*, tome iii, Paris, 1889), pl. lvii, lxi, lxxiii.

   The monuments most similar in style to this have been obtained at Erment (Hermonthis). Those in the Gizeh Museum will be found photographically reproduced in the volume on Coptic Monuments by W. E. Crum, forming part of the *Catalogue Général.*

**943.** CIRCULAR SLAB of limestone carved in relief with a dove upon a branch with an olive branch in its beak.   Round its neck is suspended a rectangular object.
   *Coptic.*   *7th or 8th century.*

   D. 13.75 in.
   Cf. Gayet, as above, pl. xvi, and lix–lxi.

**944.** LIMESTONE FRAGMENT carved in relief with scrolls of foliage enclosing a human face and a panther (?).
   *See* figure.   *5th or 6th century.*

   H. 11 in.   Given by the Rev. G. J. Chester, 1870.   From Medinet el-Fayûm (Crocodilopolis).
   Cf. Naville, *Ahnas el Medineh*, pl. xv, xvi (Eleventh Memoir of the Egypt Exploration Fund, London, 1894) ; Gayet, as above, pl. vi ; Riegl, *Spätrömische Kunstindustrie*, fig. 54, p. 147.

**945.** SIMILAR FRAGMENT ; the head and shoulders of a lion within similar foliage.

   H. 10.5 in.   Given by the Rev. G. J. Chester, 1870.   From Medinet el-Fayûm (Crocodilopolis).

**946.** CAPITAL of an engaged column, of grey stone, rudely carved with two figures, one bearded standing on the *r.*, the other kneeling. The head of the second figure has been destroyed. In the top is a deep cavity.

*See* figure.

H. 20 in.

**947.** CORNICE of grey stone; in the centre an equal-armed cross in high relief; background in low relief, consisting of an arcade of rounded arches supported on double columns which rest on bases of two steps. Beneath each arch is a conventional tree.

L. 31 in. H. 6.5 in.

**948.** SLAB OF GREY STONE, imperfect, carved in relief with a cross pattée within a circle.

L. 28 in. H. 18.5 in.

**949.** SMALL LIMESTONE SLAB; in the centre is painted the Virgin seated with the Child in her arms, the colours almost entirely lost. On each side stands an angel once similarly painted, the background being cut away, leaving the figures in outline; engraved border, at the top and bottom of cross-hatching with a medallion containing a cross pattée in the centre, on the two sides, of conventional palms; at each corner an engraved quatrefoil.

L. 8.2 in. H. 5.8 in. 1855.

**950.** CORNER OF ANOTHER SLAB, with somewhat similar border.

L. 4.1 in. 1855.

# IX. MISCELLANEOUS.

## I. Textiles, &c.

### (6th—8th century.)

**951**. LINEN TUNIC, with applied tapestry ornament. The front and back both have two vertical stripes (*clavi*) terminating in medallions, and connected at the neck by broader transverse bands. Below each of the stripes is a larger medallion (*orbiculus* or *segmentum*), while a similar medallion is seen on each shoulder. Apart from the horizontal bands, which have animals in different arrangements, only two designs are used, one for the stripes, the other for the medallions; but

variety and symmetry are attained by employing each in two forms, direct and reversed, an example of one matching an example of the other on each side of the garment. The design of the stripes is a series of superimposed panels within conventional borders containing figures, the central panel representing the Virgin and Child. That of the larger medallions is the scene of the Adoration of the Magi (*see* figure). The colours employed are crimson for the ground, and yellow, dark and pale green, brown, pink, dark and light blue, purple-brown, black, and white, for the figures.

L. 52 in.   Given by the Executors of Major W. J. Myers.   1901.   From Egypt.

The tunic resembles those discovered at Akhmím (Panopolis), and perhaps came from that

place.   It is very ragged in parts, and the tapestry on one side and on the shoulders is greatly frayed and faded.   It should be compared with the garments worn by the attendants on the left end of the Casket of Projecta (pl. xviii).

**952.** FRAGMENT OF A TUNIC (?), ornamented with narrow inwoven purple lines, and a square of the same colour containing a cross between four smaller crosses.

L. 46 in.   W. 28 in.   Given by the Rev. G. J. Chester, 1873.   From Tell Atrîb (Athribis).

**953.** SIMILAR FRAGMENT, with a narrow inwoven purple stripe down the centre.

L. 36 in.   W. 24 in.   Given by the Rev. G. J. Chester, 1873.   From Tell Atrîb (Athribis).

**954.** ANOTHER, ornamented with H. inwoven in purple.

L. 24 in.   W. 20 in.   Given by the Rev. G. J. Chester, 1873.   From Tell Atrîb (Athribis).

**955.** LINEN HOOD, with an inwoven cross and a narrow line in purple on each side.

L. 13 in.   Given by the Rev. G. J. Chester, 1873.   From Tell Atrîb (Athribis).

Z

**956**. ANOTHER ; on the outside horizontal rows of tags and knots.

L. 11 in.   Given by the Rev. G. J. Chester, 1873.   From Tell Atrîb (Athribis).

**957**. CROSS of gilt leather, with looped ends.   It stands upon a base of four steps, and is ornamented with cut designs ; upon each limb a plaited band, and upon the base bands of zigzag, with small pounced circles in the angles.   A narrow black border runs round the whole.

L. 30 in.   Given by J. Gardner Wilkinson, Esq., 1834.   From Medinet Habu, Thebes.   Said to be from a vestment.

## II. Plaster and Clay.

Nos. 958—965, seals from wine-jars, of the 4th to 7th century.

**958**. PLASTER SEAL OF A WINE-JAR, with the sacred monogram ☧ and inscription XM(Γ)/////ωMΔ.

D. 3·5 in.   Given by the Egypt Exploration Fund, 1888.

Cf. *C. I. L.* vol. xv, nos. 4886, 4888–4890.   The letters XMΓ stand for Χριστὸς Μιχάηλ Γαβρίηλ, and are usually a sign of Syrian origin.   *See* de Rossi, *Bullettino*, 1890, p. 42, and 1894, p. 104 ; Le Blant in *Rev. Arch.* 1872, p. 130 ; *Bulletin de Correspondance Hellénique (École française d'Athènes)*, 1894, p. 24 ; Renan, *Mission de Phénicie*, p. 592 ; V. Strazzulla in *R. Q. S.* 1899, p. 132.

**959**. ANOTHER ; the *crux monogrammatica* ⳨ and a mutilated inscription.

D. 3·1 in.   Given by the Egypt Exploration Fund, 1888.   From Naucratis.

**960**. ANOTHER ; in the centre R W, surrounded by a border with the inscription : VTHMANARITANO.

D. 3·6 in.   Given by H. Martyn Kennard, Esq., 1894.   From Coptos, Egypt.

For an example of a wine-jar closed by a similar seal *see* La Blanchère et Gauckler, *Cat. du Musée Alaoui*, no. 390, p. 251 (Paris, 1897).

**961**. ANOTHER ; in the sunk top is a ligatured inscription. In the back are imbedded five fragments of red pottery.

D. 4·8 in.   Given by H. Martyn Kennard, Esq., 1894.   Coptos, Egypt.

**962**. ANOTHER, impressed with the figure of St. Menas between two camels.   Pieces of reed adhere to the back of the seal.

D. 4 in.   Franks Coll. 1880.

*See* C. H. Smith in *Journ. Hellenic Studies*, vol. iv (1883), p. 159.

**963**. ANOTHER, with cruciform monogram between letters forming the word καλοκἀγα(θοῦ).   The proper name may be ᾿Ιωάννου.

D 4·1 in.   1882.

**964.** ANOTHER, with a cruciform monogram and a cross.

     D. 4·1 in.   Franks Coll. 1880.

**965.** ANOTHER, with the name IOYΛIANOY, and the seven-branched candlestick.

     D. 3·6 in.   Franks Coll. 1880.

**966.** MEDALLION, (impression of a seal?) of pale clay.   The Entry into Jerusalem ; our Lord riding an ass to *l.* and carrying a cross.   Before him stand two figures carrying palm-branches.   In the field, a star.

     D. 1·9 in.   Blacas Coll. 1867.

**967.** ANOTHER ; our Lord with cruciform nimbus riding to *r.* on an ass.   He holds up his *r.* hand, and carries a cross in his left ; before the ass walks a bearded figure.

     D. 1·82 in.   1889.   From Smyrna.

**968.** ANOTHER ; the Annunciation (?).   The Virgin is seated to *l.* on a folding stool, and holds up her *r.* hand towards the angel who stands before her.   On the ground between the two figures is the basket ? containing the wool which the Virgin has been spinning.

     D. 1·64 in. 1882.   From Edfu, Egypt.

## III. Small Objects of Stone.

**969.** LIMESTONE STAMP, oblong and of triangular section, pierced for suspension ; the rectangular face engraved : MARTIAN//| VIVASI////, in two lines, the letters reversed.   *Martiane vivas i(n Deo).*

    *4th century.*

     L. 6·75 in.   Given by the Egypt Exploration Fund, 1888.   From Benha.   Imperfect.

**970.** ANOTHER, conical and pierced for suspension.   The face is rudely engraved in intaglio with a bird.

    *5th or 6th century.*

     H. 2·5 in.   1877.   From the Fayûm.

**971.** ANOTHER, of similar shape, also pierced ; engraved

     L. 2·26 in.   1876.

**972.** ANOTHER; a cylinder drilled longitudinally and engraved in intaglio with a cross pattée within a circle of radiating lines.

*About the 6th century.*

L. ·86 in. 1880. From Alexandria.

**973.** ANOTHER, pyramidal, engraved as in figure ('Ιησοῦς Χριστὸς νικᾷ).

| IC | XC |
|----|----|
| NI | K/// |

*About the 6th century.*

L. 2·15 in. 1892. From Cyprus.

Cesnola, *Salaminia*, fig. 117. Possibly a stamp for the Eucharistic bread; cf. É. Michon, in *Mélanges G.-B. de Rossi* (*École française de Rome*), 1892, p. 199.

**974.** ANOTHER, of black stone, flat and circular, engraved with a cross pattée within a circle of zigzag bands interrupted by four small crosses.

D. 2·3 in. 1879.

Possibly a stamp for the Eucharistic bread; cf. É. Michon, as above.

**975.** MOULD, of dark green stone, flat and oblong, engraved on one side with a rosette of eight petals within a pearled border. Pierced at both ends.

L. 1·7 in. 1879.

Perhaps a mould for casting jewellery; cf. Doublet et Gauckler, *Le Musée de Constantine*, p. 54 (Paris, 1892); S. Reinach, *Esquisses archéologiques*, ch. v; *Mat. Russ. Arch.* no. 23 (1899), p. 27.

**976.** PECTORAL CROSS, of steatite.

*About the 6th century.*

L. 1 in. 1875. From Egypt.

**977.** ANOTHER.

L. 1 in. 1876. From Egypt.

**978.** ANOTHER.

L. 1 in. 1884. From Egypt.

**979.** ANOTHER.

L. 1 in. 1879.

**980.** ANOTHER, within a lozenge; cut from the solid.

L. 9 in. 1879.

## IV. Wood.

**981.** CYLINDRICAL STAMP, grooved round sides. On one face is engraved in intaglio a lion (?) rampant with head turned back; in front of the breast, a small cross. On the other face is engraved Solomon's seal with a star in the centre.

*6th or 7th century.*

D. 2·44 in. 1890. From Akhmîm (Panopolis).

**982.** ANOTHER; on one side is engraved a monogram, *see* figure; on the other, another cruciform monogram.

*6th or 7th century.*

D. 3.2 in. 1890. From Minyeh, Egypt.

**983.** PANEL, with holes for pegs along both the side-edges, and carved on both surfaces in low relief. On one side is a row of nine rosettes within a zigzag border; on the other, six medallions containing formal flowers (?) separated by as many crosses, and bordered above and on the left side by a band of guilloche.

L. 23.3 in. Imperfect.

**984.** FRAGMENT OF A PANEL, carved on one side in low relief with a fish to *l.* between two geometrical designs. On the back, part of a much weathered inscription in three lines.

L. 10.5. 1881. From Egypt.

**985.** CANDLESTICK of soft, brown wood carved with geometrical patterns. The base is in openwork standing on four feet; the body is barrel-shaped, and the upper part cylindrical with two pierced projections, one on either side.

H. 8.7 in. 1891. From Egypt.

**986.** CARVED CEDAR PANELS from a door, four purely ornamental, the remaining six with scriptural subjects. The panels of the former class are identical in design, each having a large central cross with floriated extremities and two medallions containing smaller crosses upon the vertical limb; the ground is covered with a rich decoration of interlacing floral scrolls (*see* figure). The panels of the second class represent the following scenes: the Annunciation; Nativity and Adoration of the Magi; Baptism; Entry into Jerusalem; Ascension; Descent into Hell; and Pentecost; the Annunciation and Baptism being on the same panel.

*The Annunciation* (pl. xxxiv, lower part of central panel). The angel Gabriel approaches from the *l.*, extending his *r.*

arm towards the Virgin, who stands before him with her *r*. hand raised and holding a book in her *l*.

*The Nativity* (pl. xxxv, left hand).    In the centre the Virgin, wearing a richly embroidered mantle, is seated to *l*.; behind her is the Child in the manger, above which are seen the heads of the ox and the ass.    Behind are three shepherds. From the *r*. approach the Magi with their gifts.    Below to *l*. is seated Joseph, and at the bottom two nurses are washing the Child, while an ass is feeding in the *l*. hand corner; above is a choir of angels, above whom is a star.

*The Baptism* (pl. xxxiv, upper part of central panel).    Our Lord, an adult bearded figure with cruciferous nimbus, stands up to the waist in the Jordan; to *r*. stands St. John in a garment of skins with his *r*. hand extended over our Lord's head, and a long cross in his *l*.    Above is the dove, and to *l*. are three angels holding garments.

*The Entry into Jerusalem* (pl. xxxiv, left panel).    Above is our Lord, full-face, riding sideways upon an ass.    He has the cruciferous nimbus with the addition of a small cross above the head, and his garments are richly embroidered. Behind him is visible the top of a palm-tree, which rises from the lower part of the panel; in it are seated four small figures cutting branches; *see* the Painter's Guide of Mount Athos, Didron, *Manuel d'Iconographie Chrétienne*, p. 186 (Paris, 1845).    Below is a group of Jewish spectators of both sexes.

*The Descent into Hell* (pl. xxxv, *r*. hand).    In the middle is our Lord holding a long cross in his *l*. hand and helping Adam and Eve to rise from an open tomb.    Behind him stands King David, and in the background are the prophets and just men of the Old Testament.    Below, two angels are binding with chains the prostrate figure of Beelzebub.

*The Pentecost* (pl. xxxiv, right panel).    The twelve Apostles are seated round a table which terminates in front in a rounded arch.    In the background are buildings, and at the top is the dove descending from heaven.

*The Ascension* (pl. xxxv, central panel).    Above, our Lord in a *mandorla* supported by two angels; with his *r*. hand he makes the gesture of benediction. Below stand the twelve Apostles, in front of whom is the Virgin between two angels.

*Plates* XXXIV and XXXV.

1*3th century.*

H. of the panels, 12 in.    1878.    From the church of *Sitt Miriam* (*Al Mu'Allaka*), Cairo.

*See Arch. Journ.* vol. xxix (1872), p. 128, and cf. Strzygowski in *R. Q. S.* 1897 (*Die christlichen Denkmäler Aegyptens*).    The arabesques which form the principal ornament of some of the panels, and are introduced to fill up the background of the others, are in the style of contemporary Arab art.

The treatment of the gospel scenes is in general in accord with the rules of the Painter's Guide of Mount Athos, but there are marked divergencies, as in the case of the Annunciation, where the Virgin holds a book instead of the spindle and wool, and in the Pentecost, where the figure representing the world is absent from the arch in the foreground of the scene.

**987.** WOODEN PANEL, gilt and painted, with four scenes.

*The Annunciation.*    The Virgin stands in the traditional manner before her chair, holding the spindle in her *l.* hand. The angel approaches from the *l.* with his *r.* hand extended and holding a staff in his *l.* In the background are buildings. Inscription: O E'YⲀYYEΛICMOC, O ᴬᴦᴦABPIHΛ, M̄P ⲐY.

*The Baptism.* In the centre our Lord, adult and bearded, standing in the river ; to *l.* the Baptist, to *r.* a group of angels, and at the top the dove. Inscriptions: H̊ BAⲠTICIC, and ᴵC̄ X̄C̄.

*The Nativity.* In the centre the Virgin upon a couch ; behind her the Child in the manger and the angels with the shepherds. In the foreground, to *l.*, the washing of the Child, to *r.*, Joseph seated. Inscriptions: H X̄Y ᴦENNHCIC, and M̄P ⲐY.

*The Transfiguration.* Above, our Lord in a circular glory ; on the top of the mountain on either side Moses and Elias standing ; lower down in the foreground Peter, James and John in attitudes of amazement and adoration. Inscription: H MET MOPⲪⲰCIC, and ᴵC̄ X̄C̄.

*12th—13th century.*

L. 15.3 in. 1851. From the Monastery of the Virgin near the Natron Lakes, Syria.

## V. Bone.

**988.** Six rings, with diagonal flutings on the outer sides, and with traces of mortar adhering to them.

*About the 4th century.*

D. 1.7 to 1.1 in. Probably impressed in the mortar of the *loculi* in the Roman Catacombs.
Cf. de Rossi, *Roma Sotterranea*, vol. iii. p. 583 ; Bosio, *Roma Sotterranea, passim* ; Boldetti, pp. 504, 506.

**989.** Pectoral cross.

*6th or 7th century.*

L. .82 in. 1880. From Egypt.

**990.** Pendant, a flat tablet. On one side is very rudely carved in relief St. George riding to *r.* and transfixing with a lance a dragon (?) upon the ground before him.

*6th or 7th century.*

L. .84 in. 1882. From the Fayûm.
Cf. a similar object from Akhmîm ; *see* Forrer, *Frühchristl. Altertümer,* pl. xxi, fig. 6.

**991.** Another ; the same subject.

*6th or 7th century.*

L. 1.8 in. Given by W. Edkins, Esq., 1879.

**992.** Long bone of an animal, longitudinal section, carved on the convex side with a floral design, above which is a chevron. It is pierced with two holes at opposite corners.

*6th or 7th century.*

L. 5.5 in. 1896. From Egypt.

**993.** ANOTHER, similar.

> L. 5·25 in. 1896. From Egypt.

**994.** ANOTHER, pierced with two holes in a straight line.

> L. 3·7 in. 1896. From Egypt.

**995** ANOTHER, with a single hole.

> L. 2·62 in. 1896. From Egypt.

## VI. Lead.

NOTE.—The collection of Byzantine lead seals is in the Department of MSS.

**996.** MEDALLION, with loop for suspension; on one face in relief the standing figure of a military saint with long chlamys, supporting a shield with his *l.* hand, and holding a spear in his *r.*; on the other side, a saint standing in the attitude of an *orans* between two crouching animals. Perhaps St. Menas.

> D. ·34 in. 1882.

**997.** AMPULLA, with ornament in relief; on each side of the neck is a cross. On one side of the body are two military saints standing side by side, each holding a spear in his *l.* and an oval shield in his *r.* hand. In the field the vertical inscriptions: ѲAH|TIO(C) and O ГЄ|OP|(ГI)|OC. (Saints Aetius and George.) On the other side is a building with three round arches, above which are a gabled roof flanked by a cupola and a turret. Under the central and largest arch is our Lord lying in the manger, above which is seen the head of an ox. From each of the smaller arches a lamp (?) is suspended.

> H. 2·26 in. Franks Coll. 1876.
> C. Roach Smith, *Collectanea Antiqua*, vol. v, pl. xxix, fig. 1. St. Aetius was one of the forty military martyrs of Sebaste in Armenia under Licinius (March 10).

**998.** ANOTHER; on each side in low relief within a plaited border the bust of a military saint with circular shield on his *l.* arm and spear in his *r.* hand. In the field on one side, the remains of defaced vertical inscription.

> H. 2·22 in. Franks Coll. 1876.
> C. Roach Smith, *Collectanea Antiqua*, vol. v, pl. xxix, fig. 2.

**999.** ANOTHER; on one face within an engraved plaited border the bust of a military saint with spear and shield; in the field, on either side of the head, remains of an inscription. On the other side is a similar bust.

> H. 2 in. Franks Coll. 1876.
> C. Roach Smith, *Collectanea Antiqua*, vol. v, pl. xxix, fig. 3.

### VII. Various Small Objects.

**1000.** PENDANT OF ROCK-CRYSTAL, hemispherical, engraved on the convex side with the sacred monogram ☧; in a bronze setting with loop for suspension.

*4th century.*

L. 1·6 in. 1890. Obtained in Rome.

**1001.** PECTORAL CROSS pattée, of pearl shell, pierced for suspension.
*6th or 7th century.*

L. 1·6 in. 1883. Probably from Egypt.

**1002.** FIGURE OF A PEACOCK rudely carved from a flat piece of pearl shell.
*6th or 7th century.*

L. 1·32 in. 1879. From Thebes, Egypt.

**1003.** IRON ROD, of round section and blunt at the lower end, square in section with engraved geometrical ornament in the upper part, which terminates in a cross pattée surmounted by a hook.
*6th or 7th century.*

L. 6·75 in. 1882. Probably from Egypt. Perhaps a rod for stibium.

THE CASKET OF PROJECTA. NO. 304.

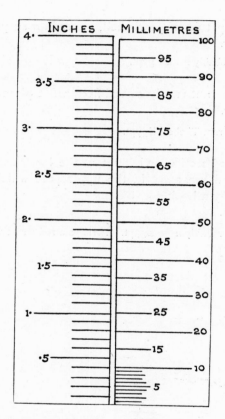

COMPARATIVE ENGLISH AND METRICAL SCALE.

# INDEX

STAMPS ON A SILVER VESSEL AT VIENNA.
(After J. Arneth, *Die antiken Gold- und Silber-Monumente &c.*, pl., S. vii.)
For comparison with No. 397 above.

Plate I

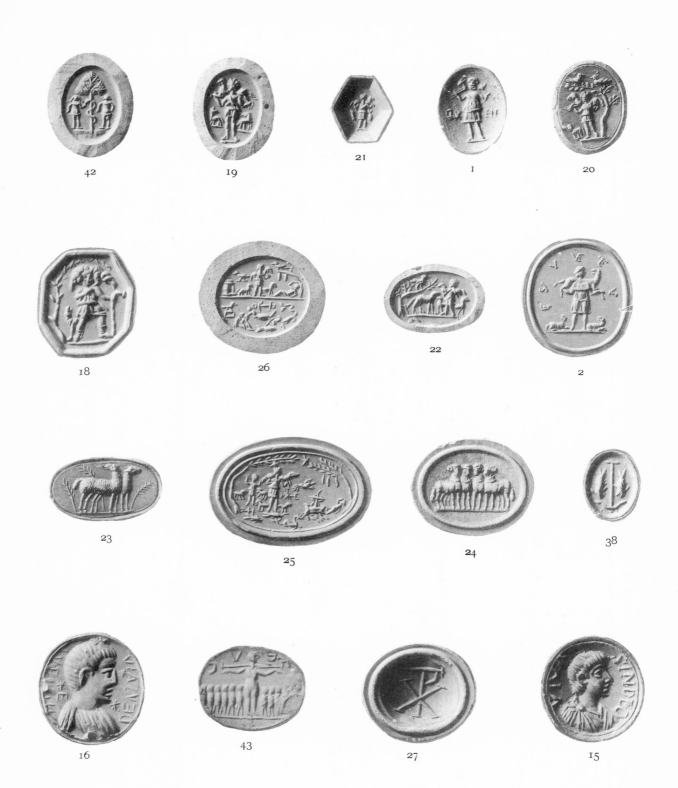

42     19     21     I     20

18     26     22     2

23     25     24     38

16     43     27     15

ENGRAVED GEMS

PLATE II

ENGRAVED GEMS AND RINGS

Plate III

CAMEOS

PLATE IV

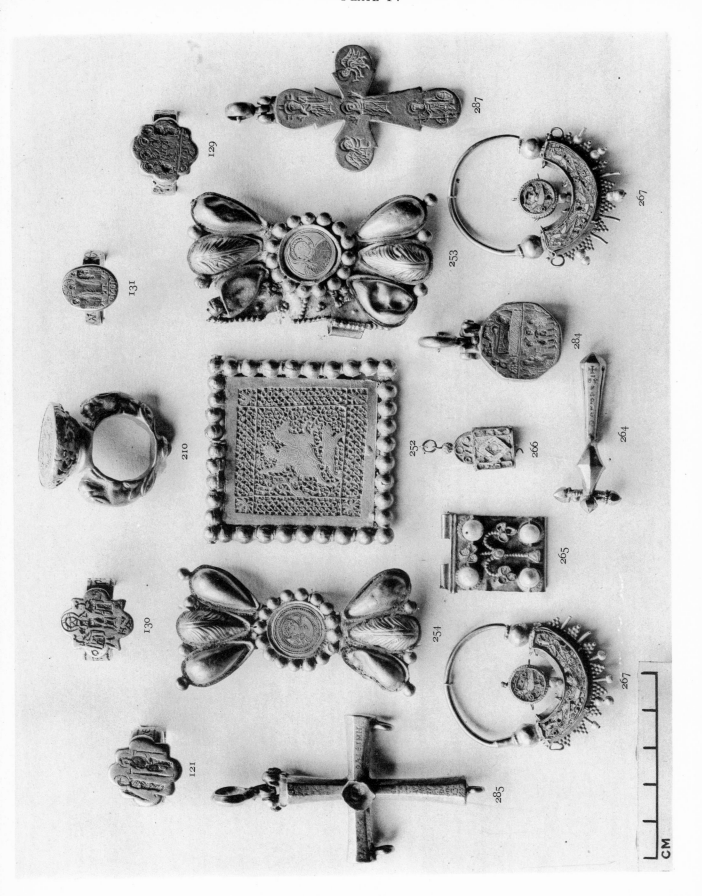

Plate V

PLATE VI

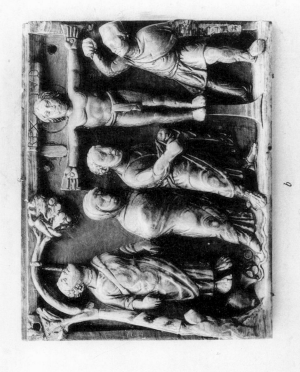

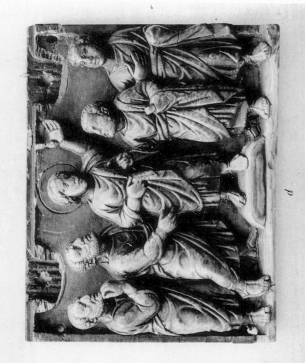

IVORY PANELS FROM A CASKET

PLATE VII

292 *a*

292 *b*

292 *c*

294

292 *d*

292 *e*

CM

IVORY PANELS

PLATE VIII

295

LEAF OF AN IVORY DIPTYCH

THE ARCHANGEL MICHAEL

PLATE IX

*a*

*b*

*d*

*c*

297

IVORY BOX (PYXIS)
WITH THE STORY OF ST. MENAS

PLATE X

IVORY BOX (PYXIS)
WITH THE STORY OF DANIEL, &c.

298

Plate XI

IVORY PANELS

PLATE XII

BONE PANELS FROM A CASKET

PLATE XIII

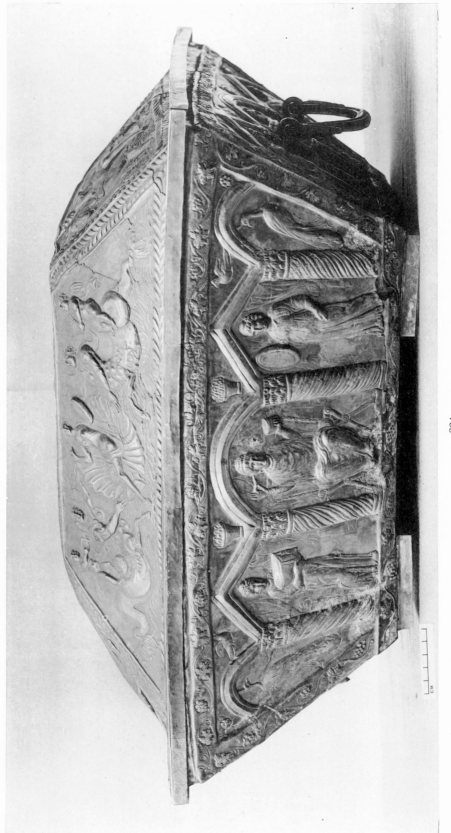

ESQUILINE TREASURE—CASKET OF PROJECTA

304

Plate XIV

304

ESQUILINE TREASURE—CASKET OF PROJECTA

TOP OF LID

PLATE XV

ESQUILINE TREASURE—CASKET OF PROJECTA

FRONT

304

PLATE XVI

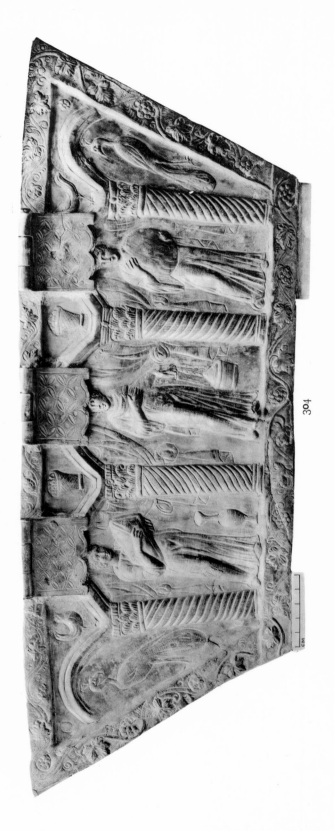

ESQUILINE TREASURE—CASKET OF PROJECTA

BACK

304

PLATE XVII

304

ESQUILINE TREASURE—CASKET OF PROJECTA
RIGHT END

PLATE XVIII

304

ESQUILINE TREASURE—CASKET OF PROJECTA

LEFT END

PLATE XIX

ESQUILINE TREASURE—DOME-SHAPED CASKET

1. FRONT.     2. RIGHT SIDE.     3. BACK.     4. LEFT SIDE

305

PLATE XX

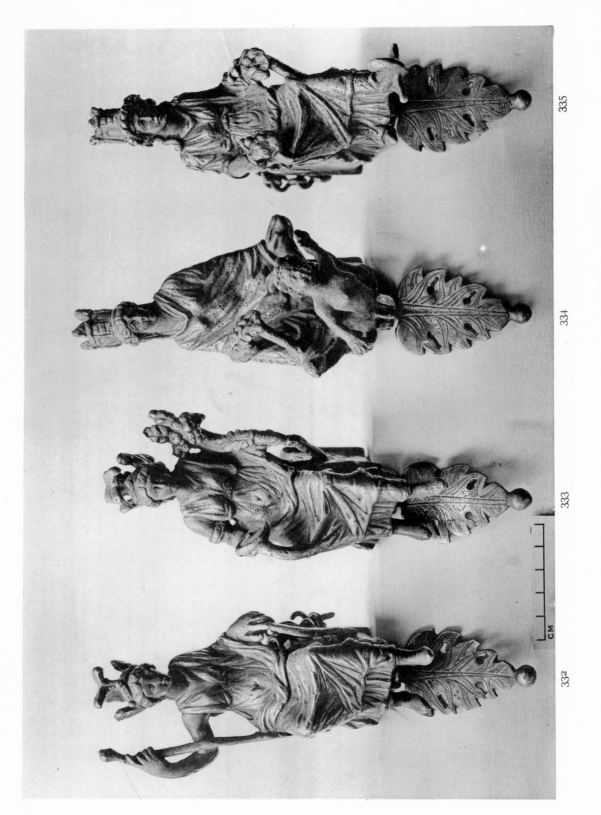

335

334

333

332

CM

ESQUILINE TREASURE—FIGURES REPRESENTING CITIES

PLATE XXI

CARTHAGE TREASURE

PLATE XXII

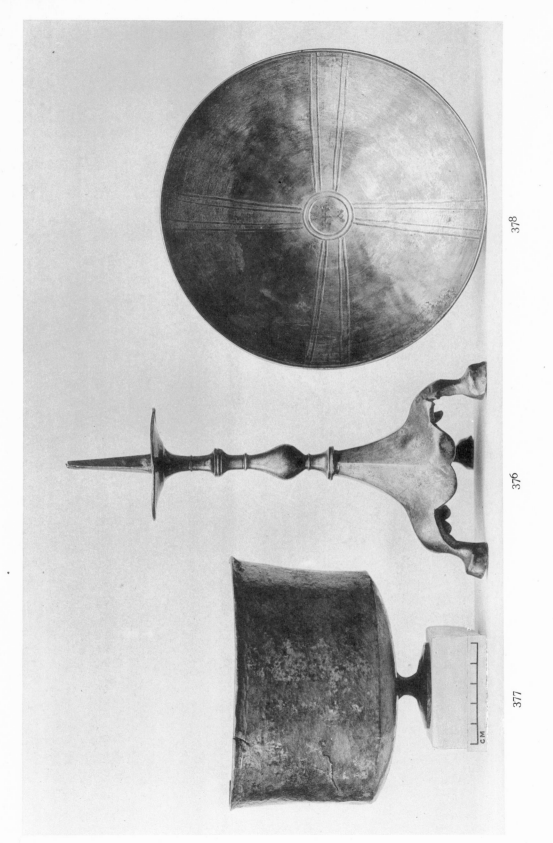

378

376

377

LAMPSACUS TREASURE

PLATE XXIII

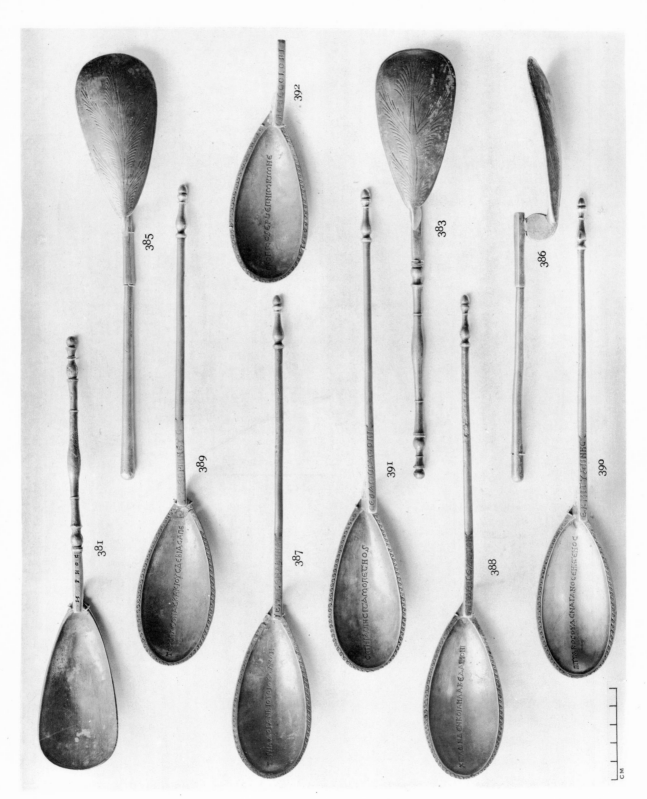

LAMPSACUS TREASURE

PLATE XXIV

398

397

CYPRUS TREASURE

PLATE XXV

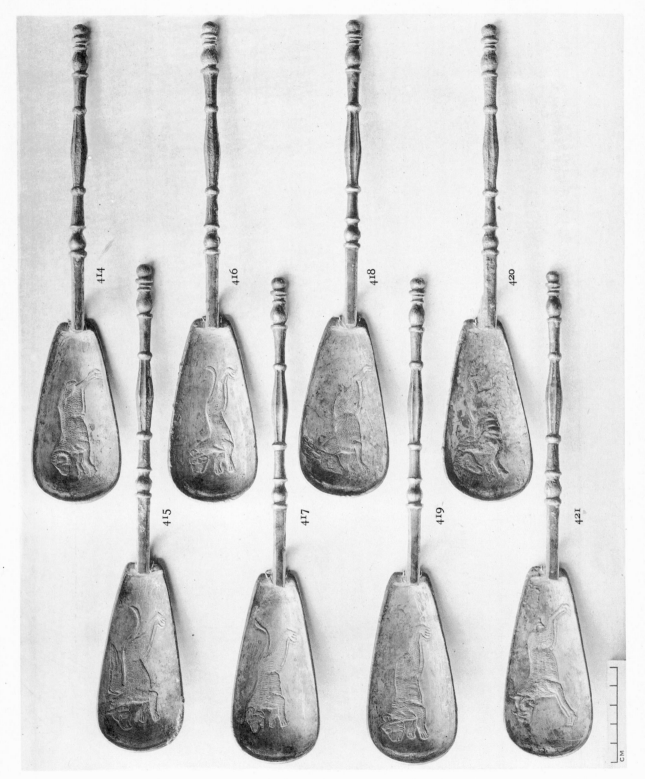

PLATE XXVI

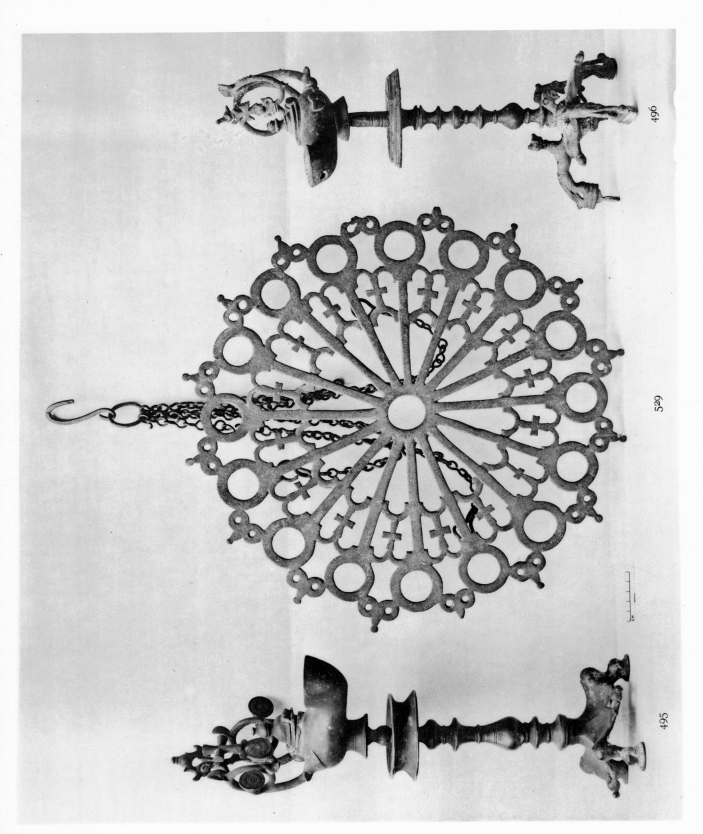

496

529

495

BRONZE LAMPS

Plate XXVII

526

508

525

527

509

507

512

502

503

501

BRONZE LAMPS

Plate **XXVIII**

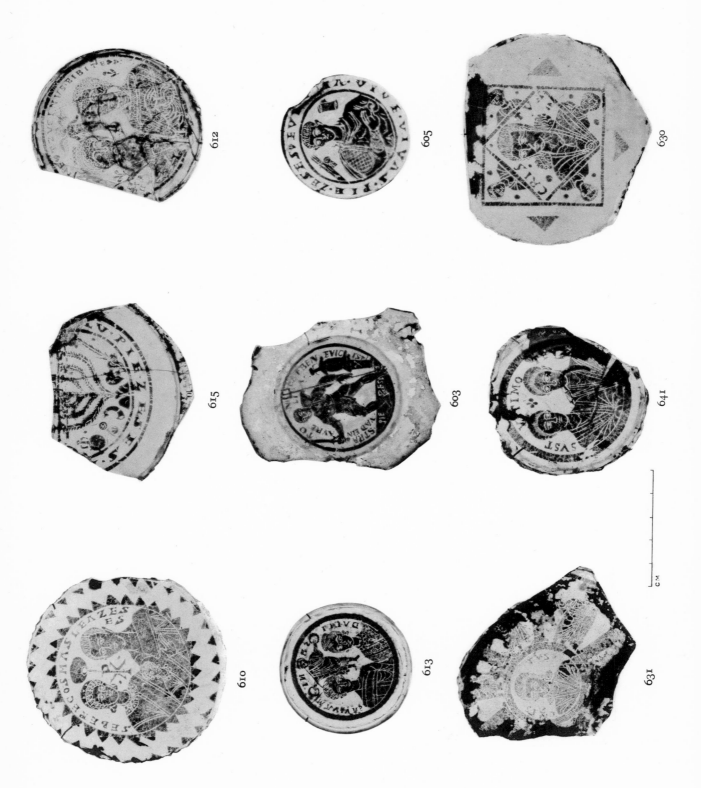

PLATE XXIX

PLATE XXX

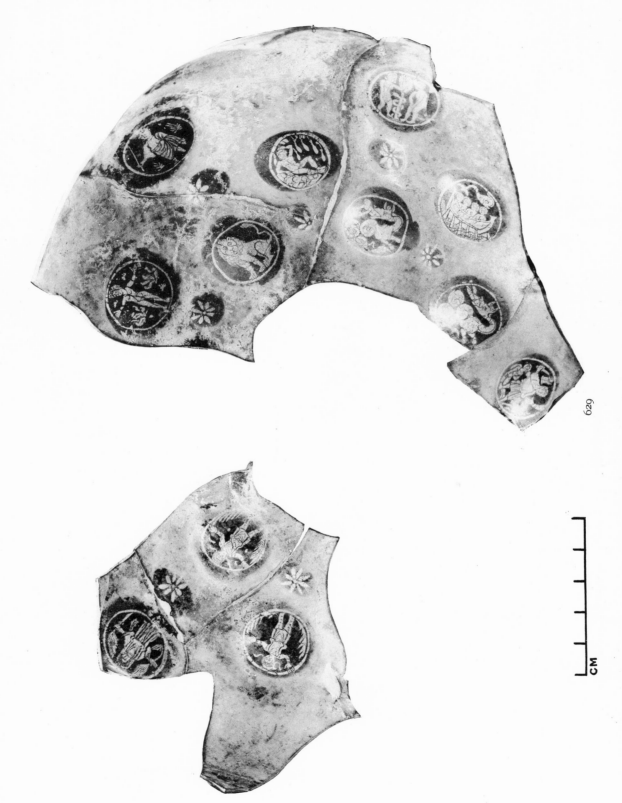

629

GILDED GLASS—FRAGMENTS OF A BOWL
WITH SMALL MEDALLIONS

PLATE XXXI

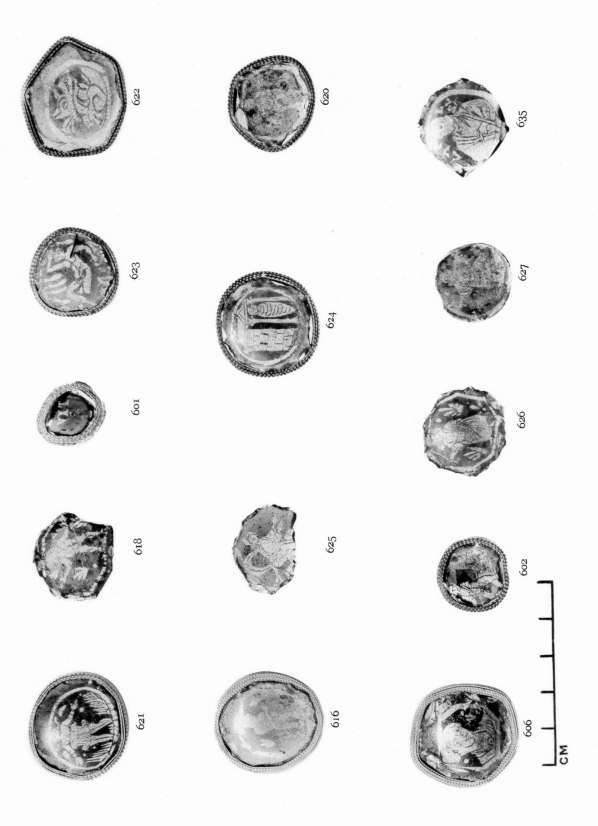

GILDED GLASS—SMALL MEDALLIONS FROM BOWLS

PLATE XXXII

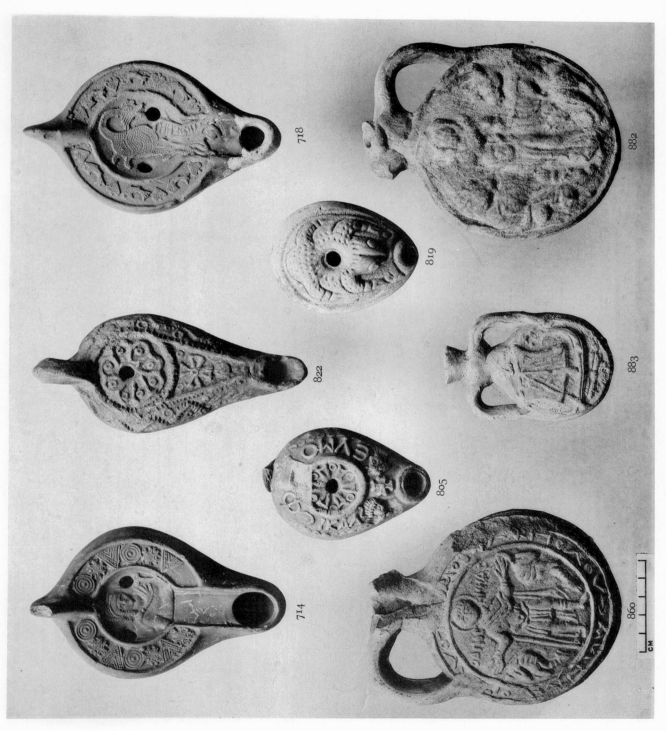

718

882

819

822

883

805

714

860

POTTERY LAMPS AND PILGRIMS' BOTTLES

Plate XXXIII

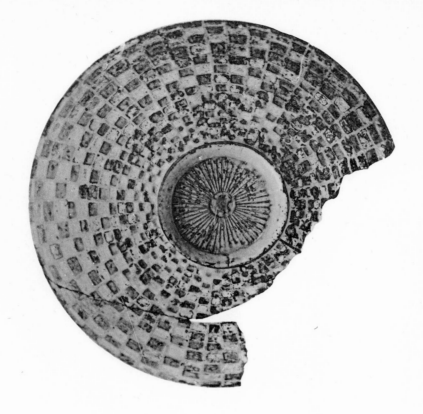

916

THE CONSTANTINE BOWL

DIAMETER, 5·06 IN.   HEIGHT, 2 IN.

Plate XXXIV

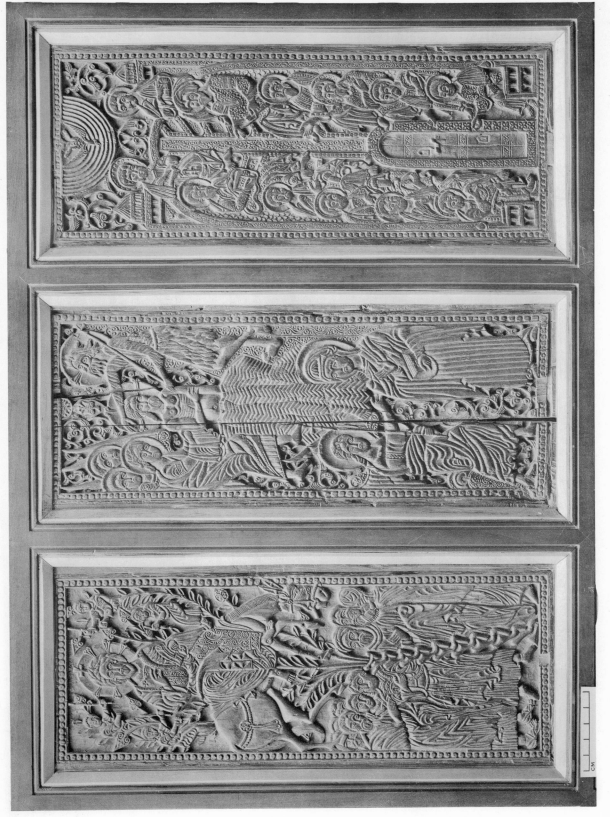

CARVED WOODEN PANELS FROM CAIRO

Plate XXXV

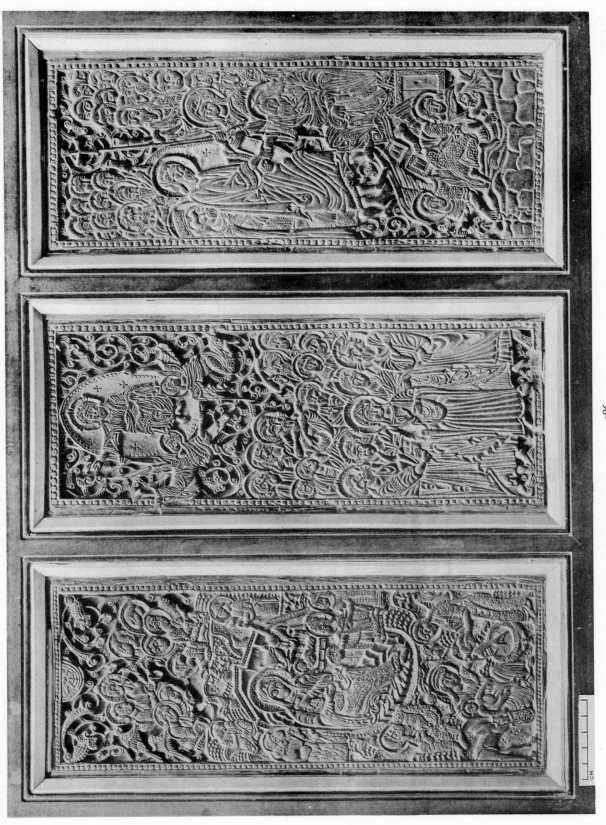

CARVED WOODEN PANELS FROM CAIRO

OXFORD: HORACE HART
PRINTER TO THE UNIVERSITY